Glencoe Science

BIOLOGY

The Dynamics of Life

Unit 10 Resources
The Human Body

McGraw Hill Glencoe

New York, New York Columbus, Ohio Chicago, Illinois Peoria, Illinois Woodland Hills, California

A GLENCOE PROGRAM

BIOLOGY: THE DYNAMICS OF LIFE

Glencoe Online SCIENCE

Visit the Glencoe Science Web site
bdol.glencoe.com

You'll find:
Standardized Test Practice, Interactive Tutor, Section and Chapter Self-Check Quizzes, Online Student Edition, Web Links, Microscopy Links, WebQuest Projects, Internet BioLabs, In the News, Textbook Updates, Teacher Bulletin Board, Teaching Today

and much more!

McGraw Hill Glencoe

The McGraw-Hill Companies

Send all inquiries to:
Glencoe/McGraw-Hill
8787 Orion Place
Columbus, OH 43240-4027

ISBN 0-07-860221-1

Printed in the United States of America.

3 4 5 6 7 8 9 10 009 08 07 06 05

Contents

To the Teacher

This unit-based booklet contains resource materials to help you teach this unit more effectively. You will find in chapter order:

Reproducible Pages

Hands-on Activities

MiniLab and BioLab Worksheets: Each activity in this book is an expanded version of each BioLab or MiniLab that appears in the Student Edition of ***Biology: The Dynamics of Life***. All materials lists, procedures, and questions are repeated so that students can read and complete a lab in most cases without having a textbook on the lab table. Data tables are enlarged so that students can record data in them. All lab questions are reprinted with lines on which students can write their answers. In addition, for student safety, all appropriate safety symbols and caution statements have been reproduced on these expanded pages. Answer pages for each MiniLab and BioLab are included in the Teacher Support and Planning section at the back of this book.

Real World BioApplications: These two-page activities provide students with the opportunity to explore a technological or everyday application of biology. Each activity is directly related to a major concept in the Student Edition, and several examine principles from the physical sciences that underlie the biology content. While some activities are more hands-on, all require critical thinking and creativity. The teaching notes in the Teacher Support and Planning section at the back of this book suggest chapters and topics with which to correlate the activities, explain the purpose of each activity, offer materials tips and teaching strategies, and provide answers to all questions on the student pages.

Extension and Intervention

Reinforcement and Study Guide in English and Spanish: These pages help students understand, organize, and compare the main biology concepts in the textbook. The questions and activities also help build strong study and reading skills. There are four study guide pages for each chapter and two pages for the BioDigest. Students will find these pages easy to follow because the section titles match those in the textbook. Italicized sentences in the study guide direct students to the related topics in the text.

The *Reinforcement and Study Guide* exercises employ a variety of formats including short-answer questions, multiple-choice, matching, true/false, ordering, labeling, completion, and short essay. The clear, easy-to-follow exercises and the self-pacing format are geared to build your students' confidence in understanding biology. The English pages are followed immediately by the study guide pages in Spanish.

Concept Mapping: The *Concept Mapping* worksheets reinforce and extend the graphic organizational skills introduced in the Skill Handbook in the Student Edition of ***Biology: The Dynamics of Life***. Concept maps are visual representations of relationships among particular concepts. By using these worksheets, students will gain experience with three different types of concept maps: the *network tree*, which shows causal information, group hierarchies, and branching procedures; the *events chain*, which describes the stages of a process, the steps in a linear procedure, or a sequence of events; and the *cycle map*, which shows how a series of events interacts to produce a set of results again and again.

There is one *Concept Mapping* worksheet for each chapter in the Student Edition. Each worksheet is geared toward a specific section or sections in the chapter so that you can assign it at the most relevant time. An entire section may be mapped or just a few key concepts from the section. Answers to all *Concept Mapping* worksheets are provided in the Teacher Support and Planning section at the back of this book.

Critical Thinking/Problem Solving: For each chapter of ***Biology: The Dynamics of Life***, a one-page *Critical Thinking* or *Problem Solving* worksheet is provided to extend the material in the Student Edition. Each worksheet is geared to a specific section or sections in the chapter so that you can assign it at the most relevant time. Answers to all worksheets are provided in the Teacher Support and Planning section at the back of this book.

The worksheets follow Bloom's taxonomy of problem solving. Each worksheet tests the students' abilities on one or more of the following areas:

- to use knowledge
- to comprehend what that knowledge means
- to apply that knowledge to a new but related situation
- to analyze the different aspects of new information
- to synthesize new information in order to respond to a particular situation in a creative and logical way

Transparency Activity Masters

Section Focus Transparencies: A *Section Focus Transparency* is provided for every section in the Student Edition. Each transparency contains two questions related to the transparency image. In addition, each transparency is reproduced as a master in this book. These masters are designed to generate interest and focus students' attention on the topic being presented in that section. Teaching strategies background information, and possible answers to the questions for each transparency in this unit can be found in the Teacher Support and Planning section at the back of this book.

Basic Concepts Transparencies: This book contains a blackline master version of each color *Basic Concepts Transparency* for this unit. In most cases, the transparency illustration is different than the illustration in the textbook, providing optimum support for your visual learners. The accompanying worksheet for each transparency master focuses students' attention on the topic, requiring them to analyze the illustration and relate it to the concepts being taught in the textbook. The use of the masters makes the worksheets convenient homework assignments.

Teaching strategies as well as worksheet answers are provided for each transparency. Several transparencies utilize overlays for maximum teaching benefit, and explanations of how to use these overlays are included in the teaching suggestions in the Teacher Support and Planning section at the back of this book.

Reteaching Skills Transparencies: This book contains a blackline master version of each color *Reteaching Skills Transparency* for this unit. The transparencies and masters provide visual tools for reteaching important concepts. To make your reteaching more powerful, the transparencies and masters are developed around basic skills. These skills include, but are not limited to, interpreting scientific illustrations, sequencing, recognizing cause and effect, comparing and contrasting, observing and inferring, and classifying.

The accompanying worksheet for each transparency master focuses students' attention on the topic skill. Students may find it helpful to take notes on the master and use it as a study tool for the chapter. Teaching strategies as well as worksheet answers are provided for each transparency. Several transparencies utilize overlays for maximum teaching benefit, and explanations of how to use these overlays are included in the teaching suggestions in the Teacher Support and Planning section at the back of this book.

Assessment

Chapter Assessment: These worksheets provide materials to assess your students' understanding of concepts from each chapter in this unit. Each chapter test includes several sections that assess students' understanding at different levels.

The *Reviewing Vocabulary* section tests students' knowledge of the chapter's vocabulary. A variety of formats is used, including matching, multiple-choice, and completion.

The *Understanding Main Ideas* section consists of two parts. Part A tests recall and basic understanding of facts presented in the chapter. Part B is designed to be more challenging and requires deeper comprehension of concepts than does Part A. Students may be asked to explain biological processes and relationships or to make comparisons and generalizations.

The *Thinking Critically* section requires students to use several high-order learning skills. For some questions, students will need to interpret data and discover relationships presented in graphs and tables. Other questions may require them to apply their understanding of concepts to solve problems, to compare and contrast situations, and to make inferences or predictions.

In the final section, *Applying Scientific Methods*, students are put into the role of researcher. They may be asked to read about an experiment, simulation, or model, and then apply their understanding of chapter concepts and scientific methods to analyze and explain the procedure and results. Many of the questions in this section are open-ended, giving students the opportunity to demonstrate both reasoning and creative skills. This section, as well as the other sections of each test, begins on a separate page, so that if you wish to omit a section from a test, you can easily do so.

Answers or possible responses to all questions for the chapters in this unit are provided in the Teacher Support and Planning section at the back of this book.

Student Recording Sheet: *Student Recording Sheets* allow students to use the Chapter Assessments in the Student Edition as a practice for standardized testing, giving them an opportunity to use bubble answer grids and number grids for recording answers. There is a recording sheet for each chapter in this unit and a recording sheet for the Unit Assessment at the end of the BioDigest for this unit. Answers for the *Student Recording Sheets* can be found in the side wrap of the Teacher Wraparound Edition on the Chapter Assessment and Unit Review pages.

Teacher Support and Planning

Foldables™ Study Organizer: These pages provide an additional Foldables strategy for each chapter in this unit. The strategy is presented at the top of the page along with more challenging options or suggestions for students who prefer their Foldables to be more creative or informative. The bottom of the page provides instructions for how to make Foldables and can be reproduced and distributed to students who may benefit from the illustrated instructions.

Teacher Guide and Answers: Answers or possible answers for questions in this booklet can be found in chapter order in this section. Materials, teaching strategies, and content background along with chapter references are found where appropriate.

Contents

Chapter 34 Protection, Support, and Locomotion

MiniLab 34.1 Examine Your Fingerprints

Comparing

Fingerprints play a major role in any police investigation. Because a fingerprint is an individual characteristic, extensive FBI fingerprint files are used for identification in criminal cases.

Procedure

1. Press your thumb lightly on the surface of an ink pad.
2. Roll your thumb from left to right across the corner of an index card, then immediately lift your thumb straight up from the paper.
3. Repeat the steps above for your other four fingers, placing the prints in order across the card.
4. Examine your fingerprints with a magnifying lens, identifying the patterns in each by comparing them with the diagrams on page 895 of your text.
5. Compare your fingerprints with those of your classmates.

Analysis

1. Are the fingerprint patterns on your five fingers identical?

____

____

2. Do any of your fingerprints show the same patterns as those of a classmate?

____

____

3. How can a fingerprint be used to identify a person?

____

____

MiniLab 34.2 Examining Muscle Contraction

Interpreting

Muscle fibers are composed of a number of small functional units called sarcomeres. Sarcomeres, in turn, are composed of protein filaments called actin and myosin. The sliding action of these filaments in relation to each other results in muscle contraction.

Procedure

1. Look at Diagrams A and B on page 907 of your text. Diagram A shows a sarcomere in a relaxed muscle. Diagram B shows a sarcomere in a contracted muscle.
2. Using a centimeter ruler, measure and record the length of a(n): sarcomere in Diagram A, myosin filament in Diagram A, actin filament in Diagram A. Record your data in a table.
3. Repeat step 2 for Diagram B.

Analysis

1. When a muscle contracts, do actin or myosin filaments shorten? Use specific data from your model to support your answer.

2. How does the sarcomere shorten?

Name Date Class

DESIGN YOUR OWN BioLab

Does fatigue affect the ability to perform an exercise?

Chapter 34

PREPARATION

Problem

How does fatigue affect the number of repetitions of an exercise you can accomplish?

Hypotheses

Hypothesize whether or not muscle fatigue has any effect on the amount of exercise muscles can accomplish. Consider whether fatigue occurs within minutes or hours.

Objectives

In this BioLab, you will:

- **Hypothesize** whether or not muscle fatigue affects the amount of exercise muscles can accomplish.
- **Measure** the amount of exercise done by a group of muscles.
- **Make a graph** to show the amount of exercise done by a group of muscles.

Possible Materials

stopwatch or clock with second hand
graph paper
small weights

Skill Handbook

Use the **Skill Handbook** if you need additional help with this lab.

Safety Precautions

CAUTION: ***Do not choose an exercise that is too difficult. Do not overexert yourself. Wear appropriate footwear and clothing for exercise.***

PLAN THE EXPERIMENT

1. Design a repetitive exercise for a particular group of muscles. Make sure you can count single repetitions of the exercise, for example, one jumping jack.
2. Work in pairs, with one member of the team being a timekeeper and the other member performing the exercise.
3. Compare your design with those of other groups.

Check the Plan

1. Be sure the exercises are ones that can be done rapidly and cause a minimum of disruption to other groups in the classroom.
2. Consider how long you will do the activity and how often you will record measurements.

Data Table

Time interval	Number of repetitions
First minute	
Second minute	
Third minute	
Fourth minute	
Fifth minute	

3. ***Make sure your teacher has approved your experimental plan before you proceed further.***
4. Use the data table above to record the number of exercise repetitions per time interval.
5. Carry out the experiment.
6. On a piece of graph paper, plot the number of repetitions on the vertical axis and the time intervals on the horizontal axis.

DESIGN YOUR OWN BioLab

Does fatigue affect the ability to perform an exercise?, *continued*

Chapter 34

Analyze and Conclude

1. **Making Inferences** What effect did repeating the exercise over time have on the muscle group?

2. **Comparing and Contrasting** As you repeated the exercise over time, how did your muscles feel?

3. **Recognizing Cause and Effect** What physiological factors are responsible for fatigue?

4. **Thinking Critically** How well do you think your fatigued muscles would work after 30 minutes of rest? Explain your answer.

5. **Hypothesize** Form a hypothesis about how different amounts of resistance would affect the rate of fatigue. Design an experiment to test your hypothesis. Identify the independent and dependent variables.

6. **Error Analysis** Compare your results to those of other student groups. How can you explain the differences in results? If you were to perform this experiment again, how would you improve it?

Chapter 34 **Biceps Biomechanics**

Real World BioApplications

To the trained eye of an engineer, the human skeleton is a remarkable masterpiece of both strength and efficiency. Made up of 206 bones lashed together at the joints by tough ligaments, the skeleton forms a rigid framework that protects and supports a mass of tissues and organs. On a mechanical level, the skeleton may also be thought of as a system of bony levers, activated by muscles, that work together to produce movement. In this activity, you will analyze the lever mechanics of some body parts and learn how biomechanics can be applied to such fields as prosthetic design, robotics, sports medicine, and surgery.

Part A: Lever Mechanics

Levers form one of the most important groups of simple machines. At its simplest, a lever is a rigid bar that can turn freely around a fixed point, known as a fulcrum. The load that is lifted or moved is referred to as the resistance, and the force used in moving it is called the effort. Figure 1 illustrates the three different classes of levers.

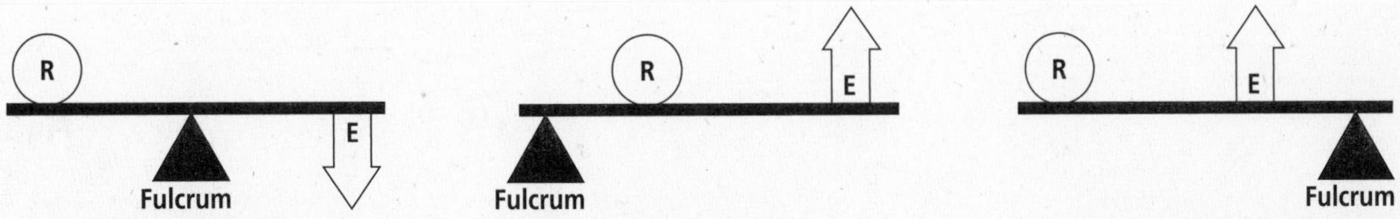

First-Class Lever: Fulcrum is between resistance and effort.

Second-Class Lever: Resistance is between fulcrum and effort.

Third-Class Lever: Effort is between resistance and fulcrum.

Figure 1

1. For each bone/muscle system in Figure 2, indicate which class of lever is illustrated and label the fulcrum, effort force, and resistance force.

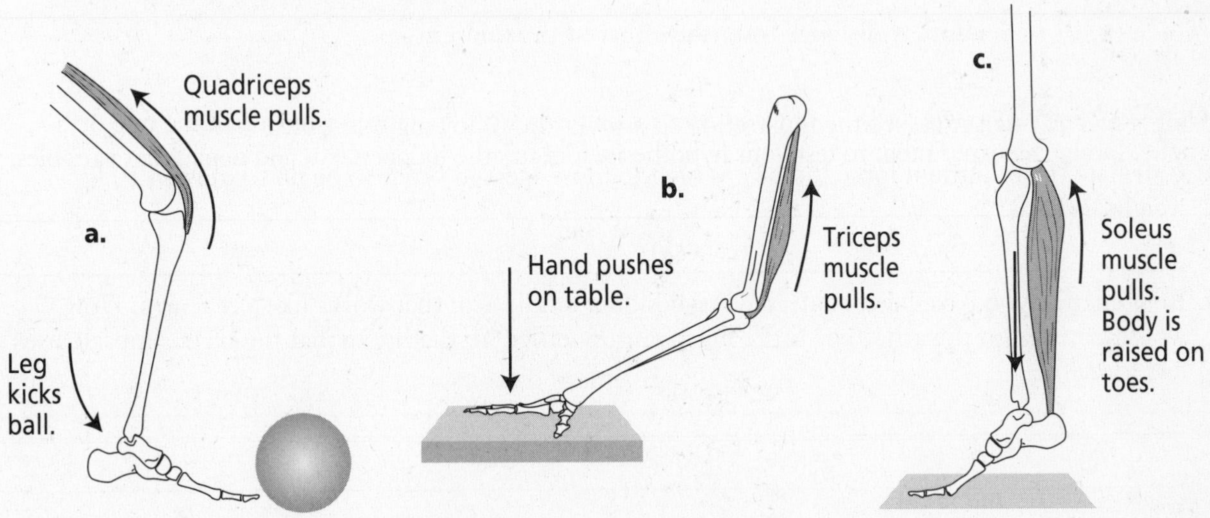

Figure 2

Class of lever **a.** ______________ **b.** ______________ **c.** ______________

Chapter 34 **Biceps Biomechanics**

Real World BioApplications

Part B: Biceps Biomechanics

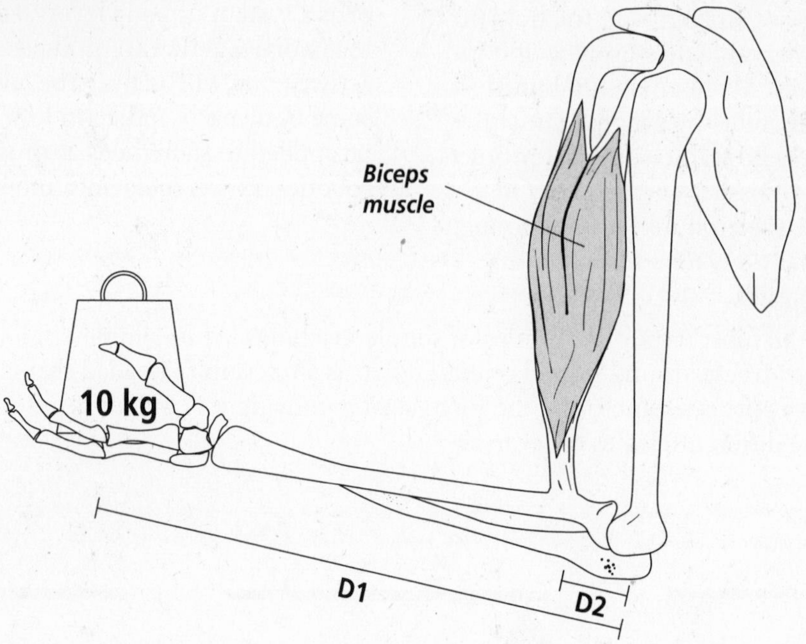

Figure 3

1. Examine the illustration in Figure 3. Label the resistance, fulcrum, and effort. What class of lever does this illustrate?

____

2. For all levers operating without friction, the following equation applies:

resistance × distance from the resistance to the fulcrum =
effort × distance from the effort to the fulcrum

Using a metric ruler, measure the illustration to answer the following questions.

a. Calculate the minimum force the biceps muscle must exert in order to begin to move a 10 kg weight upward.

____

b. Imagine that you have been contracted to design a bionic arm that works like a real arm. How would you design the arm to be more mechanically efficient, that is, so that the biceps muscle uses less force?

____

____

____

Chapter 34 **Real World BioApplications**

Analyzing Dietary Fiber

Leading nutritionists are now recommending that humans go back to a diet more similar to that of our ancestors 20 000 years ago. No, this doesn't mean that you'll soon find mastodon burgers at your favorite fast-food restaurant. But it is a strong suggestion that people incorporate more plant foods such as whole grains, nuts, fruits, and vegetables into their diets in order to get more dietary fiber. Dietary fiber is the part of plants that can't be digested, so it passes through the digestive system without being broken down. Composed mainly of cellulose and derived from the tough cell walls of plant cells, dietary fiber has been shown to lower cholesterol, reduce the risk of colon cancer, and effectively treat common intestinal ills, such as constipation. In this activity, you will examine the fiber content of certain foods and learn how you can incorporate more fiber into your diet.

Part A: Dietary Fiber Content in Foods

Table 1 shows the dietary fiber content of some common foods. Use the table to answer the questions below.

Table 1: Dietary Fiber Content of Some Foods

Food	Portion	Fiber (g)
Breads		
bagel	1	1.2
English muffin	1	1.6
white bread	1 slice	0.5
whole-wheat bread	1 slice	2.1
doughnut	1	negligible
Grains and grain products		
puffed-rice cereal	1 cup	1.2
crisped-rice cereal	1 cup	0.3
toasted-oat cereal	1 cup	2.5
high-fiber cereal	1 cup	9.0
white rice	1/2 cup	1.0
brown rice	1/2 cup	1.7
Fruits and Vegetables		
apple, with peel	1 small	3.7
apple, peeled	1 small	1.4
pear, with peel	1 small	4.3
pear, peeled	1 small	2.4
banana	1	1.8
orange	1	3.1
carrot, raw	1	2.3
broccoli, cooked	1/2 cup	2.0
tomato, raw	1 medium	1.6
iceberg lettuce	1 cup	1.4
sweet potato, skin	1 medium	3.4
Beans		
chick-peas, canned	1/2 cup	7.0
black-eyed peas	1/2 cup	8.3
lentils	1/2 cup	5.2
pinto bean chili	1/2 cup	4.6
Snacks		
potato chips	3 cups	1.0
popcorn	3 cups	2.7

1. Based on Table 1, which group of foods is the best source of dietary fiber?

____

2. The American Dietetic Association recommends 20 to 35 grams of dietary fiber daily. What is your daily fiber intake? In your science notebook or journal, list the amount and types of foods you ate yesterday. Then use Table 1 to find the fiber content of each food. For foods not listed in the table, consult additional reference sources.

Name Date Class

Chapter 34

Analyzing Dietary Fiber

Real World BioApplications

Part B: Fitting Fiber into Your Diet

Does fitting fiber into your diet mean a great change in how you eat? Actually, changing your diet to include more fiber is easy; one way it can be done is by simply substituting a high-fiber food for a low-fiber food in the same food group. For example, at breakfast, a slice of whole-wheat toast, a carbohydrate with 2.1 grams of dietary fiber, can be substituted for a doughnut, a carbohydrate with negligible fiber content. You may wish to include more foods from certain food groups, such as beans. Use Table 1 and other references to adjust the menu below so that it forms a balanced diet that includes at least 35 grams of dietary fiber.

Old Menu

Breakfast	**Fiber (g)**
doughnut	negligible
orange juice	0.1
corn flakes	0.5
Lunch	
hamburger on white bun	0.7
french fries	3.1
Dinner	
lettuce and tomato salad	3.0
chicken	negligible
white rice	0.2
Snacks	
apple	3.0
potato chips	1.0
Daily Total:	**11.6 g**

New Menu

Breakfast	**Fiber (g)**
Lunch	
Dinner	
Snacks	
Daily Total:	

Name Date Class

Chapter 34

Protection, Support, and Locomotion

Reinforcement and Study Guide

Section 34.1 Skin: The Body's Protection

In your textbook, read about the structure and function of the skin.

Complete the table by checking the correct column for each description.

Description	Epidermis	Dermis
1. The outermost layer of skin		
2. Contains connective tissue, glands, and muscles		
3. The thicker, inner layer of skin		
4. Partly composed of dead, keratin-containing cells		
5. Contains pigmented cells that protect against the sun's rays		
6. Hair follicles grow out of this layer		
7. Site of continual mitotic cell divisions		
8. Richly supplied with blood vessels and nerves		

Answer the following questions.

9. Describe the change that takes place in your skin when you are exposed to ultraviolet light.

____

____

____

____

10. How does skin help regulate body temperature?

____

____

____

____

11. List three other functions of skin.

____

____

____

____

Chapter 34

Protection, Support, and Locomotion, *continued*

Reinforcement and Study Guide

Section 34.2 Bones: The Body's Support

In your textbook, read about the structure of the skeletal system and joints.

Identify the following as being part of the axial or appendicular skeleton.

_______________ **1.** the tarsals, metatarsals, and phalanges in your foot

_______________ **2.** the seven vertebrae in your neck

_______________ **3.** your rib cage

_______________ **4.** the bones in your shoulder

_______________ **5.** your lower jaw

_______________ **6.** the humerus in your arm

For each answer below, write an appropriate question.

7. Answer: They are bands of connective tissue that attach muscles to bones.

Question: ____

8. Answer: Fluid-filled sacs that reduce friction between bones in a joint.

Question: ____

9. Answer: They connect bones to other bones.

Question: ____

10. Answer: One allows the bones to move back and forth; the other allows the bones to rotate.

Question: ____

In your textbook, read about the formation of bone and bone growth.

Complete each sentence.

11. In a human embryo's skeleton, _______________ is gradually replaced by _______________ except in a few places like the tip of the _______________ .

12. Some cells in cartilage are stimulated to become _______________ . They secrete a substance in which _______________ _______________ and other minerals are deposited.

13. Your bones increase in length near their _______________ .

14. Even after you reach your full adult height, the bone-forming cells in your body will still be involved in _______________ and _______________ .

Chapter 34 Protection, Support, and Locomotion, *continued*

Reinforcement and Study Guide

Section 34.2 Bones: The Body's Support

In your textbook, read about compact and spongy bone and skeletal system functions.

Answer the following questions.

15. If you cut through to the center of a large leg bone, what bone components (in order, from the outside in) would you encounter?

____

____

16. How do blood vessels and nerves reach individual bone cells in compact bone?

____

17. What role does bone marrow play in the functioning of your circulatory system?

____

____

18. In what way is the skeleton a storehouse?

____

____

____

In your textbook, read about growth, mineral storage, and injury and disease in bone.

Determine if the statement is <u>true</u> or <u>false</u>.

______________ **19.** Once you have finished growing, your bones no longer change.

______________ **20.** Calcium is both deposited in and removed from bones.

______________ **21.** Calcium removed from bone is rapidly excreted in the urine as an unnecessary body waste.

______________ **22.** As a person ages, his or her bone density usually decreases.

______________ **23.** Because bones in an adult's skeleton are harder than children's bones, adults are less likely to break a bone in a fall.

______________ **24.** Osteoporosis is most common in older women because they rarely include milk in their diet.

Chapter 34

Protection, Support, and Locomotion, *continued*

Reinforcement and Study Guide

Section 34.3 Muscles for Locomotion

In your textbook, read about three types of muscles and skeletal muscle contraction.

Complete the table by checking the correct column for each description.

Description	Type of Muscle		
	Smooth	Skeletal	Cardiac
1. under voluntary control			
2. striated			
3. slow, prolonged contractions			
4. attached to bones			
5. found only in the heart			
6. not under voluntary control			
7. lines cavities and surrounds organs			

In your textbook, read about muscle strength and exercise.

If the statement is true, write *true*. If it is not, rewrite the italicized part to make it true.

8. Muscle strength depends on *the number of fibers in a muscle.*

____

9. When oxygen is limited, *aerobic respiration* becomes a muscle's primary source for ATP.

____

10. During lactic acid fermentation, *oxygen* builds up in muscle cells.

____

11. A drop in the amount of lactic acid in the bloodstream indicates that muscular activity has *decreased.*

____

Nombre Fecha Clase

Capítulo 34 Protección, sostén y locomoción

Refuerzo y Guía de estudio

Sección 34.1 La piel: la protección del cuerpo

En tu libro de texto, lee sobre la estructura y las funciones de la piel.

Completa la tabla indicando la columna correcta para cada enunciado.

Enunciado	Epidermis	Dermis
1. Capa más externa de la piel		
2. Contiene tejido conectivo, glándulas y músculos		
3. Forma la capa más gruesa e interna de la piel		
4. Formada en parte por células muertas que contienen queratina		
5. Contiene células pigmentadas que protegen contra los rayos solares		
6. Los folículos pilosos nacen en esta capa		
7. Sitio donde ocurren continuas divisiones mitóticas		
8. Rica en vasos sanguíneos y nervios		

Contesta las siguientes preguntas.

9. Describe los cambios que sufre tu piel cuando te expones a la luz ultravioleta.

____

____

____

____

10. ¿Cómo ayuda la piel a regular la temperatura corporal?

____

____

____

____

11. Anota otras tres funciones de la piel.

____

____

____

____

Capítulo 34

Protección, sostén y locomoción, *continuación*

Refuerzo y Guía de estudio

Sección 34.2 Los huesos: el sostén del cuerpo

En tu libro de texto, lee sobre la estructura del sistema óseo y las articulaciones.

Indica si cada una de las siguientes estructuras pertenece al esqueleto axial o al esqueleto apendicular.

______________ **1.** el tarso, el metatarso y las falanges de tu pie

______________ **2.** las siete vértebras de tu cuello

______________ **3.** las costillas

______________ **4.** los huesos del hombro

______________ **5.** la mandíbula

______________ **6.** el húmero

Escribe la pregunta adecuada para cada una de las siguientes respuestas.

7. Respuesta: Son bandas de tejido conectivo que unen los músculos a los huesos.

Pregunta: ____

8. Respuesta: Sacos llenos de líquido que reducen la fricción entre los huesos de una articulación.

Pregunta: ____

9. Respuesta: Unen un hueso con otro.

Pregunta: ____

10. Respuesta: La primera permite que los huesos se muevan de adelante hacia atrás; la segunda permite la rotación de huesos.

Pregunta: ____

En tu libro de texto, lee sobre la formación y el crecimiento de los huesos.

Completa los siguientes enunciados.

11. En el esqueleto de un embrión humano, el ______________ es reemplazado paulatinamente por ______________, excepto en algunos sitios como la punta de la ______________.

12. Algunas células cartilaginosas son estimuladas para convertise en ______________ y empiezan a secretar una sustancia en que se depositan ______________ ____ ______________ y otros minerales.

13. Los huesos crecen en longitud cerca de sus ______________.

14. Aún después de que alcances la etapa de adulto, las células formadoras de hueso de tu cuerpo seguirán funcionando en la ______________ y el ______________.

Capítulo 34

Protección, sostén y locomoción, *continuación*

Refuerzo y Guía de estudio

Sección 34.2 Los huesos: el sostén del cuerpo

En tu libro de texto, lee sobre el hueso compacto, el hueso esponjoso y las funciones del sistema óseo.

Contesta las siguientes preguntas.

15. Si cortas un hueso largo por el centro, ¿qué componentes encontrarás, en orden, de afuera hacia adentro?

____

____

16. ¿Qué estructura ayuda a que los vasos sanguíneos y los nervios se acerquen a las células óseas individuales del hueso compacto?

____

17. ¿Cuál es la importancia de la médula ósea en el funcionamiento de tu sistema circulatorio?

____

____

18. ¿Por qué el hueso funciona como almacén?

____

____

____

En tu libro de texto, lee sobre el crecimiento, el almacenamiento de minerales, las lesiones y las enfermedades de los huesos.

Indica si cada uno de los enunciados es verdadero o falso.

__________ **19.** Una vez que terminas de crecer, tus huesos ya no cambian.

__________ **20.** El calcio se deposita y se elimina de los huesos.

__________ **21.** El calcio eliminado de los huesos rápidamente se excreta en la orina como desecho.

__________ **22.** Por lo general, al envejecer, la densidad de los huesos de una persona disminuye.

__________ **23.** Debido a que los huesos son más duros en el esqueleto adulto que en el esqueleto infantil, es menos probable que los adultos se rompan un hueso al caerse.

__________ **24.** La osteoporosis es más común en mujeres de edad avanzada porque casi nunca incluyen leche en sus dietas.

Capítulo 34

Protección, sostén y locomoción, *continuación*

Refuerzo y Guía de estudio

Sección 34.3 Músculos para la locomoción

En tu libro de texto, lee sobre los tres tipos de músculos y la contracción del músculo esquelético.

Completa la tabla indicando la columna o columnas correspondientes a cada enunciado.

Enunciado	Tipo de músculo		
	Liso	Esquelético	Cardiaco
1. bajo control voluntario			
2. estriado			
3. contracciones lentas y prolongadas			
4. unido a huesos			
5. se encuentra sólo en el corazón			
6. no está bajo el control voluntario			
7. rodea cavidades y órganos			

En tu libro de texto, lee sobre la relación entre la fortaleza de un músculo y el ejercicio.

Si el enunciado es verdadero, escribe *verdadero*; de lo contrario, modifica la sección en itálicas para hacer verdadero el enunciado.

8. La fuerza de un músculo depende *del número de fibras en el músculo.*

____

9. Cuando hay escasez de oxígeno, la *respiración aeróbica* se convierte en la fuente primaria de ATP para el músculo.

____

10. Durante la fermentación del ácido láctico se acumula *oxígeno* en las células musculares.

____

11. Una reducción en la cantidad de ácido láctico en la sangre indica que la actividad muscular ha *disminuído.*

____

Name Date Class

Chapter 34

Protection, Support, and Locomotion

Concept Mapping

Use with Chapter 34, Section 34.2

Joints in the Human Body

Complete this concept map of the types and functions of joints in the human body. Then give examples of each type. Use these words or phrases once: *wrist, ball-and-socket, fingers, toes, rotational motion, hip, shoulder, back-and-forth motion, ankle, knee, hinge, gliding, elbow, pivot.*

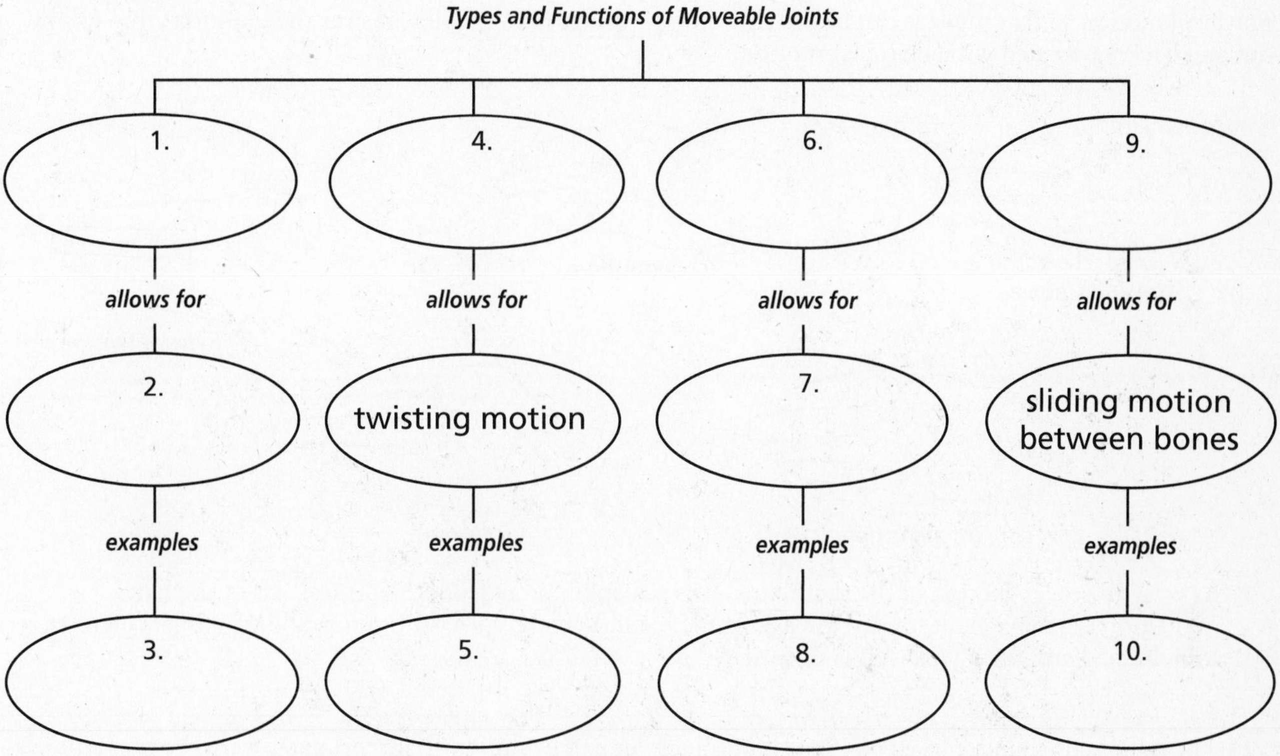

Name Date Class

Chapter 34

Protection, Support, and Locomotion

Critical Thinking

Use with Chapter 34, Section 34.2

Joints in Action

Each type of joint in the human body allows a certain range of motion. For example, the hinge joints of the knees allow leverlike motion in one plane only, permitting bending and straightening of the leg. The ball-and-socket joints of the hip allow universal motion so that the legs can be lifted, swung out and back, or rotated with a circular motion.

Another important joint is the saddle joint of the thumb. As the name implies, it looks like two saddles that fit together and can slide over each other without losing their close fit. The saddle joint of the thumb allows for a wide range of motion. Study the drawings below. Then answer the questions that follow.

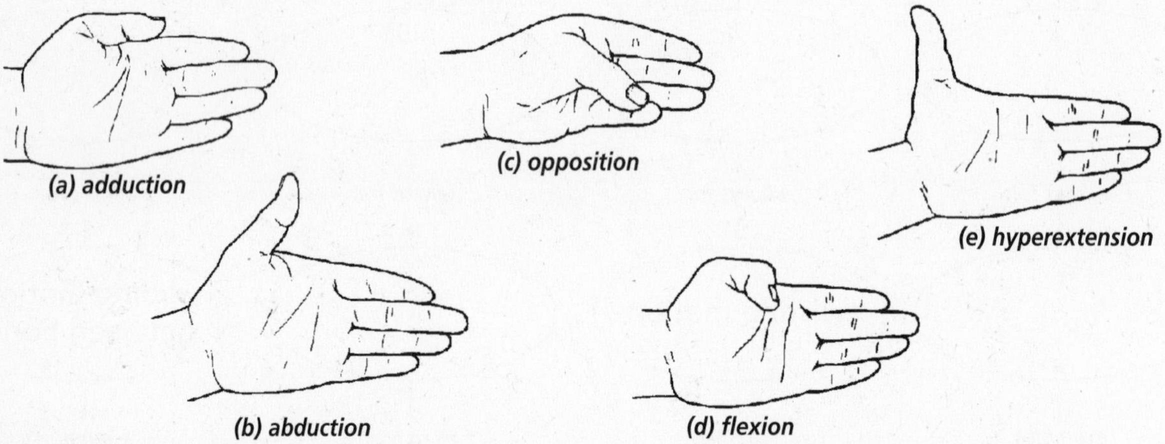

1. As you can see, abduction of the thumb involves moving it away from the central axis of the hand. Adduction is a movement toward the axis of the hand. Which type of motion would you call swinging a straightened arm from your sides outward?

2. The opposable thumb played an important role in human evolution. Early primates were the first animals in which this adaptation appeared. What advantages do you think it offers?

3. How useful is flexion as an adaptation? What does it allow us to do?

4. Suppose the saddle joint were only a hinge joint. How would the various actions of the thumb be affected?

Name Date Class

Master 81

To Cover, Contain, and Protect

Section Focus

Use with Chapter 34, Section 34.1

1. Look at the title of this transparency. How does the polyethylene container in the picture satisfy these requirements?
2. Do you think that polyethylene would be a satisfactory substitute for skin? Explain.

Master
82
Flexible Support

Section Focus

Use with Chapter 34, Section 34.2

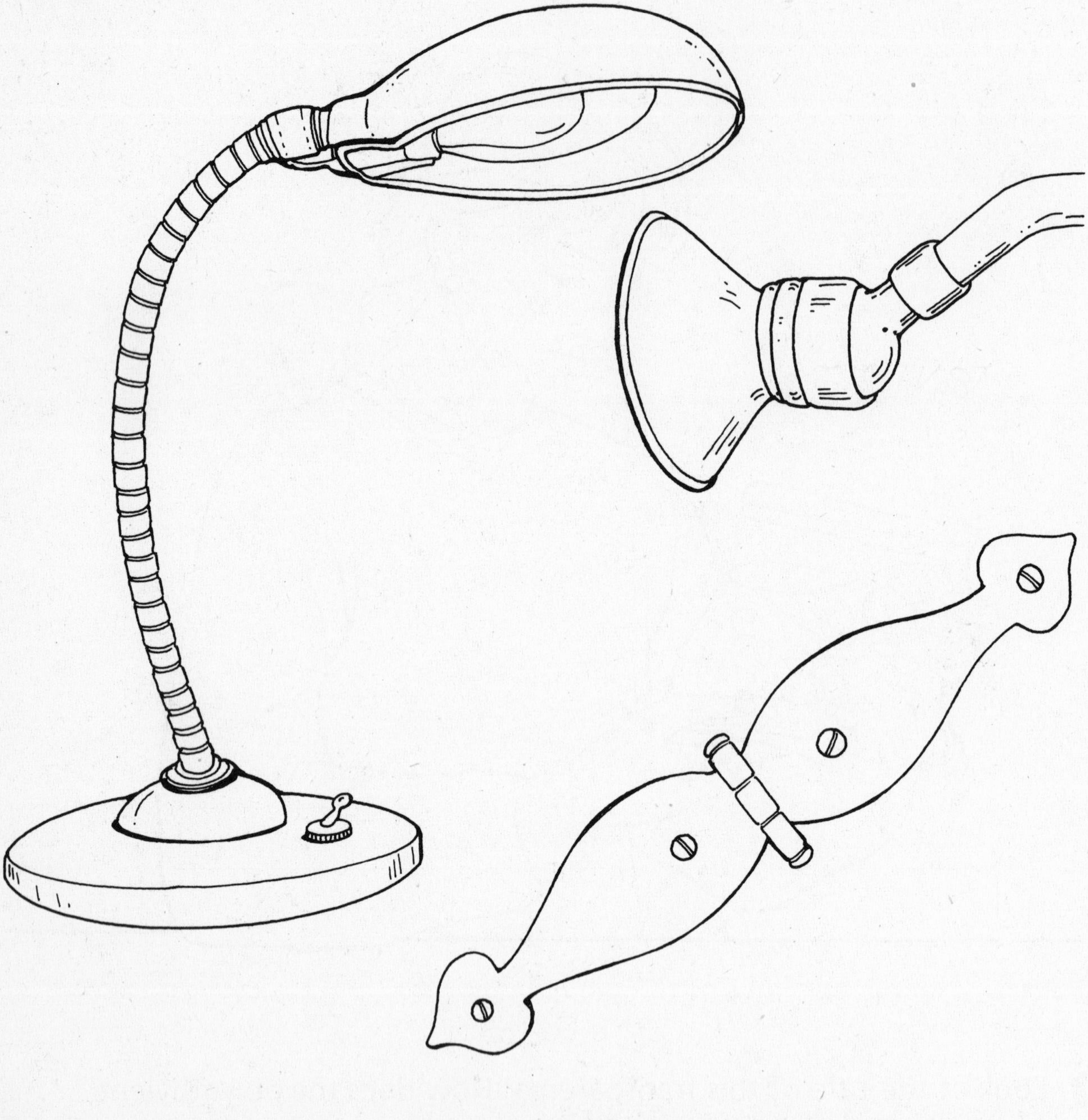

1. Describe the range of motion that is possible in each object pictured.
2. Identify a part of the human skeleton that can move like each of the objects.

Name Date Class

Master 83

Built to Move

Section Focus

Use with Chapter 34, Section 34.3

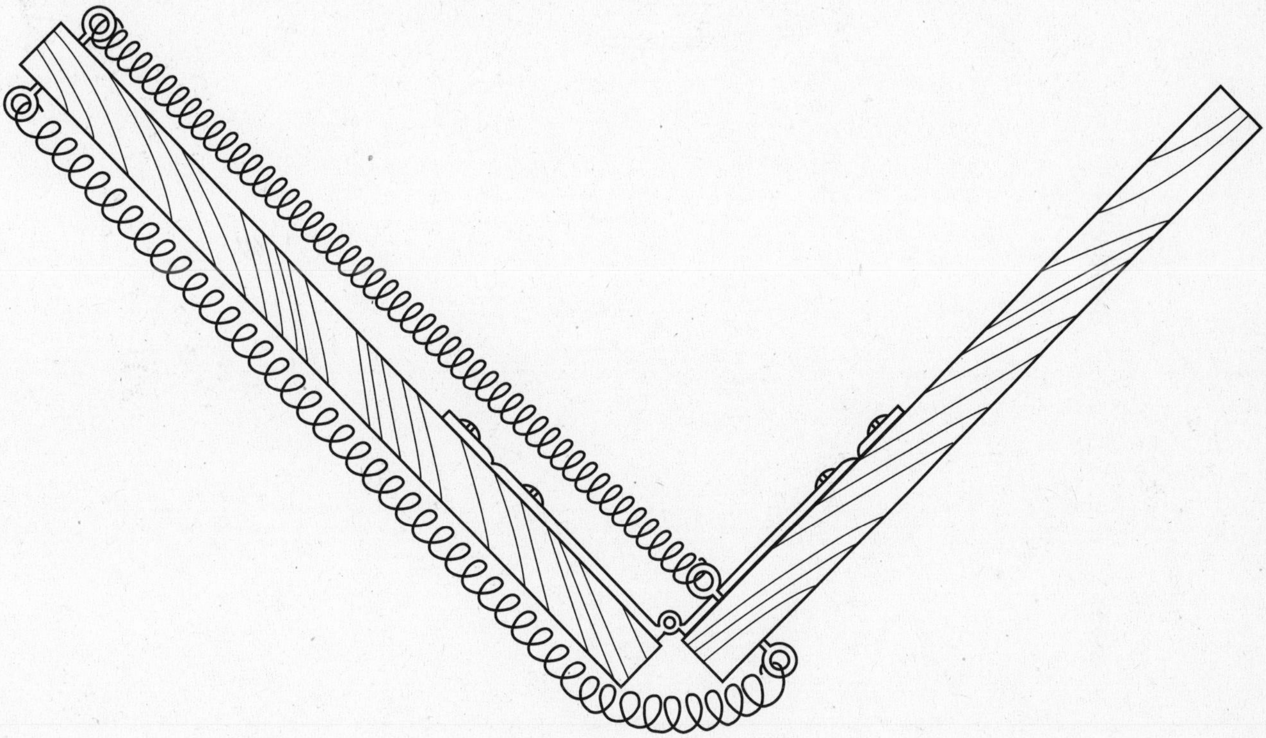

❶ How would the shape of this object change if the lower spring tightened? What would happen if the upper spring tightened instead?

❷ Where on your body is an apparatus similar to the one shown? What takes the place of a spring?

Master 61

Skin Deep

Basic Concepts

Use with Chapter 34, Section 34.1

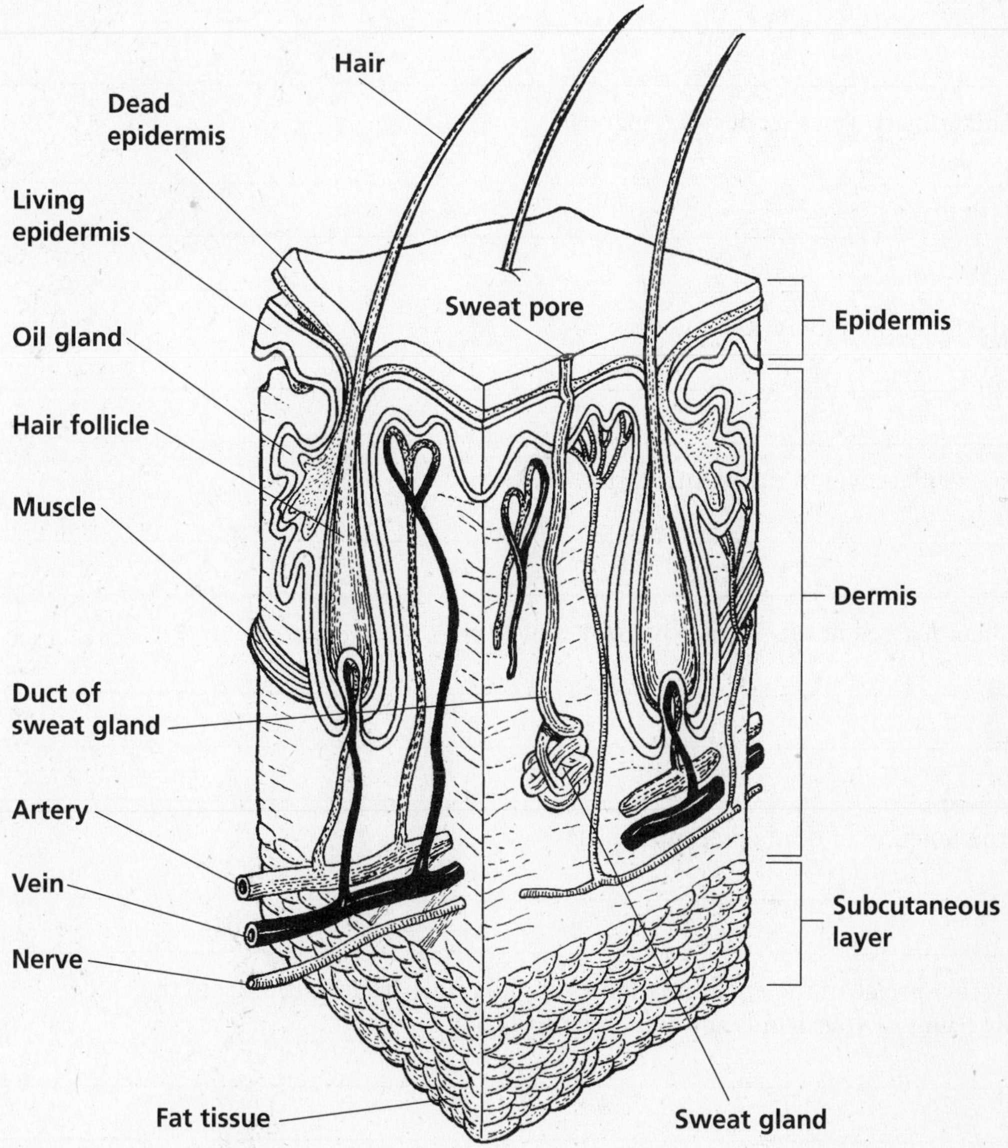

Name Date Class

Worksheet **61**

Skin Deep

Basic Concepts

Use with Chapter 34, Section 34.1

1. What are the functions of skin oils?

2. What is the primary function of sweat glands?

3. What is the function of nerves in the dermis?

4. What causes differences in the pigmentation of skin?

5. Where is hair located in the skin? What is its function?

6. What is the function of dead epidermal cells?

7. How does the surface of the epidermis shown in the transparency differ from the epidermis on the palms of your hands and soles of your feet?

8. What is the function of fat tissue in the subcutaneous layer?

Name Date Class

Master 62

Skeleton and Joints

Basic Concepts

Use with Chapter 34, Section 34.2

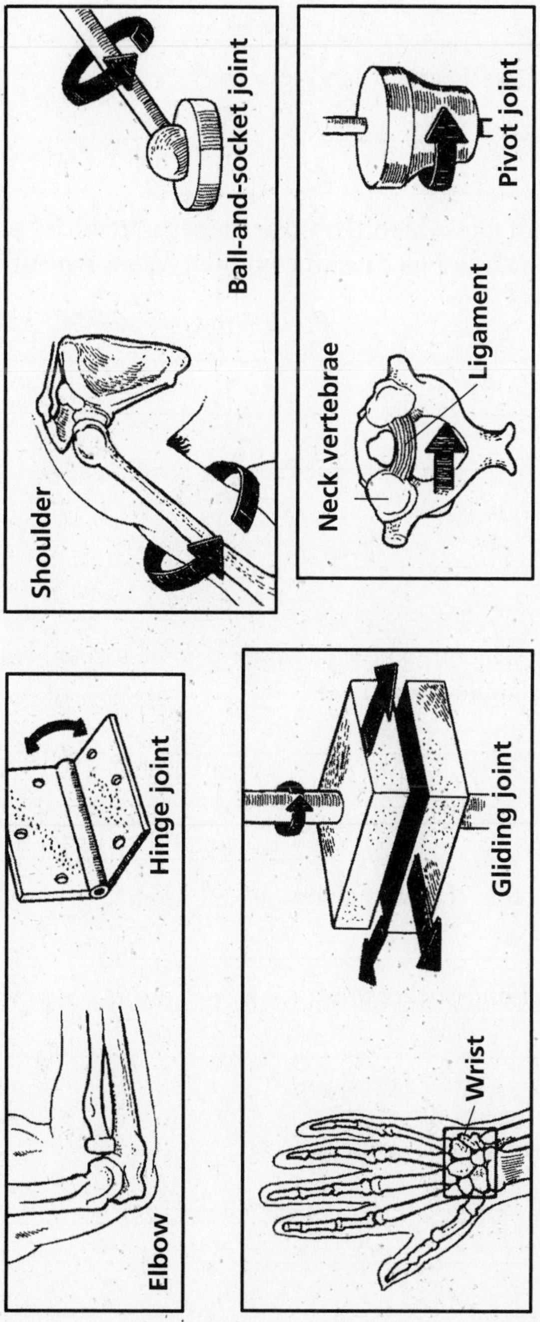

Name Date Class

Worksheet **62**

Skeleton and Joints

Basic Concepts

Use with Chapter 34, Section 34.2

1. Explain how a pivot joint works.

2. What is the difference between ligaments and tendons?

3. Look at the different types of joints highlighted in the separate boxes on the transparency. What do all of the joints have in common? What type of joint is not highlighted in a separate box?

4. Describe the action of a gliding joint.

5. Why is it important for the structure known as a bursa to be located between movable bones in places such as the shoulder and knee?

6. Identify three hinge joints other than the elbow.

7. Describe the action of a ball-and-socket joint.

8. Where do most joint injuries tend to occur? Why?

Master 63

Structure of Bone

Basic Concepts

Use with Chapter 34, Section 34.2

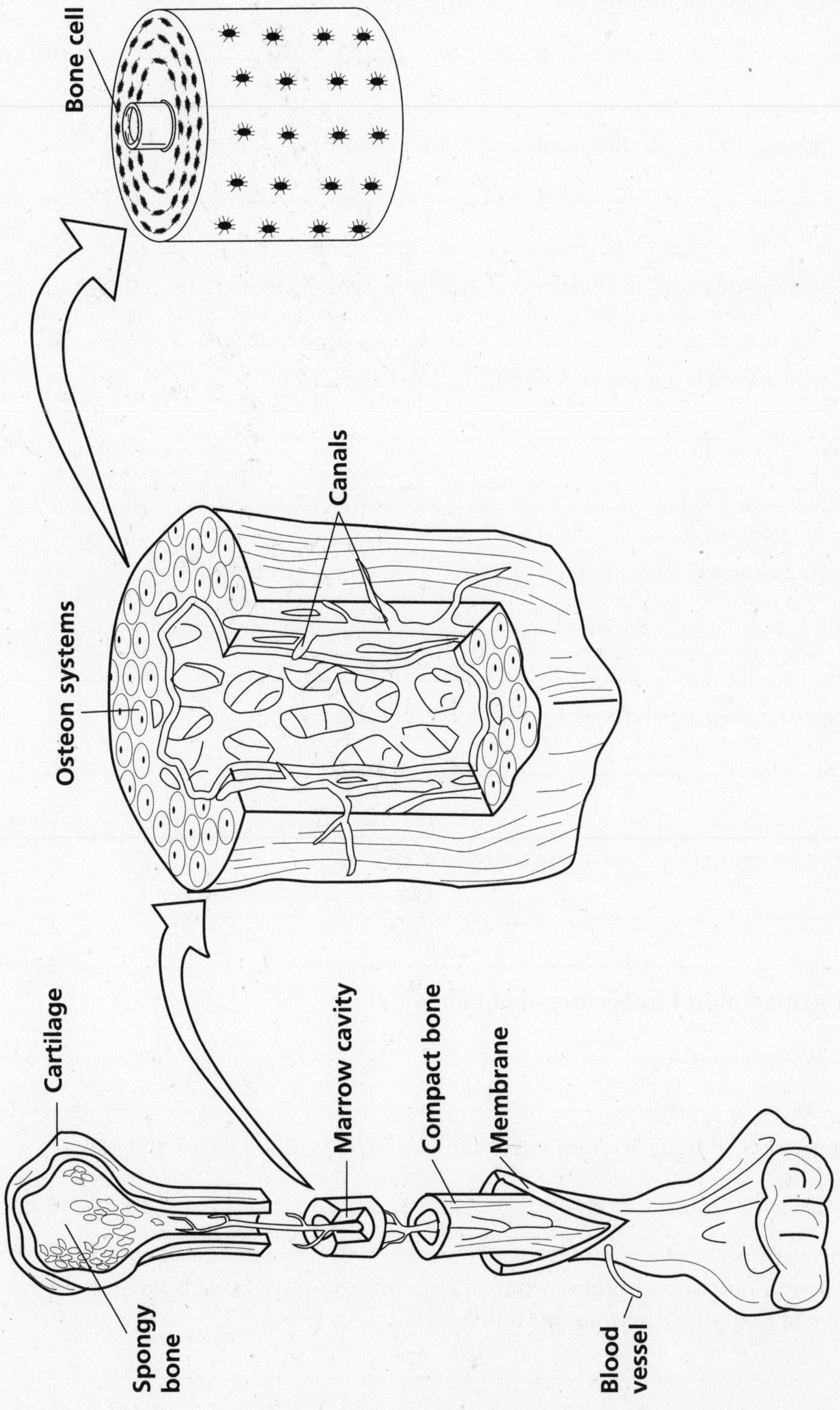

Name Date Class

Worksheet
63

Structure of Bone

Basic Concepts

Use with Chapter 34, Section 34.2

1. Describe the location and function of the osteon systems.

2. What is the function of the membrane that covers compact bone?

3. What are the various sites in the skeletal system where bone marrow can be found?

4. Briefly describe the formation of bone from cartilage.

5. Where do bones grow in diameter? Where do they grow in length?

6. What types of cells are produced by red bone marrow?

7. What is the function of yellow bone marrow?

8. What is the innermost layer component of a bone?

9. What component of bone secretes a substance in which minerals are deposited?

10. Describe a vital function of bones other than providing physical support for the body. What parts of the bone carry out this function?

Name Date Class

Master 64

Muscle Contraction

Basic Concepts

Use with Chapter 34, Section 34.3

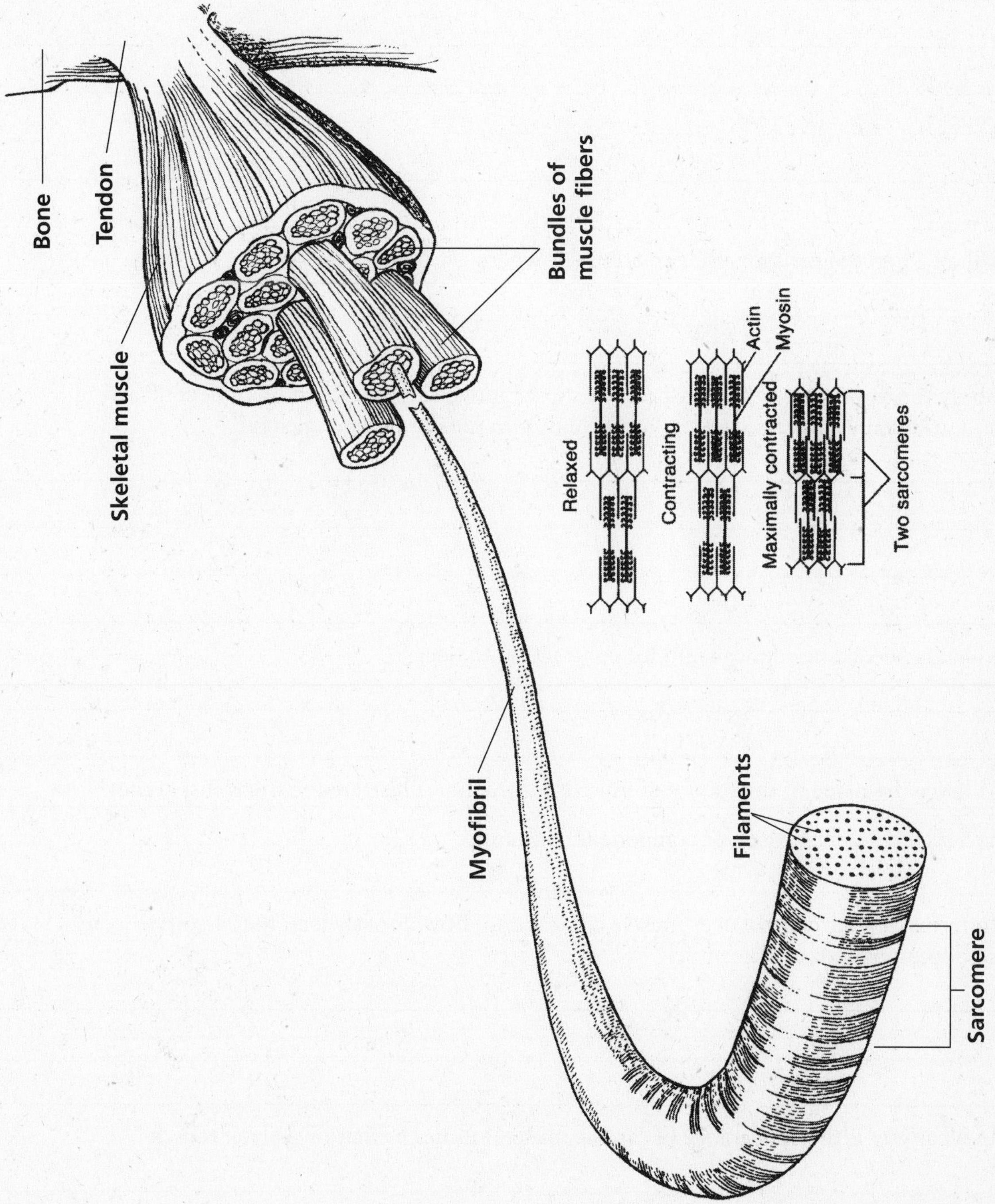

Name Date Class

Worksheet
64 Muscle Contraction

Basic Concepts

Use with Chapter 34, Section 34.3

1. What causes the striated appearance of skeletal muscles?

2. What is a sarcomere?

3. When a nerve signals a muscle to contract, where is calcium released?

4. Study the drawings in the transparency showing two sarcomeres in relaxed, contracting, and maximally contracted states. What happens in the presence of calcium?

5. What is needed besides calcium for contraction to occur?

6. What is the name of the theory of muscle contraction illustrated in the transparency?

7. In terms of your control over muscle contraction, how does skeletal muscle differ from smooth muscle or cardiac muscle?

8. In what way is the appearance of cardiac muscle similar to that of skeletal muscle?

Name Date Class

Master 49

The Muscular System

Reteaching Skills

Use with Chapter 34, Section 34.3

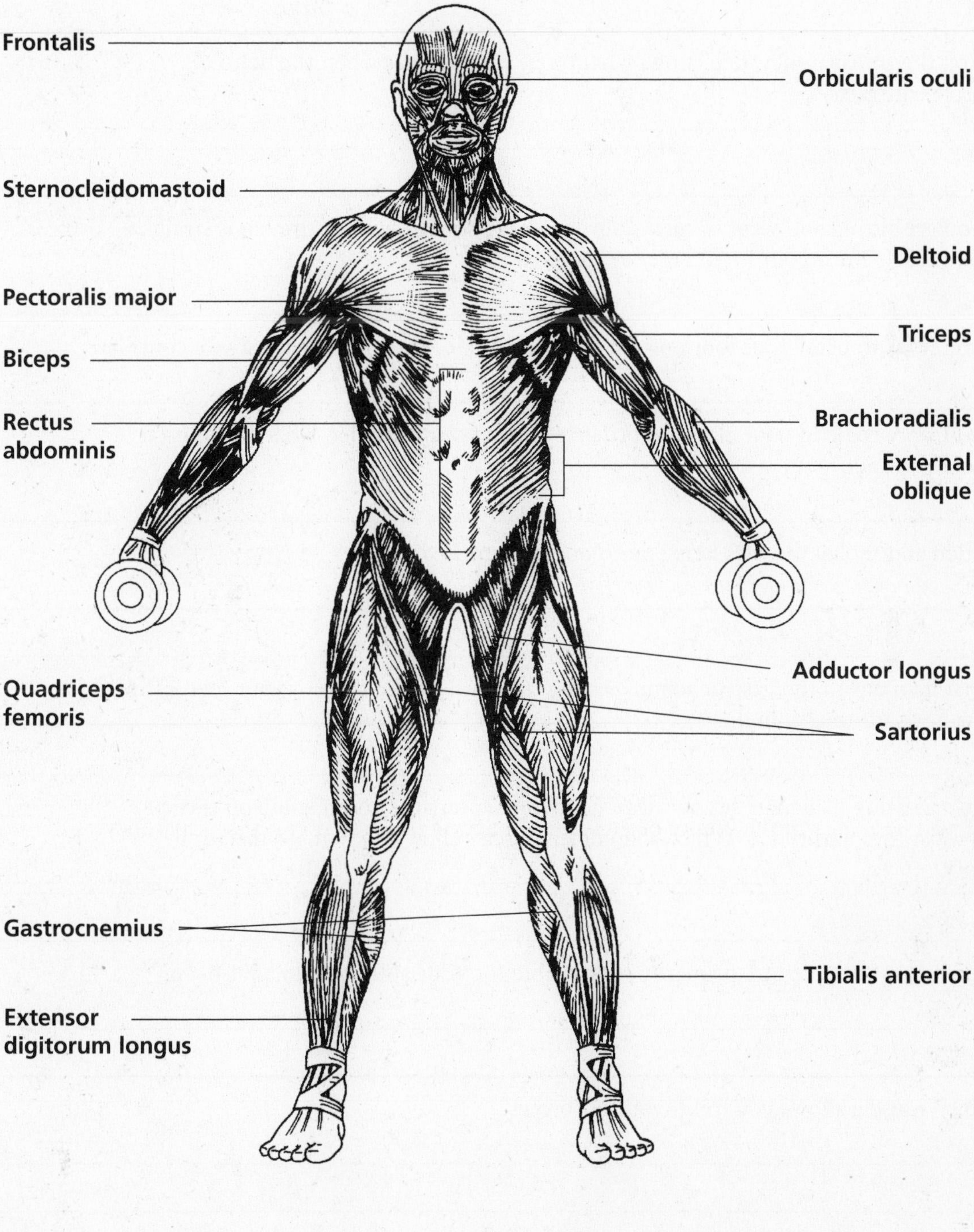

Worksheet **49**

The Muscular System

Reteaching Skills

Use with Chapter 34, Section 34.3

1. What do all the muscles shown in the transparency have in common?

2. Using the transparency, determine what movement occurs when the deltoid muscle contracts.

3. If you are sitting and want to raise your lower leg so that your entire leg is straight, what muscle must your brain order to contract?

4. If you want to bend your foot upward from the ankle, what muscle must you contract?

5. If you were to bend your elbow in order to touch your shoulder, what arm muscle would contract?

6. Which abdominal muscles help you to do a sit-up?

7. What happens to the gastrocnemius when you stand on the balls of your feet, lifting your heels off the ground?

8. You are sitting in a chair at your desk. Someone enters the room, and you turn at the waist to see who it is. Which abdominal muscles allow you to make this turn?

9. Which chest muscles are primarily responsible for your ability to do a push-up?

10. Which muscle allows you to lift your eyebrows?

Chapter 34

Chapter Assessment

Protection, Support, and Locomotion

Reviewing Vocabulary

Match the definition in Column A with the term in Column B.

	Column A	Column B
______	**1.** Where two or more bones meet	**a.** ligament
______	**2.** Fluid-filled sac on the outside of a joint	**b.** marrow
______	**3.** Potential bone cell found in cartilage of embryo	**c.** melanin
______	**4.** Soft tissue that fills center cavities of bones	**d.** osteoblast
______	**5.** Protein in dead epidermal cells that protects underlying cells	**e.** bursa
______	**6.** Cell pigment that colors skin and protects it from solar radiation	**f.** sarcomere
______	**7.** Band of tissue connecting bone to bone	**g.** keratin
______	**8.** Smaller unit in a muscle fiber	**h.** joint
______	**9.** The functional unit of a myofibril	**i.** myofibril

Compare and contrast each pair of related terms.

10. compact bone, spongy bone

____

____

11. axial skeleton, appendicular skeleton

____

____

____

12. voluntary muscle, involuntary muscle

____

____

13. epidermis, dermis

____

____

Chapter 34 **Protection, Support, and Locomotion,** *continued*

Chapter Assessment

Understanding Main Ideas (Part A)

Write the word or phrase that best completes the statement.

1. Beneath the scab of a wound, ____________________ begin to multiply to fill in the gap.

2. ____________________ produces red blood cells, some white blood cells, and cell fragments involved in blood clotting.

3. The mineral ____________________, found in dairy products, is a critical part of the diet for healthy, strong bones.

4. Contraction of ____________________ muscle, the muscle of internal organs, is slow and prolonged.

5. Bones grow in length at the ____________________ of the bone. They grow in diameter on the ____________________ surface of the bone.

6. Muscle strength depends on the ____________________ of the fibers and the number of fibers that ____________________ at one time.

7. When an inadequate supply of oxygen is available to meet a muscle cell's oxygen needs, ____________________ becomes the primary source of ATP.

Answer the following questions.

8. Why is the skin considered an organ? Name two important functions of skin.

____

____

____

____

9. Explain what causes a sprain and what the effects are.

____

____

____

Chapter 34 **Protection, Support, and Locomotion,** *continued* **Chapter Assessment**

Understanding Main Ideas (Part B)

In the space at the left, write the letter of the word, phrase, or sentence that best completes the statement or answers the question.

______ **1.** The skin regulates the temperature of the body on a hot day by
- **a.** closing the pores.
- **b.** dilating the capillaries.
- **c.** constricting the blood.
- **d.** reducing access to the exterior.

______ **2.** After suffering widespread third-degree burns, the burn victim
- **a.** is unlikely to incur bacterial infection.
- **b.** recovers in a short time.
- **c.** has a harder time regulating body temperature.
- **d.** has slight damage to cells of the dermis.

______ **3.** Which of the following examples illustrates a pivot joint in use?
- **a.** You wind up to pitch a baseball.
- **b.** You wave good-bye to a friend.
- **c.** You kick a football.
- **d.** You look behind you.

______ **4.** By age 20, a person's bones stop growing because
- **a.** bone-forming cells are no longer present.
- **b.** less calcium is present in the body.
- **c.** hormones cause the growth centers at the ends of bones to degenerate.
- **d.** bone cells receive less oxygen and nutrients at that time.

Answer the following questions.

5. How does the sliding filament theory explain muscle contraction?

____

____

____

6. How does the buildup of lactic acid in muscle cells result in more oxygen being delivered to your cells?

____

____

____

7. Explain one beneficial and one harmful effect of exposure to sunlight.

____

____

____

Chapter 34

Protection, Support, and Locomotion, *continued*

Chapter Assessment

Thinking Critically

Because it usually goes unnoticed until back pain or a spontaneous fracture occurs, osteoporosis is often referred to as the silent disease. This skeletal disease is characterized by a decrease in bone mass resulting in bones so porous they break as a result of even everyday activities. Though most prevalent after the age of 50, intervention before the age of 30 can significantly decrease the risk of developing osteoporosis later in life. The table below shows some of the risk factors associated with developing osteoporosis later in life. Use the table to answer questions 1 and 2.

Risk Factors	Description
Age	After the middle or later forties, bone mass begins to decrease.
Alcohol Intake	Excessive alcohol intake increases the risk of osteoporosis, especially in men.
Body frame/weight	Small-framed women and men are at greater risk for developing osteoporosis.
Cigarette Smoking	Smokers generally have lower bone densities than nonsmokers.
Diet	Calcium intake below the RDA throughout life increases the risk of osteoporosis.
Genetics	Having a close relative with osteoporosis or an osteoporotic fracture increases the risk of developing the disease.
Gender	Though both men and women develop osteoporosis, women are about four to five times more likely to develop the disease.
Physical Activity	Regular physical activity, especially weight-bearing exercise, increases bone density.

1. Which of the factors listed in the table are controllable? Which are not controllable?

____

____

2. Why would weight-bearing exercises increase bone density? ______________________________

____

____

Answer the following questions.

3. Bone fractures in children are often different from fractures in adults. Explain why this may be so.

____

____

____

4. A paramedic at an accident is aware of pressure points, areas where a major blood vessel crosses a bone close to the body surface. How might the paramedic use these points to stop bleeding?

____

____

Chapter 34 **Protection, Support, and Locomotion,** *continued*

Chapter Assessment

Applying Scientific Methods

The different function of skeletal, smooth, and cardiac muscle is reflected in the way each of the muscles contracts. Study the graphs below to see how the contractions compare. The black line indicates the electrical impulse that stimulates the muscle. The dotted line represents the muscle contraction.

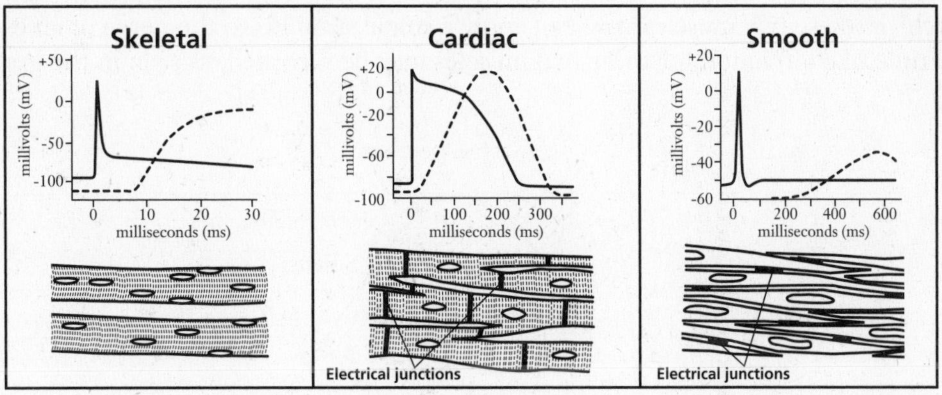

1. Study the graphs. Which of the three muscle types contracts most quickly following electrical impulse? Slowest? Explain the basis for your answer.

2. Compare the electrical impulses in each of the muscle types. How does the electrical impulse for cardiac muscle reflect the function of the heart?

3. Using the graphs and the illustrations, compare the contraction in smooth muscle to skeletal muscle.

4. Explain how the structure of cardiac muscle helps to stimulate muscle cells more quickly than in other muscle types.

Applying Scientific Methods *continued*

Two muscles in your leg, the gastrocnemius and soleus muscles, help you to extend your foot. The gastrocnemius is used in jumping and performing other rapid movements of the foot. The soleus is used principally for support against gravity. In the laboratory, you can study muscle contraction by causing "muscle twitch" in these two muscles. You can apply a single stimulus to the nerve of an excised frog muscle. The time of contraction for these two muscles may be recorded, as seen in the graph below.

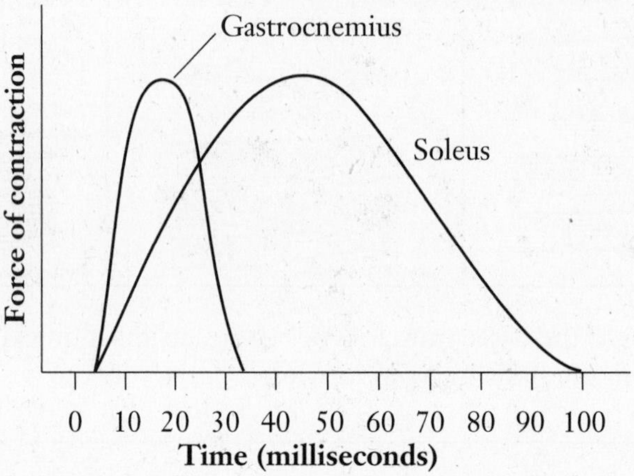

5. Use the graph to decide whether the gastrocnemius or the soleus has the longer duration of contraction. About how many times longer is this contraction than the other?

____

____

____

____

6. Why do you suppose the one leg muscle contracts so much more quickly than the other one?

____

____

____

____

Name Date Period

Chapter 34 Assessment
Student Recording Sheet

Chapter Assessment

Use with pages 914–915 of the Student Edition

Vocabulary Review

Write the vocabulary words that match the definitions in your book.

1. ______________________
2. ______________________
3. ______________________
4. ______________________
5. ______________________

Understanding Key Concepts

Select the best answer from the choices given and fill in the corresponding oval.

6. Ⓐ Ⓑ Ⓒ Ⓓ
7. Ⓐ Ⓑ Ⓒ Ⓓ
8. Ⓐ Ⓑ Ⓒ Ⓓ
9. Ⓐ Ⓑ Ⓒ Ⓓ
10. Ⓐ Ⓑ Ⓒ Ⓓ

11. Fill in the correct terms to complete the concept map.

1.______________________ 3.______________________

2.______________________ 4.______________________

Constructed Response

Record your answers for Questions 12–14 on a separate sheet of paper.

Thinking Critically

Record your answers for Questions 15, 17, and 18 on a separate sheet of paper.

16. **REAL WORLD BIOCHALLENGE** Follow your teacher's instructions for presenting your BioChallenge answer.

Standardized Test Practice

The Princeton Review

Part 1 Multiple Choice

Select the best answer from the choices given and fill in the corresponding oval.

19. Ⓐ Ⓑ Ⓒ Ⓓ
20. Ⓐ Ⓑ Ⓒ Ⓓ
21. Ⓐ Ⓑ Ⓒ Ⓓ
22. Ⓐ Ⓑ Ⓒ Ⓓ
23. Ⓐ Ⓑ Ⓒ Ⓓ

Part 2 Constructed Response/Grid In

Record your answers for Questions 24 and 25 on a separate sheet of paper.

Contents

Chapter 35 The Digestive and Endocrine Systems

Name Date Class

Interpreting the Data

MiniLab 35.1 Evaluate a Bowl of Soup

As a consumer, you are bombarded by advertising that promotes the nutritional benefits of specific food products. Choosing a food to eat on the basis of such ads may not make nutritional sense. By examining the product labels that list ingredients of processed foods, you can learn important things about their nutritional content.

Data Table

Percentage of Daily Value (DV)	
Carbohydrates	60%
Fat	30%
Saturated Fats	10%
Cholesterol	1.5%
Protein	10%
Total Calories	2000

Procedure

1. Examine the information in the table listing the daily value (DV) of various nutrients. DV expresses what percent of Calories should come from certain nutrients. For instance, in the proposed diet of 2000 Calories, 60 percent of the Calories should come from carbohydrates.
2. Examine the nutritional information on the soup can label on page 927 of your text and compare it with the DV table.

Analysis

1. Does your bowl of soup provide more than 30 percent of any of the daily nutrients? Which ones?

____

2. Calculate the percentage of Calories in soup that are provided by saturated fat.

____

3. Is this soup a nutritious meal? Explain.

____

____

MiniLab 35.2 Compare Thyroid and Parathyroid Tissue

Observing

Although their names seem somewhat similar, the thyroid and parathyroid glands perform rather different functions within the body.

Procedure

Data Table

Tissue	Drawing	Name of hormone(s) produced
Thyroid		
Parathyroid		

1 Use the data table on the right.

2 Use low-power magnification to examine a prepared slide of thyroid and parathyroid endocrine gland tissue. Note: Both tissues appear on the same slide. **CAUTION:** ***Use caution when working with a microscope and prepared slides.***

3 The image on page 934 of your text is a photograph of thyroid and parathyroid tissue. Use it as a guide in locating the two types of endocrine gland tissue under low power and in answering certain analysis questions.

4 Now locate each type of gland tissue under high-power magnification. Draw what you see in the table above. Then use what you learned in the chapter to identify the names of the hormones produced by each gland.

Analysis

1. Compare the microscopic appearance of parathyroid tissue to that of thyroid tissue.

2. a. Which tissue type contains follicles (large liquid storage areas)?

b. What may be present within the follicles?

c. Hypothesize what the function may be for the thin layer of tissue that surrounds each follicle.

3. How might you explain the fact that both thyroid and parathyroid tissue can be seen on the same slide?

INVESTIGATE BioLab

Chapter 35

The Action of the Enzyme Amylase on Breakfast Cereals

PREPARATION

Problem

How long does it take amylase to digest all of the starch in breakfast cereals?

Objectives

In this BioLab, you will:

- **Compare** the relative rate of starch digestion by amylase on three breakfast cereals.

Materials

variety of dry cereals
mortar and pestle
test tubes
water
Bunsen burner or hot plate
graduated cylinder
test tube racks
filter paper
funnel
balance
beaker
iodine solution in dropper bottles
watch glasses
plastic droppers
amylase solution

Safety Precautions

CAUTION: ***Never eat laboratory materials. Iodine can irritate and will stain skin.***

Skill Handbook

Use the **Skill Handbook** if you need additional help with this lab.

PROCEDURE

1. Copy the data table.
2. Label the breakfast cereals and three corresponding test tubes **A**, **B**, and **C**.
3. Grind a small portion of each of the breakfast cereals to a powder using the mortar and pestle.
4. Place a piece of filter paper in the funnel. Place the funnel over test tube **A**.
5. Using the balance, measure out 0.5 g of ground cereal **A** and transfer it to the funnel.
6. Filter 10 mL of boiling water over the cereal and allow the filtrate to collect in the bottom of the test tube.
7. Repeat steps 4, 5, and 6 for cereals **B** and **C**. Rinse the funnel and replace the filter paper before each filtration.
8. Add 2 drops of the iodine solution to a watch glass, followed by 2 drops of filtrate **A**. A dark blue/black color indicates the presence of starch. Record your results.
9. Using a separate eyedropper for each solution, repeat step 8 on cereals **B** and **C**. Clean the watch glass between each test.
10. Add 2 mL of amylase solution to each filtrate. Immediately take a sample, and repeat steps 8 and 9 to retest for the presence of starch.
11. Test each filtrate every 30 seconds until all of the starch has been digested to simple sugars in each sample. Record your results.
12. **Cleanup and Disposal** Clean all equipment as instructed by your teacher. Make wise choices as to the disposal or recycling of materials. Wash your hands thoroughly.

Data Table

Time (sec)	Presence of Starch		
	Cereal A	Cereal B	Cereal C
Initial test			
0			
30			
60			

INVESTIGATE BioLab

The Action of the Enzyme Amylase on Breakfast Cereals, *continued*

Chapter 35

Analyze and Conclude

1. **Analyze** Did all of the breakfast cereals contain starch? What action did the amylase have on the starch?

2. **Observe and Infer** Did all of the breakfast cereals contain starch? What action did the amylase have on the starch?

3. **Think Critically** Does the amount of starch versus simple sugars make a difference in the Calorie content of the cereal?

Name Date Class

Real World BioApplications

Chapter 35 The Abdominal Thrust

Would you know what to do if someone around you started choking on a piece of food? With choking consistently ranked as one of the leading causes of accidental death in the United States, knowing what to do in such a respiratory emergency is an important skill. When food or some other object gets stuck in the throat, permanent brain damage or death from asphyxiation may occur. One important first-aid technique for choking is the abdominal thrust, developed in 1973 by Dr. Henry Heimlich. In this activity, you will take an inside look at the abdominal thrust to see how and why it works.

Part A: The Abdominal Thrust

Swift, decisive action is needed when someone begins to choke on an object blocking the air passage. The abdominal thrust is an emergency technique designed to quickly and effectively dislodge food or another object from the respiratory passage. Follow the steps of the abdominal thrust and then answer the questions below.

1. If the choking victim cannot breathe and is standing, quickly stand behind him or her and place your fist with the thumb side against the victim's stomach. The correct placement of the fist is slightly above the navel but below the ribcage, as shown in Figure 1.
2. Grab your fist with the other hand and give four quick and forceful upward thrusts. Do not squeeze on the ribs with your arms. Just use your fist in the abdomen. It may be necessary to repeat this procedure several times until the airway is clear.
3. When the obstructing object comes free and moves into the victim's mouth, remove it quickly.
4. The victim should be seen by a doctor or sent to a hospital as soon as possible for observation.

Figure 1

Thinking Critically

1. Why is quick action important in choking emergencies?

____

____

2. In most cases of choking, the air passage isn't completely blocked. What signs might indicate a total blockage of the air passage?

3. When performing the abdominal thrust on a choking victim, the correct placement of your arms and hands is very important. What problems may result if the abdominal thrust isn't performed properly?

Part B: Analyzing the Abdominal Thrust

A detailed look at the anatomy involved in the abdominal thrust can give a better appreciation of this important technique. Study Figure 2 and answer the questions below.

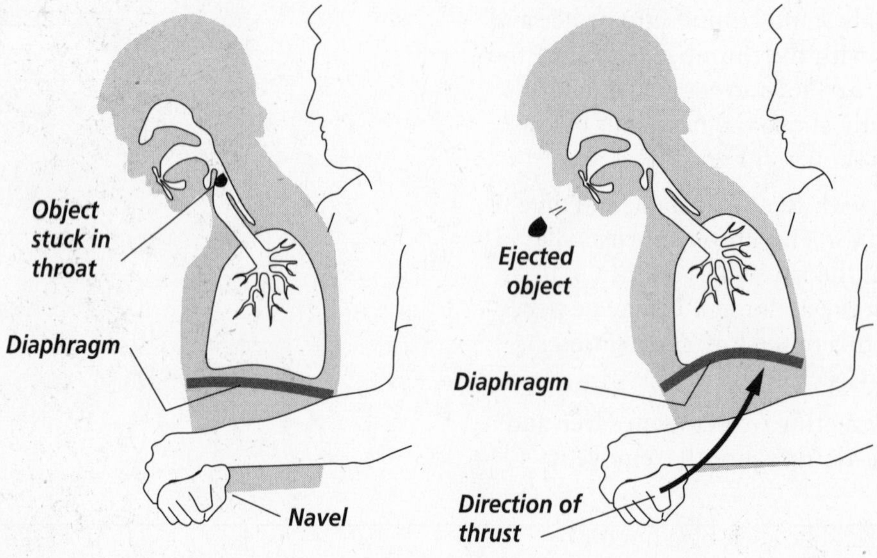

Figure 2

Thinking Critically

1. Use anatomical terms to describe what is meant when someone says that food or drink "has gone down the wrong pipe."

2. Use your knowledge of the respiratory system to explain how a force applied in the abdominal area can dislodge an object caught in the throat.

Name _______________ Date _______________ Class _______________

Chapter 35

The Digestive and Endocrine Systems

Reinforcement and Study Guide

Section 35.1 Following Digestion of a Meal

In your textbook, read about the functions of the digestive tract, the mouth, and the stomach.

Complete each statement.

1. The entire process of digestion involves first ____________________ food, then ____________________ it into simpler compounds, then ____________________ nutrients for use by body cells, and, finally, ____________________ wastes.

2. By chewing your food, you ____________________ its surface area.

3. Various enzymes play a role in ____________________ digestion, while the action of teeth, tongue, and muscles are involved in ____________________ digestion.

4. In your mouth, the enzyme ______________ is released from ______________ glands to begin the chemical breakdown of ____________________.

5. Your ____________________ are adapted for cutting food, while your ____________________ are best suited for grinding food.

If the statement is true, write *true*. If it is not, rewrite the italicized part to make it true.

6. During swallowing, the epiglottis covers the *esophagus* to prevent choking.

____

7. Food is moved through the digestive tract by rhythmic waves of *voluntary muscle contractions* called peristalsis.

____

8. The churning actions of the stomach help mix the food with *pancreatic juices.*

____

9. Pepsin is a *protein-digesting enzyme* that only works in an acidic environment.

____

10. The stomach releases its contents into the small intestine *suddenly, all at once.*

____

In your textbook, read about the small intestine and the large intestine.

Answer the following questions.

11. What role do the enzymes secreted by the pancreas play in the digestive process?

____

____

____

12. Explain the relationship between the liver, the gallbladder, and bile.

____

____

____

13. Once in the small intestine, what happens to

a. digested food?

____

____

b. indigestible materials?

____

____

Complete the table by checking the correct column(s) for each function.

Function	Small Intestine	Large Intestine
14. Water is absorbed through walls.		
15. Digestion is essentially completed.		
16. Vitamin K is produced.		
17. Nutrients are absorbed by villi.		
18. Contents are moved by peristalsis.		
19. Indigestible material is collected.		
20. Bile and pancreatic juices are added.		

Chapter 35

The Digestive and Endocrine Systems, *continued*

Reinforcement and Study Guide

Section 35.2 Nutrition

In your textbook, read about carbohydrates, fats, and proteins.

Complete the table by checking the correct column(s) for each description.

Description	Carbohydrates	Fats	Proteins
1. the most energy-rich nutrients			
2. sugars, starches, and cellulose			
3. broken down into amino acids			
4. part of a nutritious, balanced diet			
5. normally used for building muscle, but can be used for energy			
6. broken down into glucose, fructose, and other simple sugars			
7. used to insulate the body from cold			

In your textbook, read about minerals and vitamins, water, and metabolism and calories.

Complete each statement.

8. ______________________ are inorganic substances that help to build tissue or take part in chemical reactions in the body.

9. Unlike minerals, ______________________ are organic nutrients that help to regulate body processes.

10. The two major vitamin groups are the ______________________ and the ______________________ vitamins.

11. The energy content of food is measured in ______________________, each of which is equal to ______________________ calories.

12. Despite the claims of many fad diets, the only way to lose weight is to ______________________ more calories than you ______________________.

Chapter 35

The Digestive and Endocrine Systems, *continued*

Reinforcement and Study Guide

Section 35.3 The Endocrine System

In your textbook, read about control of the body and negative feedback control.

Complete each statement.

1. Internal control of the body is handled by the ______________________________ system and the ______________________________ system.

2. Most endocrine glands are controlled by the action of the ______________________________, or master gland.

3. A(n) ______________________________ is a chemical released in one part of the body that affects another part.

4. The amount of hormone released by an endocrine gland is determined by the body's ______________________________ for that hormone at a given time.

5. A ______________________________ system is one in which hormones are fed back to inhibit the original signal.

6. When your body is dehydrated, the pituitary releases ADH hormone, which reduces the amount of ______________________________ in your urine.

7. When you have just eaten and your blood glucose levels are high, your pancreas releases the hormone ______________________________, which signals the liver to take in glucose, thereby lowering blood glucose levels.

In your textbook, read about hormone action, adrenal hormones and stress, and other hormones.

For each item in column A, write the letter of the matching item from Column B.

	Column A	Column B
________	**8.** Determines the body's food intake requirements	**a.** steroid hormones
________	**9.** Made from lipids and diffuse freely into cells through the plasma membrane	**b.** glucocorticoids and aldosterone
________	**10.** Bind to receptors embedded in the plasma membrane of the target cell.	**c.** calcitonin and parathyroid hormone
________	**11.** Produce a feeling called "adrenaline rush"	**d.** epinephrine and norepinephrine
________	**12.** Help the body prepare for stressful situations	**e.** amino acid hormones
________	**13.** Regulate calcium levels in blood	**f.** thyroxine

Capítulo 35

El sistema digestivo y el sistema endocrino

Refuerzo y Guía de estudio

Sección 35.1 Ruta de la digestión de una comida

En tu libro de texto, lee sobre las funciones del tracto digestivo, la boca y el estómago.

Completa cada enunciado.

1. La primera etapa del proceso completo de la digestión es la ____________________ de alimentos, seguida por la ____________________ de los alimentos en compuestos más simples. A continuación, sigue la ____________________ de nutrientes para uso en las células del cuerpo y, finalmente, la ____________________ de los desechos.

2. Al masticar los alimentos ____________________ el área de su superficie.

3. Varias enzimas participan en la ____________________ química, mientras que la digestión ____________________ es realizada por los dientes, la lengua y músculos.

4. La enzima ____________________ es liberada en la boca por las glándulas ____________________ para iniciar la desintegración química del ____________________.

5. Los ____________________ están adaptados para cortar los alimentos, mientras que los ____________________ están diseñados para moler la comida.

Si el enunciado es verdadero, escribe *verdadero*; de lo contrario, modifica la sección en itálicas para hacer verdadero el enunciado.

6. La epiglotis cubre el *esófago* al tragar los alimentos, para evitar el atorarse con los alimentos.

____

7. Los alimentos son transportados a lo largo del tracto digestivo por las ondas rítmicas de las *contracciones de los músculos voluntarios*, conocidas como peristalsis.

____

8. La mezcla de contenidos que realiza el estómago ayuda a revolver los alimentos con los *jugos pancreáticos*.

____

9. La pepsina es una *enzima que digiere proteínas* y sólo funciona en un medio ácido.

____

10. El estómago libera sus contenidos en el intestino delgado *súbitamente* y *de una sola vez*.

____

Capítulo 35

El sistema digestivo y el sistema endocrino, *continuación*

Refuerzo y Guía de estudio

Sección 35.1 Ruta de la digestión de una comida

En tu libro de texto, lee sobre el intestino delgado y el intestino grueso.

Contesta las siguientes preguntas.

11. ¿Cuál es la función de las enzimas secretadas por el páncreas durante el proceso digestivo?

____

____

____

12. Explica la relación entre el hígado, la vesícula biliar y la bilis.

____

____

____

13. Una vez dentro del intestino delgado, ¿que ocurre con

a. la comida digerida?

____

____

b. los materiales no digeribles?

____

____

Completa la tabla indicando la columna o columnas correspondientes a cada función.

Función	**Intestino delgado**	**Intestino grueso**
14. Absorción de agua a través de las paredes.		
15. Finalización de la digestión.		
16. Producción de vitamina K.		
17. Las microvellosidades absorben los nutrientes.		
18. Los contenidos son transportados por peristalsis.		
19. Se acumula el material no digerible.		
20. Se añaden jugo pancreático y bilis.		

Capítulo 35

El sistema digestivo y el sistema endocrino, *continuación*

Refuerzo y Guía de estudio

Sección 35.2 Nutrición

En tu libro de texto, lee acerca de los carbohidratos, las grasas y las proteínas.

Completa la tabla indicando la columna o columnas correspondientes a cada enunciado.

Enunciado	Carbohidratos	Grasas	Proteínas
1. los nutrientes más ricos en energía			
2. azúcares, almidones y celulosa			
3. se desintegran en aminoácidos			
4. parte de una dieta nutritiva y balanceada			
5. normalmente se usan para formar músculo, pero se pueden usar para obtener energía			
6. se desintegran en glucosa, fructosa y otros azúcares simples			
7. aisla al cuerpo del frío			

En tu libro de texto lee sobre las vitaminas, los minerales, el agua, el metabolismo y las calorías.

Completa cada enunciado.

8. Los(Las) ______________________ son sustancias inorgánicas que participan en la formación de tejidos o en reacciones químicas del cuerpo.

9. A diferencia de los minerales, los(las) ______________________ son nutrientes orgánicos que ayudan a regular los procesos corporales.

10. Los dos grupos principales de vitaminas son las ______________________ y las ______________________ .

11. El contenido de energía de los alimentos se mide en ______________________ , cada una de las cuales equivale a ______________________ calorías.

12. A pesar de lo que afirman muchas dietas, la única manera de perder peso es ______________________ más calorías de las que se ______________________ .

Capítulo 35

El sistema digestivo y el sistema endocrino, *continuación*

Refuerzo y Guía de estudio

Sección 35.3 El sistema endocrino

En tu libro de texto lee sobre el control del cuerpo y el sistema de retroalimentación negativa.

Completa cada enunciado.

1. El sistema ______________________ y el sistema ______________________ realizan el control interno del cuerpo.

2. La mayoría de las glándulas endocrinas son controladas por la ______________________, también conocida como la glándula maestra.

3. Un(a) ______________________ es una sustancia química liberada en una parte del cuerpo que afecta otra parte del cuerpo.

4. En cierto momento, la cantidad de hormona liberada por una glándula endocrina está determinada por la ______________________ de dicha hormona por el cuerpo.

5. En el sistema de ______________________, la cantidad existente de hormona es retroalimentada para inhibir la señal original.

6. Si tu cuerpo se deshidrata, la pituitaria libera la hormona ADH, la cual se encarga de reducir la cantidad de ______________________ en tu orina.

7. Cuando acabas de comer y tus niveles de glucosa están altos, el páncreas libera la hormona ______________________. La liberación de esta hormona es la señal para que el hígado absorba glucosa, reduciendo los niveles de glucosa en la sangre.

En tu libro de texto, lee sobre la acción de las hormonas, las hormonas adrenales y el estrés y otras hormonas.

Anota la letra de la columna B que corresponda a cada enunciado de la columna A.

Columna A

_______ **8.** Determina la cantidad de alimentos que requiere el cuerpo.

_______ **9.** Formada por lípidos y se difunde libremente en el interior de las células, a través de la membrana plasmática.

_______ **10.** Se une a los receptores de la membrana plasmática de la célula blanco.

_______ **11.** Produce una sensación conocida como "adrenalinazo".

_______ **12.** Prepara el cuerpo para una situación de emergencia.

_______ **13.** Regula los niveles de calcio en la sangre.

Columna B

a. hormonas esteroides

b. glucocorticoides y aldosterona

c. calcitonina y la hormona paratiroidea

d. epinefrina y norepinefrina

e. las hormonas aminoácidos

f. tiroxina

Name Date Class

Chapter 35

The Digestive and Endocrine Systems

Concept Mapping

Use with Chapter 35, Section 35.2

Carbohydrates, Fats, and Proteins in Nutrition

Complete this concept map showing the role of carbohydrates, fats, and proteins in nutrition. Use these words or phrases once: *muscles, antibodies, carbohydrates, proteins, chemicals for blood-clotting, amino acids, glycerol, body functions, fatty acids, the liver, indigestible cellulose, glycogen, fat, body cells, hormones, cell structure, enzymes, simple sugars.*

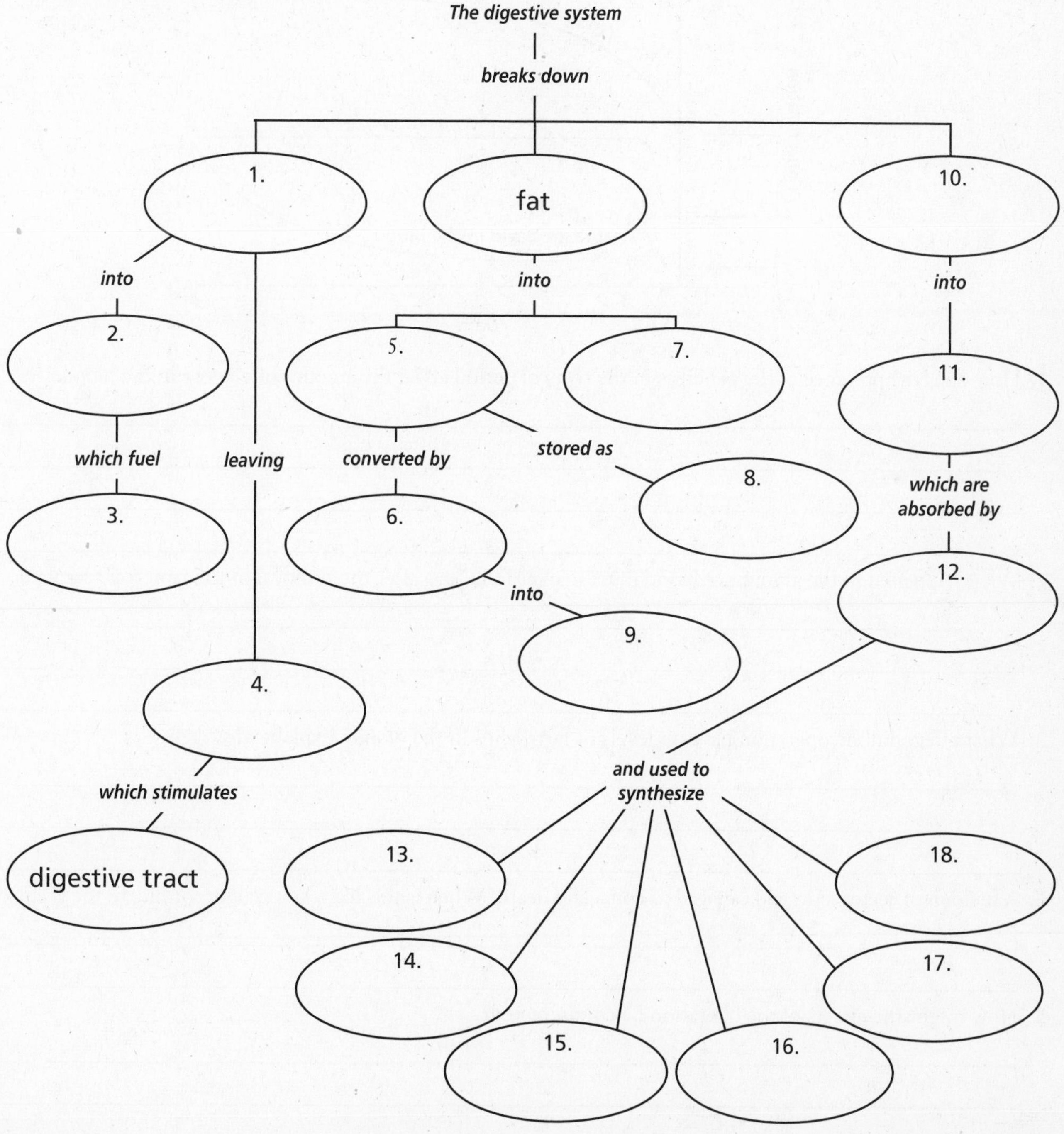

Chapter 35

The Digestive and Endocrine Systems

Problem Solving

Use with Chapter 35, Section 35.3

Interpreting a Blood Analysis Printout

Suppose that while volunteering at the hospital, you come across a printout that looks like the graph below. You recognize some of the terms on the chart and decide to try to interpret it.

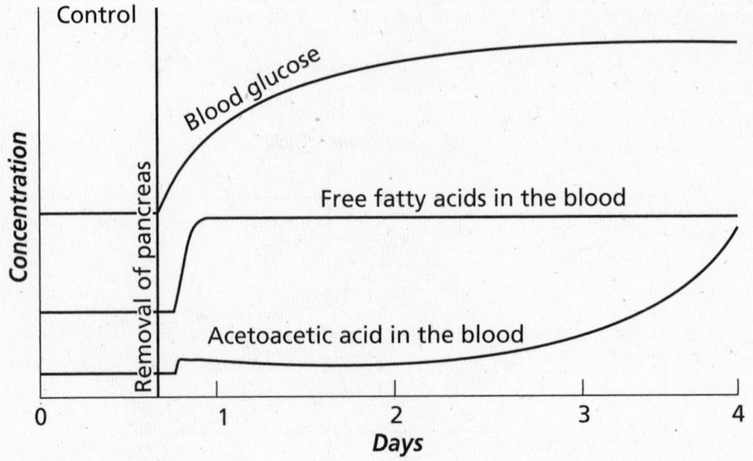

1. How does the presence of the pancreas in the control period affect the amount of glucose in the blood?

2. What happened to the amount of blood glucose over four days after the removal of the pancreas? Explain.

3. What effect did the operation have on levels of fatty acids in the blood? Explain why.

4. A buildup of acetoacetic acid can lead to coma and death. When is this likely to occur according to the graph?

5. How might the effects of the operation be counteracted?

Name Date Class

Master 84

Food Processors

Section Focus

Use with Chapter 35, Section 35.1

1. What parts of the digestive system perform functions similar to the devices shown?
2. What do you think is the overall function of the digestive system?

Master 85

All the Things You Eat

Section Focus

Use with Chapter 35, Section 35.2

1. What two or three essential nutrients are most abundant in each of the foods shown?

2. What essential nutrient is available in all the foods except the grapefruit and the orange juice?

Master **86**

Negative Feedback

Section Focus

Use with Chapter 35, Section 35.3

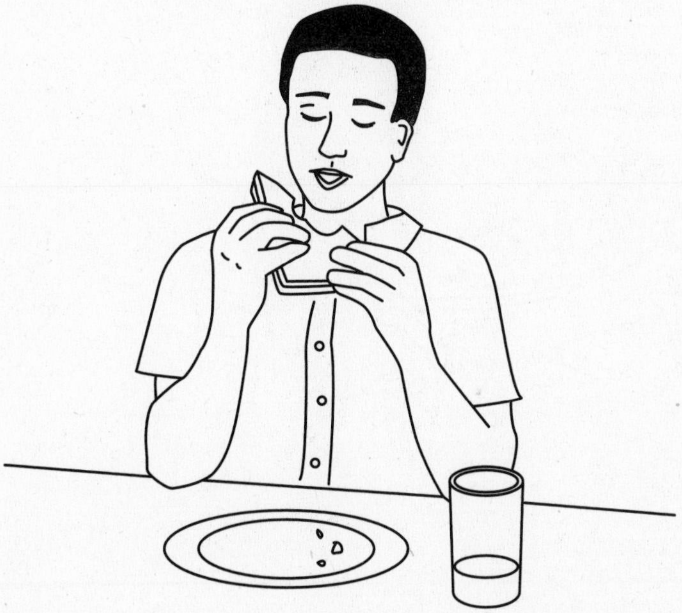

1. What is the internal result of each of these actions?
2. Describe the feedback loop involved in each situation.

Master 65

Regulation of Blood Glucose Concentration

Basic Concepts

Use with Chapter 35, Section 35.3

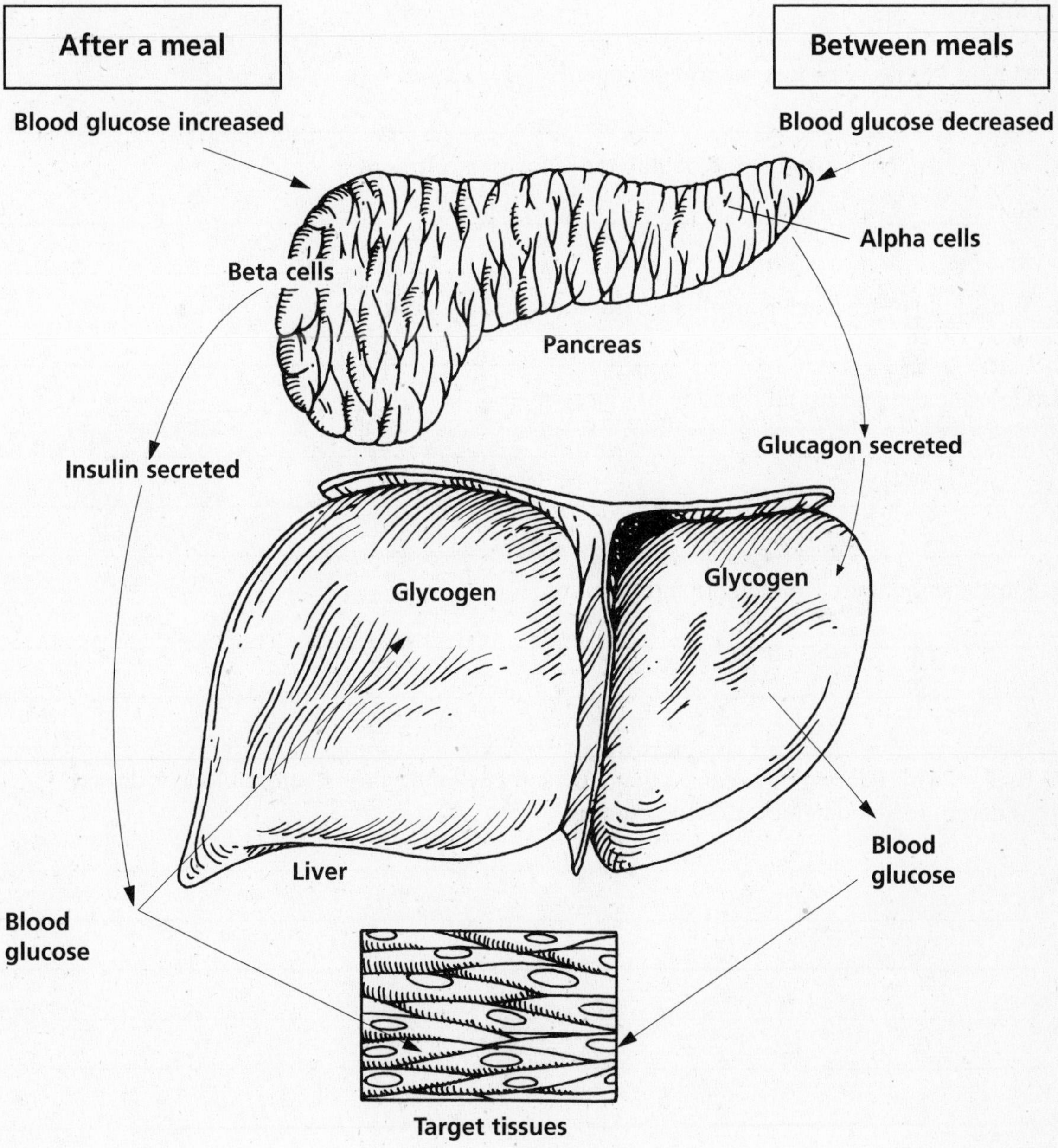

Name Date Class

Worksheet 65

Regulation of Blood Glucose Concentration

Basic Concepts

Use with Chapter 35, Section 35.3

1. What two factors influence blood glucose concentration?

2. Where is glucose converted into glycogen?

3. What triggers the production of glucose-regulating hormones?

4. What kind of feedback control does the transparency show?

5. Describe the source and function of glucagon.

6. Describe the source and function of insulin.

7. Explain why a doctor will request that a person fast for 12 hours before blood is drawn to determine blood glucose concentration.

Master 50

Function of the Small Intestine

Reteaching Skills

Use with Chapter 35, Section 35.1

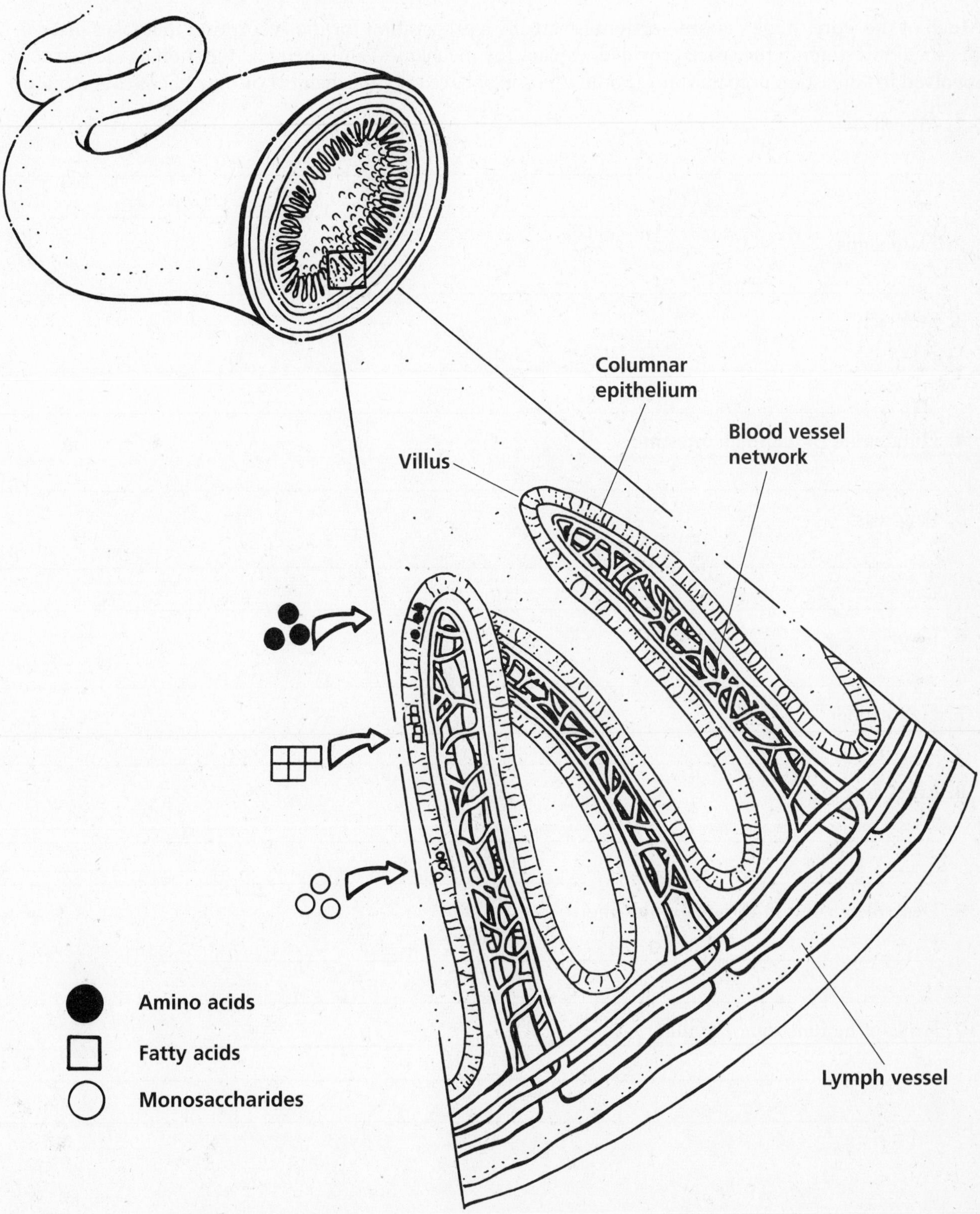

Worksheet 50

Function of the Small Intestine

Reteaching Skills

Use with Chapter 35, Section 35.1

Much of the work of the digestive system is actually a preparation for the absorption that takes place in the small intestine. In the space provided, explain the mechanical and chemical function of each structure involved in "digestion preparation." (Some items may have only mechanical or only chemical function.)

1. Mouth

____

____

2. Esophagus

____

3. Stomach

____

____

4. Duodenum of the small intestine

____

5. Pancreas

____

____

6. Liver

____

7. Gallbladder

____

8. Large intestine

____

____

9. Describe a villus in the small intestine.

____

____

10. Explain the function of a villus.

____

____

Name Date Class

Master **51**

Information on a Food Label

Reteaching Skills

Use with Chapter 35, Section 35.2

A. Conventional Soup Label

Nutrition Facts
Serv. Size 1/2 cup (120 mL) condensed soup
Servings about 2.5
Calories 70
Fat Cal. 20
*Percent Daily Values (DV) are based on a 2000 calorie diet.

Amount/serving	% DV*	Amount/serving	% DV*
Total Fat 2 g	3%	**Total Carb.** 9 g	3%
Sat. Fat 1 g	5%	Fiber 1 g	4%
Cholest. 15 mg	5%	Sugars 2 g	
Sodium 980 mg	41%	**Protein** 3 g	

Vitamin A 6% • Vitamin C 0% • Calcium 2% • Iron 4%

Daily Values

Percent Daily Values are based on a 2000 calorie diet. Your daily values may be higher or lower depending on your calorie needs:

Total Fat	Less than	65 g
Sat Fat	Less than	20 g
Cholesterol	Less than	300 mg
Sodium	Less than	2400 mg
Total Carbohydrate		300 g
Fiber		25 g

Calories per gram
Fat 9 Carbohydrates 4 Protein 4

B. "Heart Healthy" Soup Label

Nutrition Facts
Serv. Size 1/2 cup (120 mL) condensed soup
Servings about 2 1/2
Calories 90
Fat Cal. 15
*Percent Daily Values (DV) are based on a 2000 calorie diet.

Amount/serving	% DV*	Amount/serving	% DV*
Total Fat 1.5 g	2%	**Potassium** 250 mg	7%
Sat. Fat 0.5 g	3%	**Total Carb.** 18 g	6%
Polyunsat. Fat 0.5 g		Fiber 1 g	4%
Monounsat. Fat 0.5 g		Sugars 11 g	
Cholest. 0 mg	0%	**Protein** 1 g	
Sodium 460 mg	19%		

Vitamin A 8% • Vitamin C 40% • Calcium 0% • Iron 2%

Worksheet 51

Information on a Food Label

Reteaching Skills

Use with Chapter 35, Section 35.2

1. The serving size for both soups is 1/2 cup of condensed soup. Why do you think the manufacturer refers to *condensed* soup? Give your answer in scientific terms.

2. Fill in this chart to compare the nutritional content per serving of each product. Be sure to include the units of measure.

	Total Fat	Sat. Fat	Cholesterol	Sodium	Total Carb.	Fiber	Sugars	Protein	Calories	Fat Calories
A										
B										

3. People with diabetes need to be careful about their sugar intake. Which soup seems better for them?

4. People with high blood pressure need to be careful about their salt intake. Which soup seems better for them?

5. People with heart disease need to watch their cholesterol and saturated fat intake. Which soup seems better for them?

6. People with weight problems need to monitor their Calorie intake. Which soup seems better for them?

7. After comparing the two products, which would you prefer to eat? Explain your choice.

Chapter 35

The Digestive and Endocrine Systems

Chapter Assessment

Reviewing Vocabulary

Match the definition in Column A with the term in Column B.

	Column A	Column B
______	**1.** Digestive enzyme that breaks down starch into smaller molecules	**a.** epiglottis
______	**2.** Muscular tube that connects the mouth to the stomach	**b.** pepsin
______	**3.** Series of involuntary muscle contractions along the walls of the digestive tract	**c.** rectum
______	**4.** Flap of cartilage that covers the opening to the respiratory tract during swallowing	**d.** amylase
______	**5.** Muscular, pouchlike enlargement of the digestive tract	**e.** stomach
______	**6.** Digestive enzyme that begins the chemical digestion of proteins	**f.** target cells
______	**7.** Chemical that breaks down fats into small droplets	**g.** esophagus
______	**8.** Last section of the digestive system from which feces are eliminated	**h.** endocrine gland
______	**9.** Regulates metabolism, growth, and development	**i.** small intestine
______	**10.** Specific cells in the body to which hormones convey information	**j.** liver
______	**11.** Unit of heat used to measure the energy content of food	**k.** thyroid gland
______	**12.** Narrow, muscular tube in which digestion is completed	**l.** bile
______	**13.** Organ that releases hormones directly into the bloodstream	**m.** peristalsis
______	**14.** Organ that produces bile	**n.** Calorie

Chapter 35

The Digestive and Endocrine Systems, *continued*

Chapter Assessment

Understanding Main Ideas (Part A)

In the space at the left, write the letter of the word or phrase that best completes the statement or answers the question.

______ **1.** Starches are large
a. fats. **b.** proteins. **c.** polysaccharides. **d.** monosaccharides.

______ **2.** Which of the following is *not* mechanical digestion?
a. chewing food **b.** breakdown of fats by bile
c. churning of the stomach **d.** action of pepsin on proteins

______ **3.** The surface area of the small intestine is greatly increased by
a. a large number of villi. **b.** chemical digestion.
c. peristalsis. **d.** mechanical digestion.

______ **4.** Which of the following is part of the digestive tract?
a. liver **b.** small intestine **c.** gallbladder **d.** pancreas

______ **5.** Which of the following occurs in the large intestine as the work of anaerobic bacteria?
a. absorption of water
b. synthesis of vitamin K and some B vitamins
c. change of glucose to glycogen
d. elimination of indigestible matter

______ **6.** Vitamins are used by the body to
a. provide energy. **b.** maintain growth and metabolism.
c. supply building materials. **d.** digest proteins.

______ **7.** Which is the most abundant substance in the body?
a. fat **b.** water **c.** sugar **d.** protein

______ **8.** The body's preferred energy source is
a. carbohydrates. **b.** vitamins. **c.** proteins. **d.** minerals.

______ **9.** As a result of digestion, proteins are broken down into
a. monosaccharides. **b.** amino acids.
c. triglycerides. **d.** glycerol.

______ **10.** Cellulose is important in the diet as a source of
a. energy. **b.** protein. **c.** fat. **d.** fiber.

______ **11.** Pepsin works best in the presence of
a. amylase. **b.** protein.
c. saliva. **d.** hydrochloric acid.

Chapter 35

The Digestive and Endocrine Systems, *continued*

Chapter Assessment

Understanding Main Ideas (Part B)

Answer the following questions.

1. Name and describe the type of feedback mechanism that controls most endocrine glands.

2. How do glucagon and insulin affect blood glucose levels?

3. Describe how a steroid hormone affects its target cell.

4. Describe how an amino acid hormone affects its target cell.

5. Describe the relationship among the hypothalamus, the pituitary gland, and the endocrine glands that are under the control of the pituitary gland.

6. Explain why the pituitary gland is considered the master gland of the endocrine system.

Chapter 35 **The Digestive and Endocrine Systems,** *continued*

Chapter Assessment

Thinking Critically

Answer the following questions.

1. One cause of diabetes mellitus is the failure of the pancreas to secrete insulin. Describe the blood glucose levels of a person who has diabetes and goes untreated for the disease. How might a doctor test a person that he or she suspects might have diabetes?

2. Cholesterol, secreted by the liver, may cause the gallbladder to produce gallstones. At times, the gallstones block the common bile duct that leads to the duodenom. How might these gallstones affect the patient's digestion?

3. Many people have their gallbladder removed, but the absence of the gallbladder has little effect on their ability to digest fats. Explain why this is so.

4. Vitamin C is a water-soluble vitamin. Is eating a large amount of vitamin C once a week sufficient to keep the body healthy? What happens to excess amounts of vitamin C that may be consumed to prevent a cold?

5. A person suffering from diarrhea may become dehydrated. How might this cause problems in the body?

Chapter 35

The Digestive and Endocrine Systems, *continued*

Chapter Assessment

Applying Scientific Methods

Although fats are an essential part of your diet, it is important to keep total fat intake at or below 30 percent of all the Calories you consume in a day. The fatty acids in fats vary in length and in the degree to which they are saturated by hydrogen atoms. Fats that are saturated are usually solid at room temperature. Most saturated fats, such as those in butter, dairy products, and meats, come from animal sources. However, coconut oil and palm oil are highly saturated fats from plants. A diet high in saturated fat can result in high blood cholesterol levels, which can lead to heart disease. You should limit your intake of saturated fats to no more than 10 percent of your total Calories. Most of your fat Calories should come from unsaturated fats. These fats do not have all the hydrogen atoms they can carry.

1. Calculate the percentage of fat Calories in each food in the table below. (Round answers to the nearest percent.) 1 g of fat provides 9 Calories.

Notice that a hamburger contains 21 g of fat. To find the Calories from fat in the hamburger, multiply 21 g by 9 Calories = 189 Calories from fat. Divide the Calories from fat by the total Calories in a hamburger:

189 Calories ÷ 289 Calories = 0.65 or 65 percent

Food Source (100 g)	**Calories**	**Fat (g)**	**% of Calories from Fats**	**Saturated Fats (g)**
a. Regular hamburger	289	21		8
b. Beef loin	184	7		3
c. Chicken breast with skin	197	8		2
d. Chicken breast, skinless	165	4		1
e. Drumstick with skin	216	11		3
f. Drumstick, skinless	172	6		1
g. Bacon	576	49		17
h. Ham, canned, extra lean	136	5		2
i. Tuna, yellowfin	145	1		<1
j. Shrimp	99	1		<1
k. Sour cream	214	21		13
l. Whole milk	61	3		2
m. Low-fat milk	50	2		1
n. Cottage cheese	72	1		<1
o. Cheddar cheese	403	33		21

Chapter 35 **The Digestive and Endocrine Systems,** *continued*

Chapter Assessment

Applying Scientific Methods *continued*

2. Which food has the highest percentage of fat Calories?

3. Which food has the lowest percentage of fat Calories?

4. It is recommended that a female student who regularly consumes 2100 Calories per day eat only 70 g of fat per day. How many of the Calories eaten by the female student should be fat Calories?

5. A male student who consumes 2800 Calories per day should eat only 93 g of fat per day. How many fat Calories is this?

6. If a student ate a hamburger with a slice of Cheddar cheese and a glass of whole milk, how many grams of fat could the student still safely eat at the rest of his or her meals?

7. Which foods have less than one-third of their fat grams as saturated fats?

Name Date Class

Chapter 35 Assessment
Student Recording Sheet

Chapter Assessment

Use with pages 940–941 of the Student Edition

Vocabulary Review

Distinguish between the vocabulary words in each pair..

1. ______________________
2. ______________________
3. ______________________
4. ______________________
5. ______________________
6. ______________________

Understanding Key Concepts

Select the best answer from the choices given and fill in the corresponding oval.

7. Ⓐ Ⓑ Ⓒ Ⓓ
8. Ⓐ Ⓑ Ⓒ Ⓓ
9. Ⓐ Ⓑ Ⓒ Ⓓ
10. Ⓐ Ⓑ Ⓒ Ⓓ
11. Ⓐ Ⓑ Ⓒ Ⓓ
12. Ⓐ Ⓑ Ⓒ Ⓓ
13. Ⓐ Ⓑ Ⓒ Ⓓ

14. Fill in the correct terms to complete the concept map.

1.______________ 4. ______________ 5. ______________

2.______________ 5. ______________ 6. ______________

Constructed Response

Record your answers for Questions 15–17 on a separate sheet of paper.

Thinking Critically

Record your answers for Questions 18, 20, and 21 on a separate sheet of paper.

19. **REAL WORLD BIOCHALLENGE** Follow your teacher's instructions for presenting your BioChallenge answer.

Chapter 35

Assessment
Student Recording Sheet, *continued*

Chapter Assessment

Use with pages 940–941 of the Student Edition

Standardized Test Practice

The Princeton Review

Part 1 Multiple Choice

Select the best answer from the choices given and fill in the corresponding oval.

22. Ⓐ Ⓑ Ⓒ Ⓓ
23. Ⓐ Ⓑ Ⓒ Ⓓ
24. Ⓐ Ⓑ Ⓒ Ⓓ
25. Ⓐ Ⓑ Ⓒ Ⓓ
26. Ⓐ Ⓑ Ⓒ Ⓓ

Part 2 Constructed Response/Grid In

Record and bubble in your answers on the grids.

27. a. carbohydrates

0	0	0	0		0	0	0
1	1	1	1		1	1	1
2	2	2	2		2	2	2
3	3	3	3		3	3	3
4	4	4	4		4	4	4
5	5	5	5		5	5	5
6	6	6	6		6	6	6
7	7	7	7		7	7	7
8	8	8	8		8	8	8
9	9	9	9		9	9	9

b. fats

0	0	0	0		0	0	0
1	1	1	1		1	1	1
2	2	2	2		2	2	2
3	3	3	3		3	3	3
4	4	4	4		4	4	4
5	5	5	5		5	5	5
6	6	6	6		6	6	6
7	7	7	7		7	7	7
8	8	8	8		8	8	8
9	9	9	9		9	9	9

c. proteins

0	0	0	0		0	0	0
1	1	1	1		1	1	1
2	2	2	2		2	2	2
3	3	3	3		3	3	3
4	4	4	4		4	4	4
5	5	5	5		5	5	5
6	6	6	6		6	6	6
7	7	7	7		7	7	7
8	8	8	8		8	8	8
9	9	9	9		9	9	9

28. **Record your answer for Question 28 on a separate sheet of paper.**

Contents

Chapter 36 The Nervous System

MiniLab 36.1

Experimenting

Distractions and Reaction Time

Have your ever tried to read while someone is talking to you? What effect does such a distracting stimulus have on your reaction time?

Procedure

1. Work with a partner. Sit facing your partner as he or she stands.
2. Have your partner hold the top of a meterstick above your hand. Hold your thumb and index finger about 2.5 cm away from either side of the lower end of the meterstick without touching it.
3. Tell your partner to drop the meterstick straight down between your fingers.
4. Catch the meterstick between your thumb and finger as soon as it begins to fall. Measure how far it falls before you catch it. Practice several times.
5. Run ten trials, recording the number of centimeters the meterstick drops each time. Average the results.
6. Repeat the experiment, this time counting backwards from 100 by fives (100, 95, 90, . . .) as you wait for your partner to release the meterstick.

Analysis

1. Did your reaction time improve with practice? Explain.

____

____

____

2. How was your reaction time affected by the distraction (counting backwards)?

____

____

____

3. What other factors, besides distractions, would increase reaction time?

____

____

____

Name Date Class

MiniLab 36.2

Analyzing Information

Interpret a Drug Label

One common misuse of drugs is not following the instructions that accompany them. Over-the-counter medicines can be harmful—even fatal—if they are not used as directed. The Food and Drug Administration requires that certain information about a drug be provided on its label to help the consumer use the medicine properly and safely.

Procedure

1. The photograph on page 959 of your text shows a label from an over-the-counter drug. Read it carefully.
2. Use the data table below. Fill in the table using information on the label.

Information from a drug label

People with these conditions should avoid this drug	Possible side effects	This drug should not be taken with these medicines	Symptoms this drug will relieve	Correct dosage

Analysis

1. What symptoms will this product relieve? What side effects can result from using this product? Is this product appropriate for everyone to use?

____

____

2. Why should a person never take more than the recommended dosage?

____

____

Name Date Class

DESIGN YOUR OWN BioLab

What drugs affect the heart rate of *Daphnia*?

Chapter 36

PREPARATION

Problem

What legally available drugs are stimulants to the heart? What legal drugs are depressants? Because these drugs are legally available, are they less dangerous?

Hypotheses

Based on what you learned in this chapter, which of the drugs listed under Possible Materials do you think are stimulants? Which are depressants? How will they affect the heart rate in *Daphnia*? Make a hypothesis concerning how each of the drugs listed will affect heart rate.

Objectives

In this BioLab, you will:

- **Measure** the resting heart rate in *Daphnia.*
- **Compare** the resting heart rate with the heart rate when a drug is applied.

Possible Materials

aged tap water
Daphnia culture
dilute solutions of coffee, tea, cola, ethyl alcohol, tobacco, and cough medicine (dextromethorphan)
dropper
microscope
microscope slide

Safety Precautions

CAUTION: ***Do not drink any of the solutions used in this lab. Always wear goggles in the lab. Use caution when working with a microscope, microscope slides, and glassware.***

Skill Handbook

Use the **Skill Handbook** if you need additional help with this lab.

PLAN THE EXPERIMENT

1. Design an experiment to measure the effect on heart rate of four of the drug-containing substances in the Possible Materials list.
2. Design and construct a data table for recording your data.

Check the Plan

1. Be sure to consider what you will use as a control.
2. Plan to add two drops of a drug-containing substance directly to the slide.
3. When you are finished testing one drug, you will need to flush the used *Daphnia* with the solution into a beaker of aged tap water provided by your teacher. Plan to use a new *Daphnia* for each substance tested.
4. ***Make sure your teacher has approved your experimental plan before you proceed further.***
5. Begin your experiment by using a dropper to place a single *Daphnia* on a slide. Observe the animal on low power and find its heart. **CAUTION:** ***Wash your hands with soap and water immediately after making observations.***
6. **Cleanup and Disposal** Collect the used *Daphnia* in a beaker of aged tap water and give them to your teacher. Make wise choices about the disposal or recycling of other materials.

DESIGN YOUR OWN BioLab

What drugs affect the heart rate of *Daphnia*?, *continued*

Chapter 36

Analyze and Conclude

1. **Making Inferences** Which drugs are stimulants? Which are depressants?

2. **Checking Your Hypotheses** Compare your predicted results with the experimental data. Explain whether or not your data support your hypotheses regarding the drugs' effects.

3. **Drawing Conclusions** How do the drugs affect the heart rate of this animal?

4. **Error Analysis** Compare your data to that of other groups. How can you account for differences in results with other lab groups? How would you alter your experiment if you did it again?

Chapter 36

Looking Near and Far

Real World BioApplications

Look around at your classmates in the room. You will notice that some are wearing eyeglasses. Why do some people need eyeglasses and others do not? As you know, your eyes have a difficult job to perform. They are designed to bring the words on this page in focus at a distance as close as 0.5 m or focus on road signs as far away as 300 m. Some people, though, cannot focus on close objects and have a condition known as farsightedness. Others cannot see far away objects very clearly; these people are nearsighted. In this activity, you will investigate the cause of these common eye disorders and learn how eyeglasses work to correct these problems.

Part A: How the Eye Focuses on Objects

Look at the diagrams of the eyeball in Figure 1. When a normal eye looks at an object, the light rays from the object enter the eye, are bent by the lens, and come to a focus directly on the retina. The lens in your eye is soft, and its shape can be changed by eye muscles. You need a longer focal length to see a distant object than a near one. For the distant object, your eye muscles adjust your lens to be thinner and flatter. For a near object, eye muscles tighten to force the lens into a rounder shape.

Normal Vision

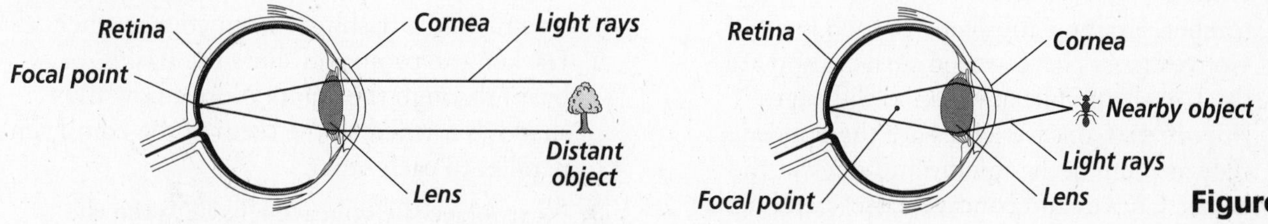

Figure 1

In nearsightedness, or myopia, the eyeball is slightly too long from front to back or the lens is too curved (Figure 2). Near objects come into focus easily. However, because the eyeball is too long, light rays from distant objects come to a focal point before they reach the retina, making the objects appear blurred.

Nearsightedness

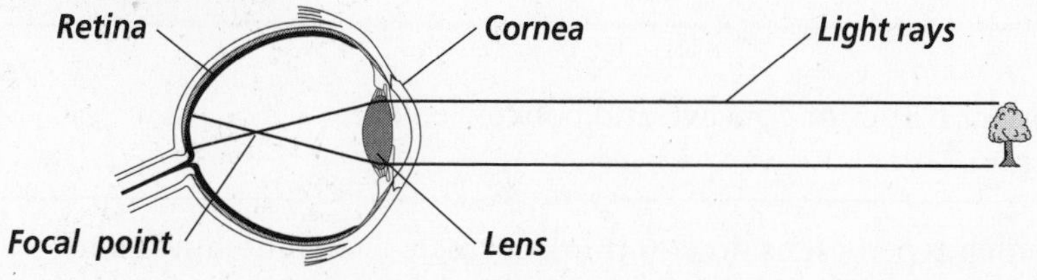

Figure 2

In farsightedness, or hyperopia, the eyeball is too short from front to back or the lens is too thin (Figure 3). Although far away objects can be seen clearly, the focal point of light coming from nearby objects falls behind the retina, making these objects appear blurred.

Farsightedness

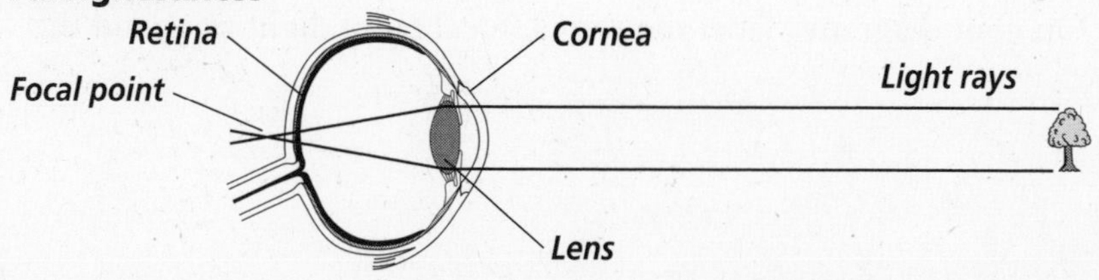

Figure 3

Name Date Class

Chapter 36 **Looking Near and Far**

Real World BioApplications

Part B: Using Lenses to Correct Vision

The most common method for helping farsighted and nearsighted people is to fit them with eyeglasses containing corrective lenses or with corrective contact lenses. In this part, you will examine how lenses are used to correct vision.

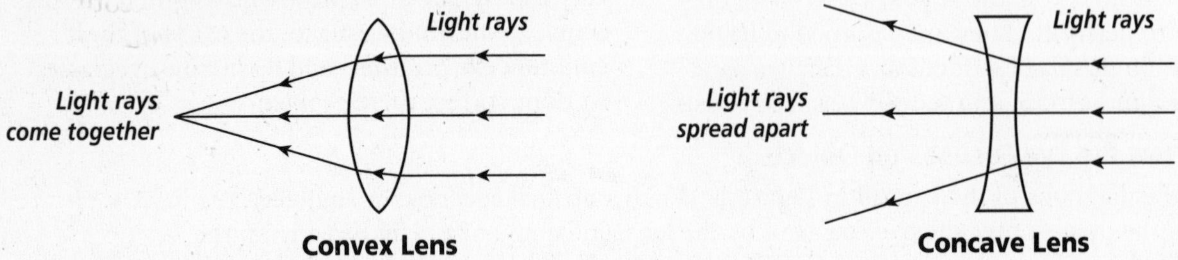

Figure 4

PROCEDURE

1. Obtain a concave and a convex lens from your teacher. Examine the shape of each lens. Convex lenses have arched surfaces and are thick in the middle and thin at the edges (Figure 4). Concave lenses are the opposite; they are thin in the middle and thick at the edges. Convex and concave lenses bend light in different ways. Light rays come together after passing through a convex lens. The lens in your eye is an example of a convex lens. Concave lenses, on the other hand, make light rays spread out.
2. To demonstrate how each lens works, obtain a comb and a flashlight from your teacher. Darken the room and shine the flashlight beam through the comb. Notice how the shadows formed by the teeth of the comb run parallel to each other.
3. Next, place the concave lens between the flashlight and the comb. Notice how the shadows of the teeth diverge from one another in this case. Repeat with the convex lens and observe how the shadows converge.

ANALYZE AND CONCLUDE

1. Why are "corrective lenses" an appropriate name for concave and convex lenses?

___

2. Based on the properties of each lens, which type of lens do you think corrects nearsightedness and which type corrects farsightedness?

___

___

3. In the space provided below, illustrate and briefly describe how each type of eyeglass lens corrects nearsightedness or farsightedness. On your diagrams, label the retina, focal point, light rays, and the type of lens.

Chapter 36

Relief from a Patch

Real World BioApplications

According to surveys, many of the nation's 50 million cigarette smokers would like to eliminate cigarettes from their lives. However, people's attempts to quit smoking often fall short because of the addictive properties of nicotine, a major component of cigarette smoke. So what can a cigarette smoker do? If you open many popular magazines or newspapers these days, you're likely to see one possible source of help—the nicotine skin patch. Nicotine patches are palm-sized circular pads that, when applied to the skin of the upper arm or back, release a stream of nicotine into the bloodstream. In this activity, you will investigate how nicotine skin patches work and examine a study on their effectiveness.

Part A: How Does the Nicotine Skin Patch Work?

Figure 1 illustrates how nicotine skin patches work. Study the diagram and then answer the questions below.

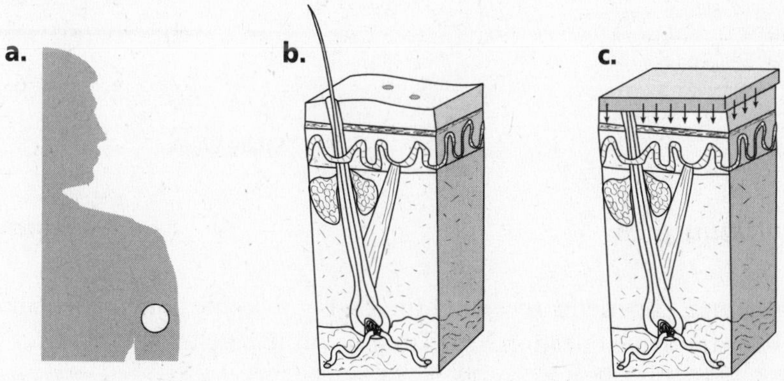

Figure 1

a. Smoker decides to quit smoking and is prescribed a nicotine patch. Patches are prescribed in heavy (21 mg), medium (14 mg), or light (7 mg) doses. Patch is applied to skin on upper arm or back every 24 hours.

b. Nicotine patches take advantage of the fact that the skin is not a uniform barrier. Rather, skin is penetrated by millions of tiny pores such as hair follicles, sweat glands, and oil glands.

c. As nicotine is released from the patch, it penetrates the pores and is absorbed by the bloodstream. The structural properties of the patch determine the rate at which nicotine is released into the blood. After a month of daily use, ex-smokers gradually withdraw from nicotine by applying successively smaller patches.

1. In your opinion, what is the major benefit of nicotine patches?

____

____

2. In your own words, describe the purpose of applying patches with successively lower doses of nicotine.

____

____

____

Chapter 36

Relief from a Patch

Real World BioApplications

Part B: Are Nicotine Patches Effective?

Figure 2 shows data from a study on the effectiveness of nicotine patches to help people quit smoking. Analyze the graphs and then answer the questions below.

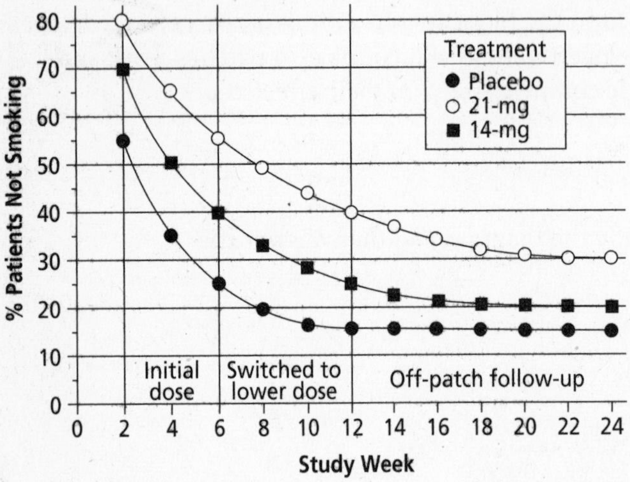

Figure 2a

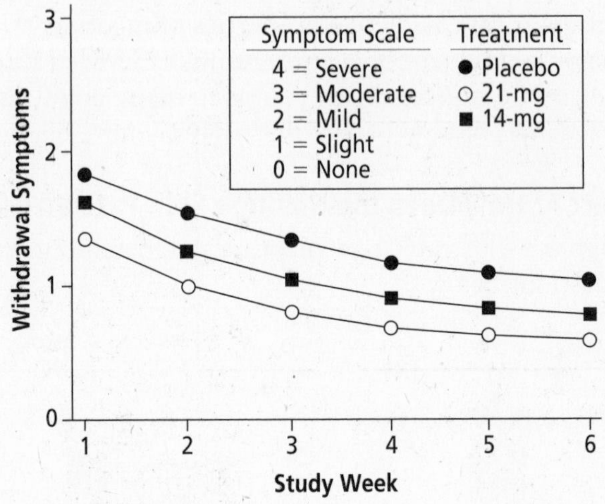

Figure 2b

1. According to Figure 2a, what percentage of patients receiving the 21-mg nicotine patches remained off cigarettes after 6 months? Answer the same question for 14-mg nicotine patches and placebo patches.

2. What was the purpose of the placebo group?

3. Figure 2b shows a graph of the withdrawal symptoms reported by the patients during the first 6 weeks of using the patch. What do these data indicate about the effectiveness of nicotine patches for reducing withdrawal symptoms?

4. What do these data suggest about the effectiveness of nicotine patches? Explain your answer.

Chapter 36

The Nervous System

Reinforcement and Study Guide

Section 36.1 The Nervous System

In your textbook, read about neurons–basic units of the nervous system.

Complete the table by filling in the missing information in each case.

Structure	Function
1.	carry impulses toward the brain and spinal cord
2. dendrites	
3. motor neurons	
4.	transmit impulses within the brain and spinal cord
5.	carry impulses away from neuron cell bodies

Order the steps in impulse transmission from 1 to 7.

______ **6.** A wave of depolarization moves down the neuron.

______ **7.** The Na^+/K^+ pump takes over again, pumping sodium ions out across the membrane, and pumping potassium ions in.

______ **8.** Sodium channels in the neural membrane open.

______ **9.** A neuron receives a stimulus.

______ **10.** As the wave of depolarization passes, sodium channels close and potassium channels open.

______ **11.** The neuron returns to a resting state.

______ **12.** Sodium ions flow into the neuron, causing the inside of the neuron to become positively charged.

Chapter 36 **The Nervous System,** *continued*

Reinforcement and Study Guide

Section 36.1 The Nervous System

In your textbook, read about the central nervous system and the peripheral nervous system.

Label the diagram of the brain to show the cerebrum, cerebellum, and brain stem.

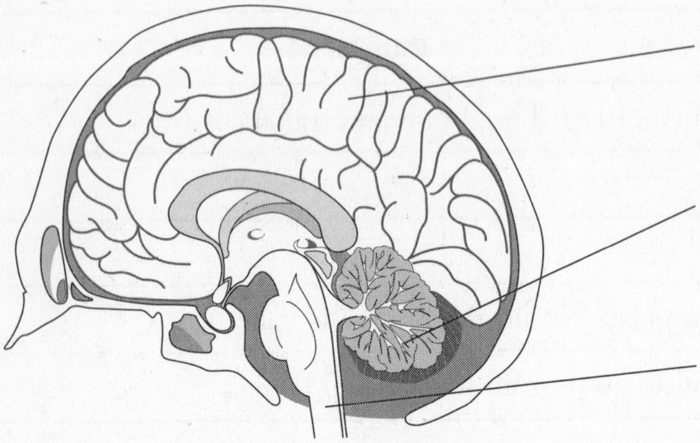

13. ______________________________

14. ______________________________

15. ______________________________

Write the name of the part labeled above that matches each description in the table.

Description	Part
16. Includes the medulla and pons	
17. Controls conscious activities and movement	
18. Important for keeping your balance	
19. If damaged, heart rate might be affected	
20. If damaged, memory might be affected	
21. Ensures that movements are coordinated	

Complete the table by checking the correct column for each description.

	Autonomic Nervous System Division	
Description	**Sympathetic**	**Parasympathetic**
22. Controls internal activities when the body is at rest		
23. Increases breathing rate		
24. Tenses muscles		
25. Slows heart rate down		
26. Activates fight or flight response		

Chapter 36 **The Nervous System,** *continued*

Reinforcement and Study Guide

Section 36.2 The Senses

In your textbook, read about sensing chemicals and sensing light.

Determine if each statement is true or false.

__________ **1.** Impulses coming from sensory receptors in your nose and mouth are interpreted as odors and tastes by the cerebrum.

__________ **2.** The senses of taste and smell are closely linked.

__________ **3.** The lens in the eye controls the amount of light that strikes the retina.

__________ **4.** On a bright sunny day, the cones in your eyes play a greater role in your sense of sight than the rods.

__________ **5.** Only the left hemisphere of the brain is involved in the sense of sight.

__________ **6.** When you are looking at an object, each of your eyes sees the object from the same perspective.

__________ **7.** The retina contains two types of light receptor cells.

In your textbook, read about sensing mechanical stimulation.

Circle the letter of the response that best completes each statement.

8. Sound waves are converted into nerve impulses inside the
a. ear canal. **b.** cochlea. **c.** malleus. **d.** optic nerve.

9. If the semicircular canals in one of your ears were damaged, you might
a. lose your ability to hear low-frequency sounds.
b. lose your ability to coordinate your neck muscles.
c. lose your sense of balance.
d. lose your sense of rhythm.

10. The malleus, incus, and stapes are found in the
a. outer ear. **b.** eardrum. **c.** middle ear. **d.** inner ear.

11. Your senses of hearing and touch *both* depend on nerve impulses being generated by
a. electrical stimulation. **b.** sound waves.
c. a change in temperature. **d.** mechanical stimulation.

12. In the skin of your fingertips, you might expect to find receptors for
a. touch. **b.** pressure. **c.** pain. **d.** all of these

Chapter 36 **The Nervous System,** *continued*

Reinforcement and Study Guide

Section 36.3 The Effects of Drugs

In your textbook, read about how drugs act on the body, their medicinal uses, and abuse of drugs.

Answer the following questions.

1. Distinguish between a drug and a medicine.

2. What is a narcotic?

3. Compare the effect of a stimulant on the CNS with the effect of a depressant.

4. What is an addiction?

5. How does a person's body develop a tolerance for a drug?

In your textbook, read about the classes of commonly abused drugs.

Complete the table by checking the correct column for each example.

Example	Stimulant	Depressant
6. Drugs that cause an increase in heart rate		
7. Alcohol		
8. Nicotine		
9. Caffeine		
10. Barbiturates		
11. Drugs that cause vasoconstriction		
12. Opiates		
13. Hallucinogens		

Capítulo 36

El sistema nervioso

Refuerzo y Guía de estudio

Sección 36.1 El sistema nervioso

En tu libro de texto, lee sobre las neuronas: la unidad básica del sistema nervioso.

Completa la tabla anotando la información que falta.

Estructura	Función
1.	transmite impulsos hacia el encéfalo y la médula espinal
2. dendrita	
3. neurona motora	
4.	transmite impulsos dentro del encéfalo y la médula espinal
5.	transmite impulsos fuera del cuerpo celular de la neurona

Ordena del 1 al 7 los pasos en la transmisión de un impulso nervioso.

_______ **6.** Una onda de despolarización atraviesa la neurona.

_______ **7.** Entra otra vez en acción la bomba de Na^+ /K^+, bombeando iones de sodio hacia afuera y iones de potasio hacia adentro, a través de la membrana.

_______ **8.** Se abren los canales de sodio de la membrana de la neurona.

_______ **9.** Una neurona recibe un estímulo.

_______ **10.** A medida que pasa la onda de despolarización, se cierran los canales de sodio y se abren los canales de potasio.

_______ **11.** La neurona regresa a su estado de reposo.

_______ **12.** Entran iones de sodio a la neurona, haciendo que la carga en el interior de la neurona se vuelva positiva.

Capítulo 36 **El sistema nervioso,** *continuación*

Refuerzo y Guía de estudio

Sección 36.1 El sistema nervioso

En tu libro de texto, lee sobre el sistema nervioso central y el sistema nervioso periférico.

Identifica el cerebro, el cerebelo y el bulbo raquídeo en el siguiente diagrama.

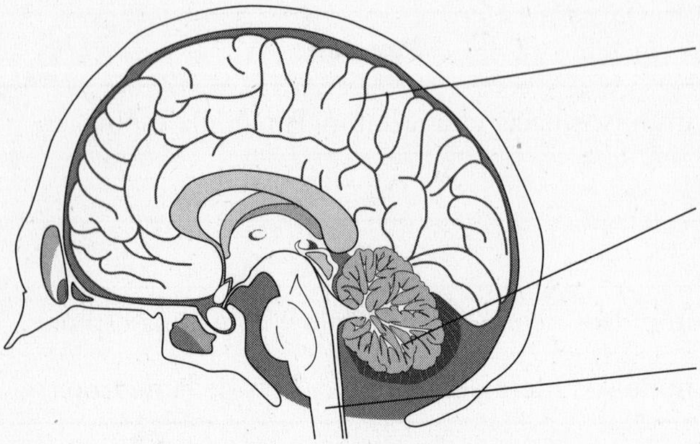

13. ______________________

14. ______________________

15. ______________________

Anota cuál parte del encéfalo del diagrama anterior corresponde a cada enunciado.

Descripción	Parte del encéfalo
16. Incluye el bulbo raquídeo y el puente de Varolio	
17. Controla las actividades conscientes y el movimiento	
18. Es importante para mantener el equilibrio	
19. Si sufre daños, se puede afectar el pulso cardíaco	
20. Si sufre daños, se puede afectar la memoria	
21. Asegura la coordinación de movimientos	

Completa la tabla indicando la columna correspondiente a cada enunciado.

	División del sistema nervioso autónomo	
Descripción	**Simpático**	**Parasimpático**
22. Controla las actividades internas del cuerpo durante el reposo		
23. Acelera la respiración		
24. Tensa los músculos		
25. Disminuye el pulso cardiaco		
26. Activa la respuesta de pelear o huir		

Capítulo 36 **El sistema nervioso,** *continuación*

Refuerzo y Guía de estudio

Sección 36.2 Los órganos de los sentidos

En tu libro de texto, lee sobre la percepción de sustancias químicas y la percepción de la luz.

Determina si cada enunciado es verdadero o falso.

__________ **1.** Los impulsos provenientes de los receptores localizados en tu boca y nariz son interpretados como sabores y olores por el cerebro.

__________ **2.** Los sentidos del gusto y del olfato están íntimamente entrelazados.

__________ **3.** El cristalino del ojo controla la cantidad de luz que llega a la retina.

__________ **4.** Durante un día soleado, los conos de los ojos son más importantes que los bastones para percibir la luz.

__________ **5.** Sólo el hemisferio izquierdo del encéfalo está relacionado con el sentido de la vista.

__________ **6.** Cuando observas un objeto, ambos ojos perciben el objeto desde la misma perspectiva.

__________ **7.** La retina contiene dos tipos de células receptoras de luz.

Estudia en tu libro la percepción de estímulos mecánicos.

Haz un círculo alrededor de la letra de la opción que completa mejor cada enunciado.

8. Las ondas sonoras se convierten en impulsos nerviosos dentro
a. del canal auditivo. **b.** de la cóclea. **c.** del martillo. **d.** del nervio óptico.

9. Si los canales semicirculares de uno de tus oídos sufre daños, es posible que
a. ya no puedas escuchar los sonidos de baja frecuencia.
b. ya no puedas coordinar los músculos del cuello.
c. pierdas el sentido del equlibrio.
d. pierdas el sentido del ritmo.

10. El martillo, el yunque y el estribo se encuentran en el
a. oído externo. **b.** tímpano. **c.** oído medio. **d.** oído interno.

11. *Tanto* el sentido del oído *como* el sentido del tacto dependen de impulsos nerviosos generados por
a. estímulos eléctricos. **b.** ondas sonoras.
c. cambios de temperatura. **d.** estímulos mecánicos.

12. Es posible que en la punta de los dedos haya receptores para
a. el tacto. **b.** la presión. **c.** el dolor. **d.** todos los anteriores

Capítulo 36 **El sistema nervioso** *(continuación)*

Refuerzo y Guía de estudio

Sección 36.3 Los efectos de las drogas

En tu libro de texto, lee sobre el efecto que las drogas tienen en el cuerpo, los usos medicinales de las drogas y el abuso de las drogas.

Contesta las siguientes preguntas.

1. ¿Cuál es la diferencia entre una droga y una medicina?

2. ¿Qué es un narcótico?

3. Compara el efecto que causa un estimulante sobre el SNC con el efecto que causa un depresor.

4. ¿Qué es una adicción?

5. ¿Cómo desarrolla el cuerpo tolerancia a una droga?

En tu libro de texto, lee sobre los tipos de drogas de las cuales se abusa comúnmente.

Completa la tabla indicando la columna correspondiente a cada ejemplo.

Ejemplo	Estimulante	Depresor
6. Drogas que aumentan el ritmo cardiaco		
7. Alcohol		
8. Nicotina		
9. Cafeína		
10. Barbitúricos		
11. Drogas que causan vasoconstricción		
12. Opiáceas		
13. Alucinógenos		

Chapter 36 **The Nervous System**

Concept Mapping

Use with Chapter 36, Section 36.2

The Sense of Touch

Complete this concept map for the sense of touch. Use these words or phrases one or more times: *dermis, temperature, nerve endings, heat, cold, light pressure, eyelids, skin surface, tip of tongue, palms of hands, epidermis, fingertips, organs, muscle tissue, lower layers, heavy pressure, soles of feet.*

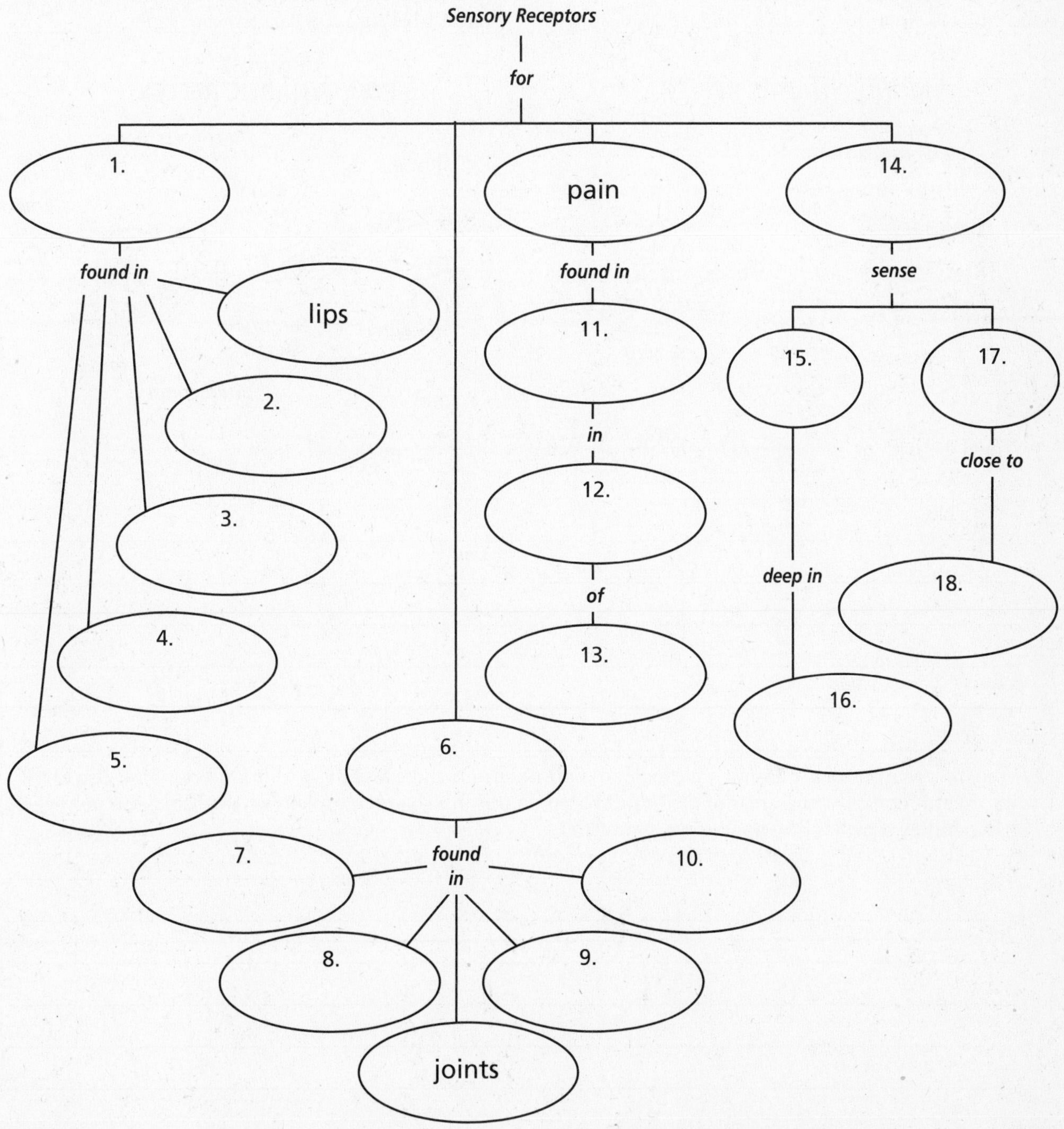

Chapter 36 **The Nervous System**

Critical Thinking

Use with Chapter 36, Section 36.1

Analyzing Sensory-Somatic Responses

There is more than one kind of reflex. Figure 1 shows the patellar reflex that occurs when a tendon in the knee is suddenly tapped. The action causes a muscle to tense and raise the leg slightly. Simple reflexes such as the patellar reflex are referred to as *monosynaptic reflexes.* Figure 2 shows what happens when the tip of the finger accidentally comes in contact with a flame. Just as with the patellar reflex, the withdrawal reflex occurs immediately, without first having to consult the brain. Yet it is more complex than the patellar reflex shown in Figure 1 because it is a *polysynaptic reflex.*

Figure 1
MONOSYNAPTIC REFLEX

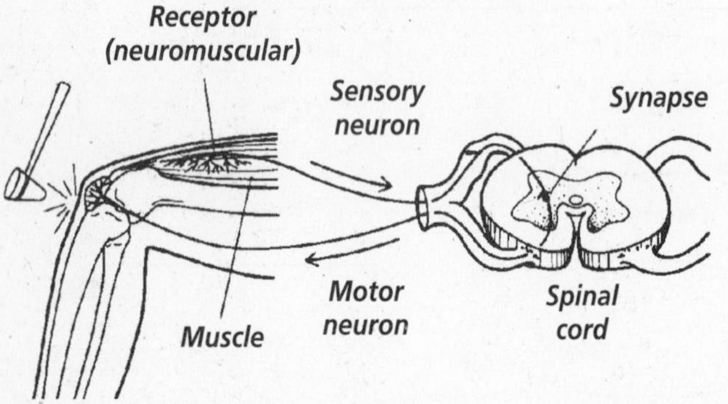

Figure 2
POLYSYNAPTIC REFLEX

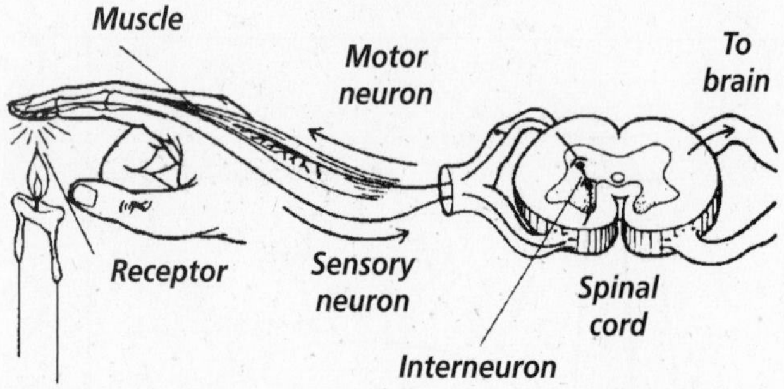

1. Trace the path of each reflex. How do the two reflexes differ in complexity?

____

____

____

____

____

____

2. The interneurons that transmit a message to motor neurons and cause the withdrawal response also carry information to conscious areas of the brain. Based on this information, explain what advantage a polysynaptic reflex provides over a monosynaptic reflex.

____

____

____

____

____

____

Name Date Class

Master 87

Take an Order

Section Focus

Use with Chapter 36, Section 36.1

1. What action causes the boy's response?
2. Give an example of a similar stimulus-response combination in the human body.

Master 88

Common Senses

Section Focus

Use with Chapter 36, Section 36.2

1. List the senses that you think the person in this scene is using.
2. Identify the stimulus for each of the senses you listed in question 1.

Master **89**

A Question of Poppies

Section Focus

Use with Chapter 36, Section 36.3

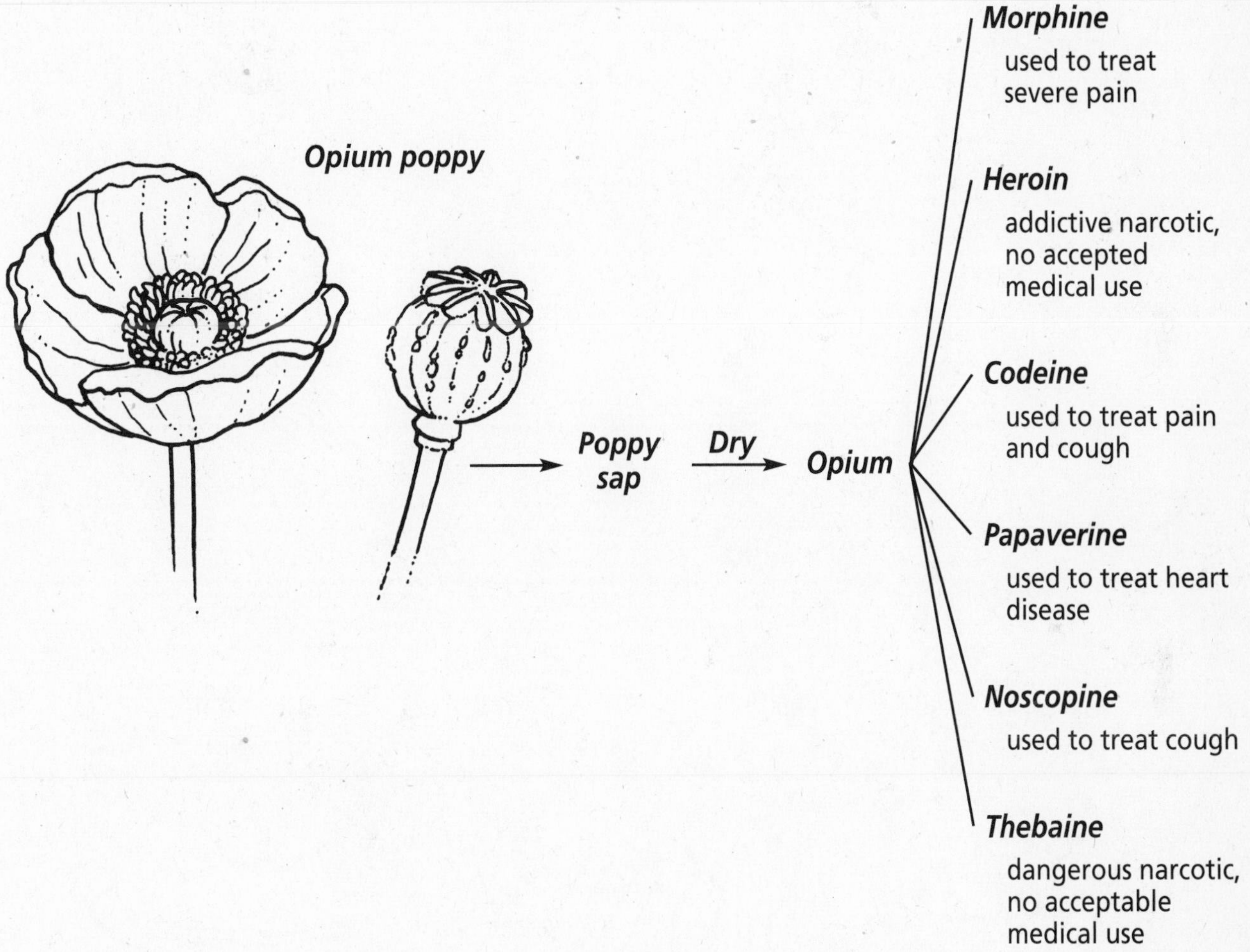

1. Examine the diagram showing products obtained from opium poppies. Which ones have you heard of?

2. Do you think it would be advisable to ban the growth of opium poppies? Explain.

Master 66

Basic Concepts

Structure of the Brain

Use with Chapter 36, Section 36.1

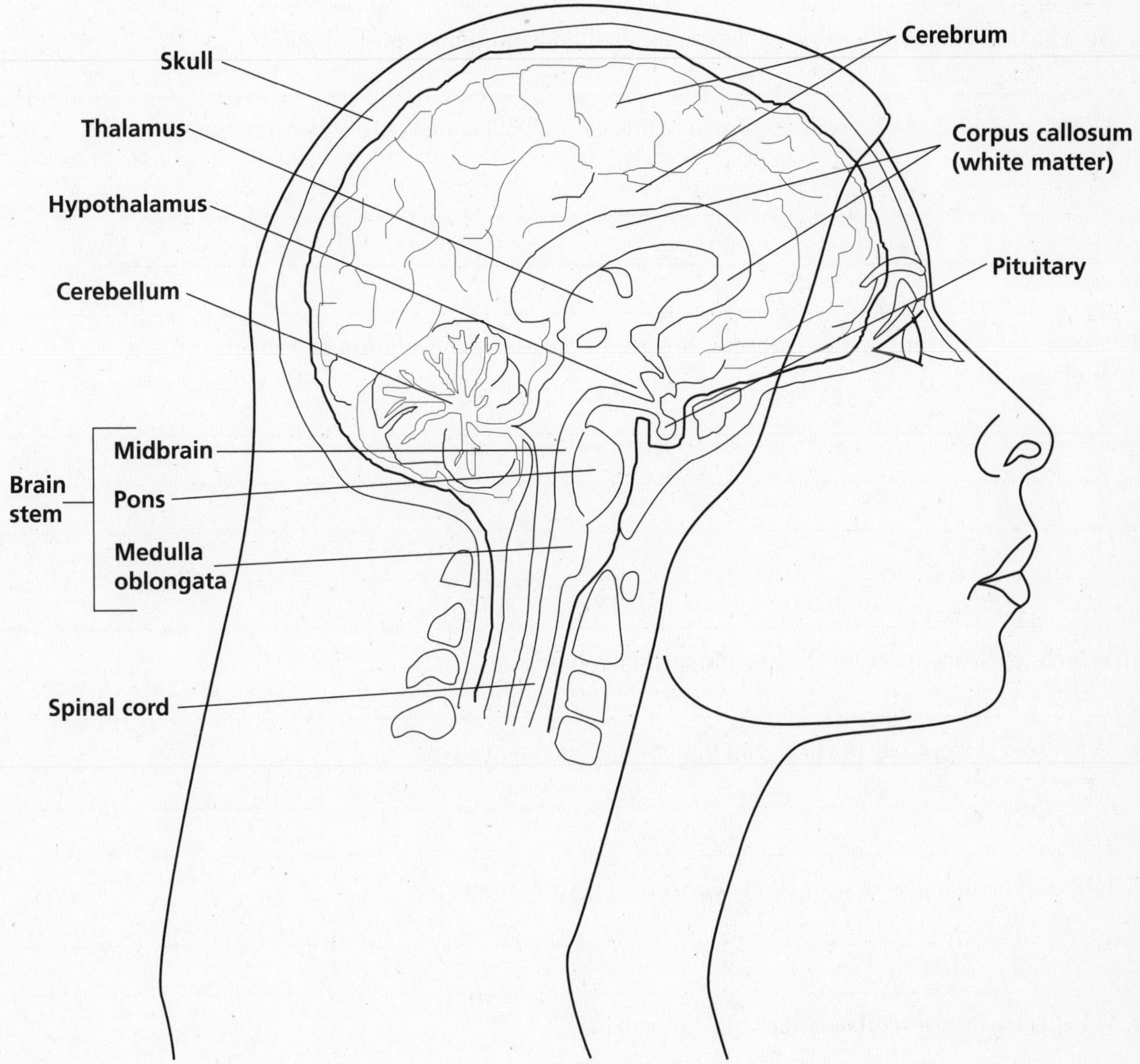

Worksheet 66

Structure of the Brain

Basic Concepts

Use with Chapter 36, Section 36.1

1. Which part of the brain controls balance, posture, and coordination?

2. To which division of the nervous system do the brain and spinal cord belong?

3. Which part of the brain consists of two hemispheres? What are some of the functions it controls?

4. How is the structure of the cerebrum thought to relate to the evolution of human intelligence?

5. Which functions are controlled by the medulla oblongata?

6. What role is played by the pons and midbrain of the brain stem?

7. How might an injury to your cerebellum affect your movements?

8. What is meant by "white matter" and "gray matter"?

Master 67

Organization of the Nervous System

Basic Concepts

Use with Chapter 36, Section 36.1

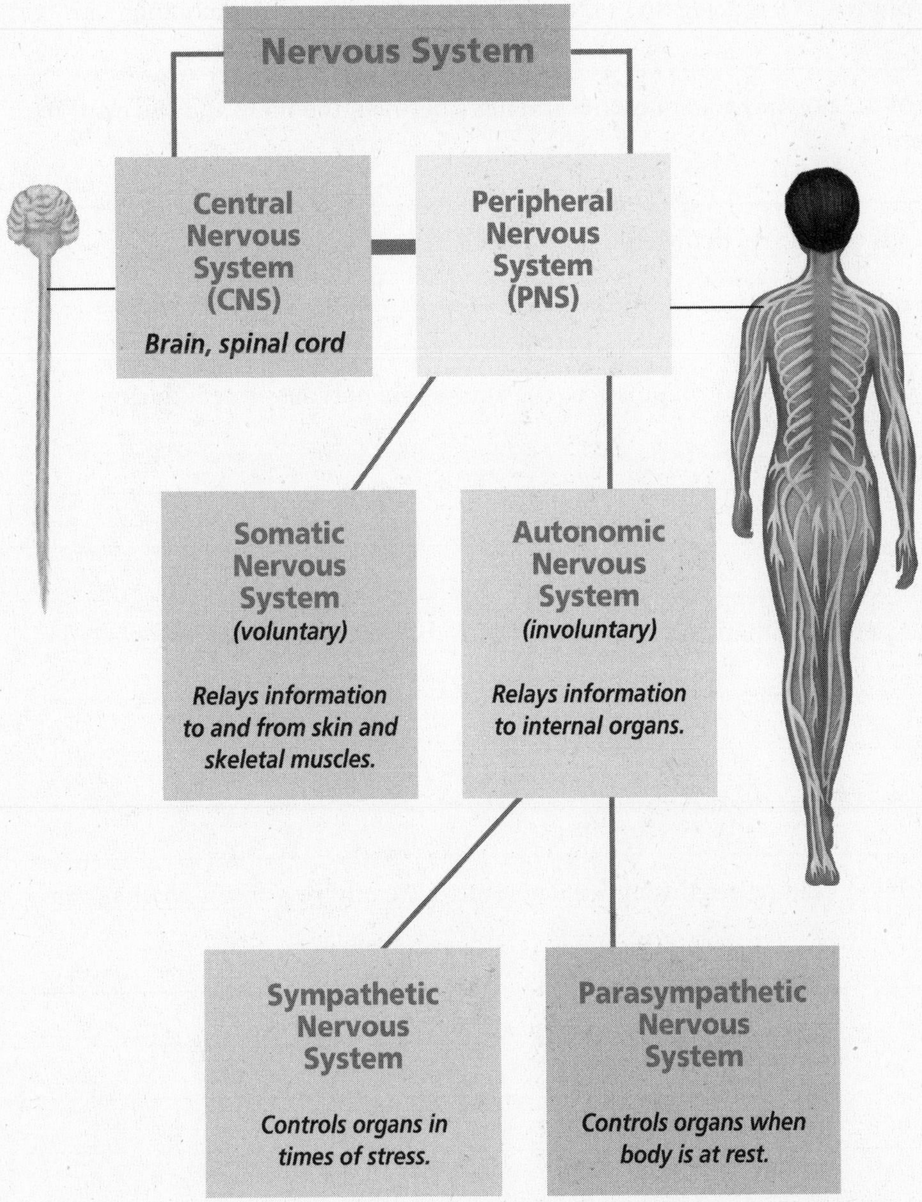
Nervous System
Central Nervous System (CNS)
Brain, spinal cord
Peripheral Nervous System (PNS)
Somatic Nervous System
(voluntary)
Relays information to and from skin and skeletal muscles.
Autonomic Nervous System
(involuntary)
Relays information to internal organs.
Sympathetic Nervous System
Controls organs in times of stress.
Parasympathetic Nervous System
Controls organs when body is at rest.

Worksheet 67

Organization of the Nervous System

Basic Concepts

Use with Chapter 36, Section 36.1

1. What is the control center of the entire nervous system?

2. Which part of the CNS is made up of the midbrain, pons, and medulla oblongata?

3. Which part of the nervous system carries impulses between the body and the central nervous system?

4. List three kinds of neurons that would be involved in a reflex impulse.

5. Which part of the brain sends impulses to the autonomic nervous system during life-threatening emergencies?

6. Compare the parasympathetic nervous system with the sympathetic nervous system.

7. Trace the pathway of impulses through the nervous system in response to feeling rain on your skin.

Name Date Class

Master 68

Structure of the Eye

Basic Concepts

Use with Chapter 36, Section 36.2

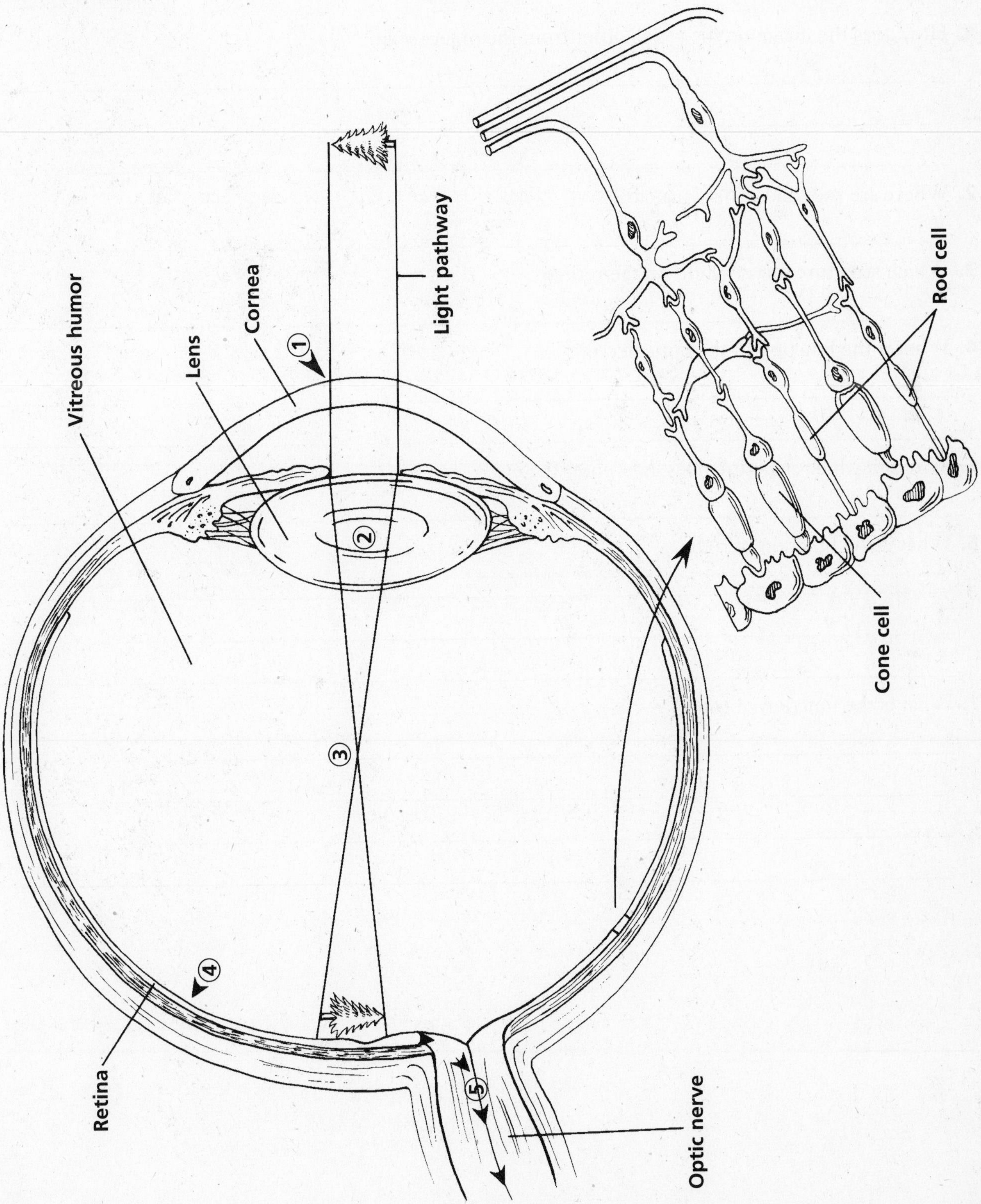

Name Date Class

Worksheet 68

Structure of the Eye

Basic Concepts

Use with Chapter 36, Section 36.2

1. How does the image on the retina differ from the object seen?

2. Where are rods and cones located?

3. Which structure focuses light on the retina?

4. What is the function of the optic nerve?

5. Through which structure does light enter the eye?

6. What is the function of rods?

7. What is the function of cones?

Name Date Class

Master
69

Process of Hearing

Basic Concepts

Use with Chapter 36, Section 36.2

A

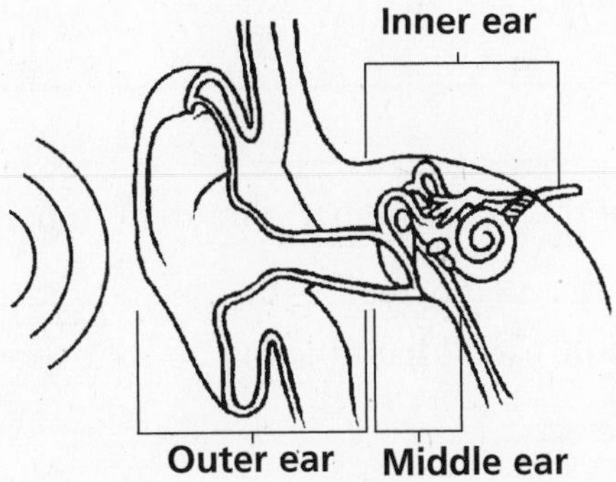

B

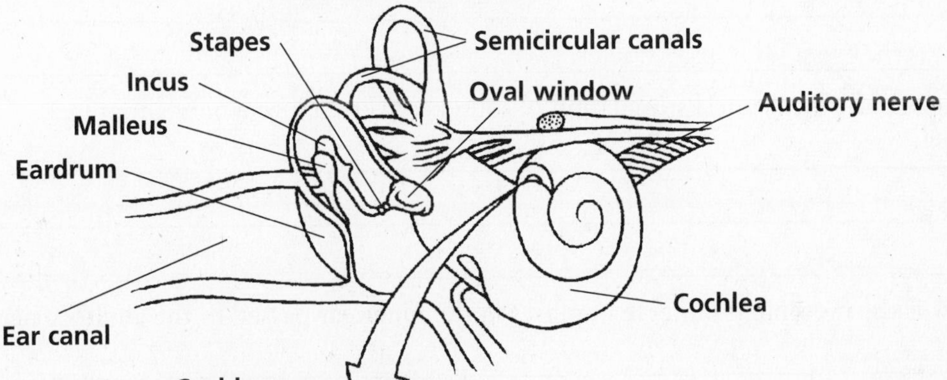

C

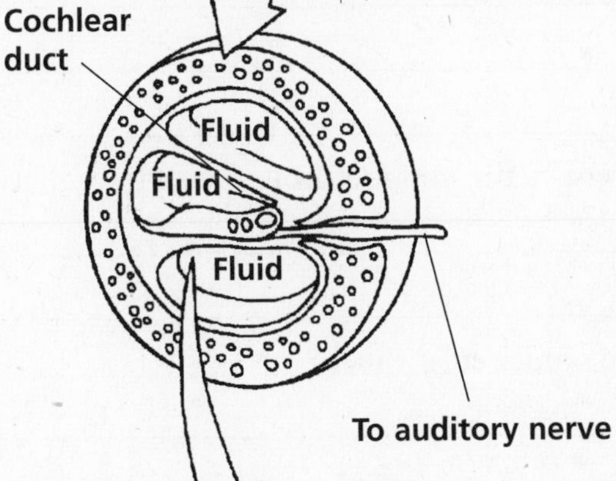

D

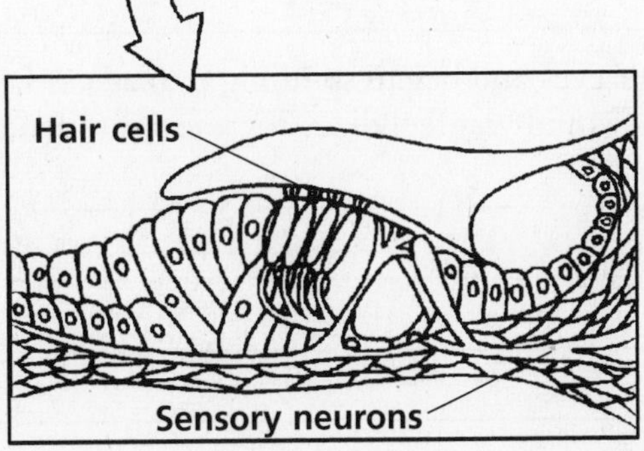

Worksheet 69

Process of Hearing

Basic Concepts

Use with Chapter 36, Section 36.2

1. What is the function of the outer ear?

2. What is the membrane at the end of the ear canal that vibrates in response to sound waves?

3. Identify the three bones of the middle ear. What function do they serve?

4. Where is the mechanical stimulation of sound converted into a nerve impulse?

5. How is the movement of nerve impulses in the inner ear passed to the auditory nerve?

6. Which parts of the brain receive the impulses from the auditory nerve?

7. What is the function of the semicircular canals?

8. Suppose you closed your eyes and began spinning in place as fast as possible and then suddenly stopped. Why would you feel dizzy for a few moments?

Name Date Class

Master 52

Structure of the Ear

Reteaching Skills

Use with Chapter 36, Section 36.2

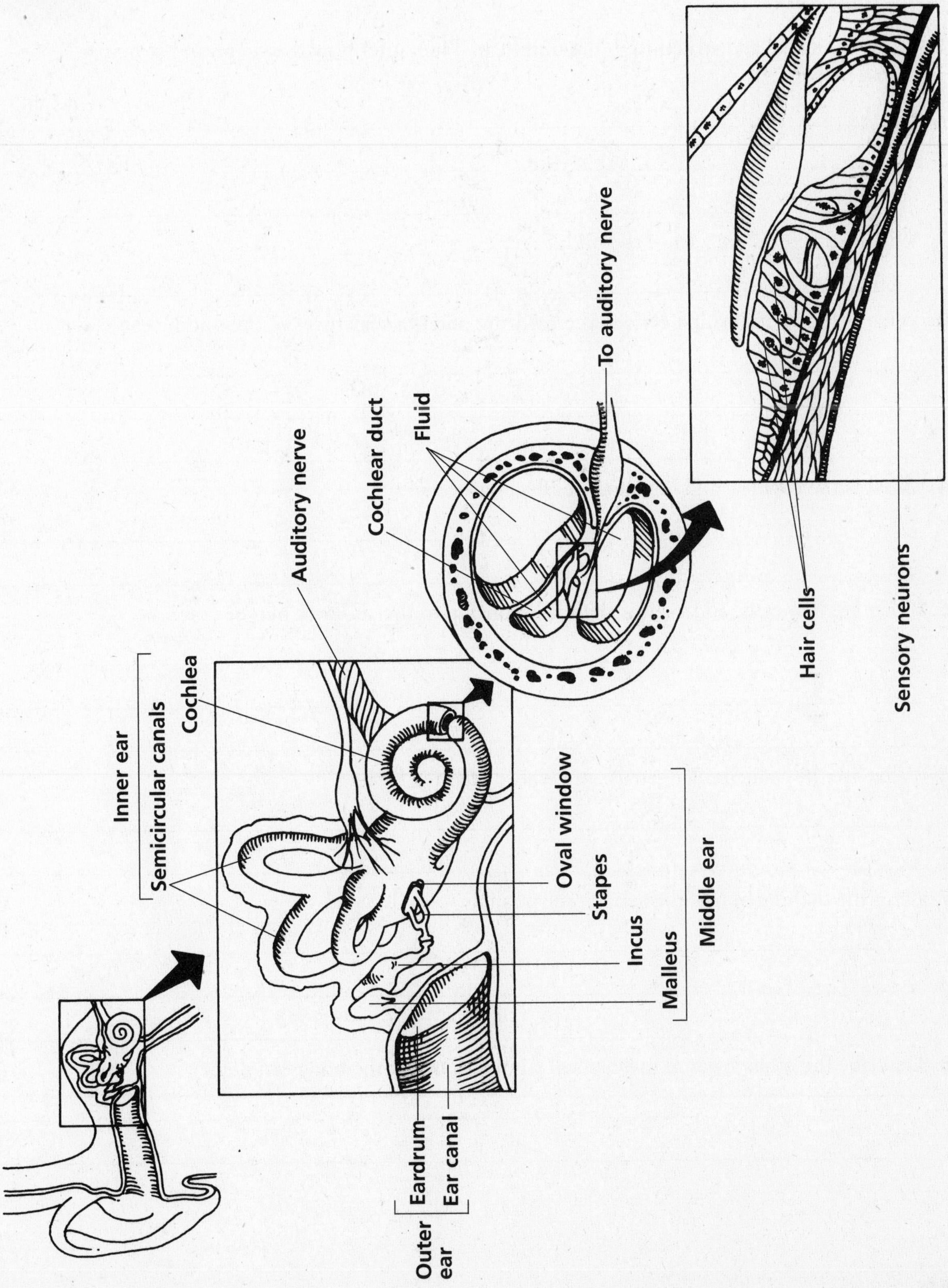

Name Date Class

Worksheet **52**

Structure of the Ear

Reteaching Skills

Use with Chapter 36, Section 36.2

1. Study the shape and structure of the outer ear. Then infer how the shape and structure help a person hear.

____

____

____

2. Which structures are part of the middle ear?

____

3. What is the relationship between the eardrum and the structures of the middle ear?

____

____

____

4. What is the cochlea, and how does it affect hair cells?

____

____

5. What are hair cells, and what is their relationship to the auditory nerve?

____

____

____

6. What are the semicircular canals, and where are they located?

____

____

7. Describe the function of the semicircular canals.

____

____

____

8. Describe the other types of mechanical stimulation that the body can detect.

____

____

Master 53

Reteaching Skills

Structure of the Skin

Use with Chapter 36, Section 36.2

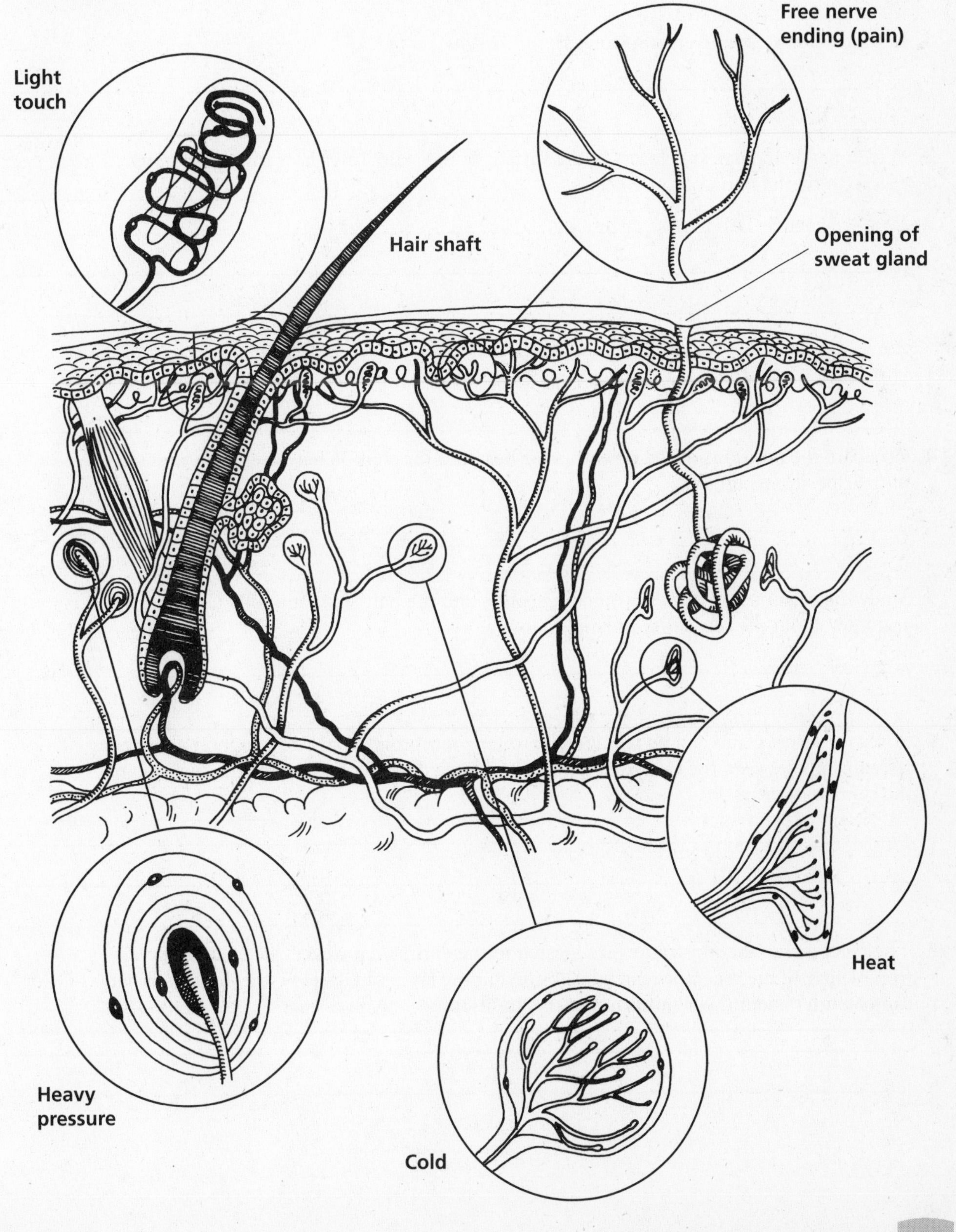

Worksheet 53

Structure of the Skin

Reteaching Skills

Use with Chapter 36, Section 36.2

1. In what layer are nerve endings found?

2. Which nerve endings are closest to the surface of the skin? Infer how this positioning relates to the function of these nerves.

3. What receptors are deeper in the dermis?

4. Compare the positions of the receptors for heat and for cold. What may the difference in their positions signify?

5. Study the relationship between touch receptors and the hair shaft and follicle. What do you infer about the sensitivity of hairs to touch?

6. Study the sweat gland and its relationship to heat receptors. What do you infer about the relationship between the two? Relate this to Chapter 34, which discusses the function of the skin.

7. The receptors in the illustration are located in the dermis. However, the "major nerve" from which all the receptors extend is located in the layer of fat below the dermis. What can you infer about the significance of this position?

Chapter 36 **Chapter Assessment**

The Nervous System

Reviewing Vocabulary

Match the definition in Column A with the term in Column B.

	Column A	Column B
______	**1.** Medicine that acts on the central nervous system to relieve pain	**a.** neutrotransmitters
______	**2.** Any drug that slows down the activities of the central nervous system (CNS)	**b.** semicircular canals
______	**3.** Psychological and physical dependence on a drug	**c.** cochlea
______	**4.** Automatic response to a stimulus	**d.** addiction
______	**5.** Single extension of a neuron that carries impulses away from the cell body	**e.** hallucinogen
______	**6.** Occurs when a person needs larger and/or more frequent doses of a drug to achieve the same effect	**f.** rods
______	**7.** Layer of nerve tissue made up of sensory neurons that respond to light	**g.** depressant
______	**8.** Light receptors adapted for vision in dim light	**h.** narcotic
______	**9.** Structure in the inner ear that helps maintain balance	**i.** retina
______	**10.** Controls involuntary activities such as breathing and heart rate	**j.** synaptic space
______	**11.** Tiny space between the axon of one neuron and the dendrites of another neuron over which nerve impulses must travel	**k.** medulla oblongata
______	**12.** Fluid-filled, snail-shaped structure in the inner ear	**l.** tolerance
______	**13.** Drug that affects the CNS, altering moods, thoughts, and sensory perceptions	**m.** reflex
______	**14.** Chemicals that diffuse across the synapse and stimulate changes in a neuron	**n.** axon

Understanding Main Ideas (Part A)

In the space at the left, write the letter of the word or phrase that best completes the statement or answers the question.

______ **1.** Sensory neurons

- **a.** process incoming impulses and pass them on to motor neurons.
- **b.** carry impulses from around the body to the brain and spinal cord.
- **c.** carry response impulses away from the brain and spinal cord.
- **d.** carry impulses across synapses.

______ **2.** A nerve impulse travels from one cell to another by passing from

- **a.** one axon to another axon.
- **b.** one dendrite to an axon.
- **c.** one axon to a dendrite.
- **d.** one dendrite to another dendrite.

______ **3.** Which controls involuntary activities of the body such as breathing and heart rate?

a. cerebrum **b.** cerebellum **c.** medulla oblongata **d.** none of these

______ **4.** You can see the colors in a picture because you are aided by the

a. rods of the retina. **b.** right visual field.
c. cones of the retina. **d.** left visual field.

______ **5.** A person who is addicted to a drug is experiencing withdrawal when he or she

- **a.** needs more of the drug to achieve the same effect.
- **b.** becomes ill after stopping its use.
- **c.** needs to take the drug more often.
- **d.** feels better when stopping its use.

______ **6.** Cocaine is a stimulant because it

- **a.** causes blood pressure to drop.
- **b.** causes heart rate to slow down.
- **c.** relieves anxiety.
- **d.** causes vasoconstriction.

______ **7.** Alcohol may act on the brain by

- **a.** dissolving through the membranes of neurons.
- **b.** blocking the movement of sodium and calcium ions.
- **c.** increasing anxiety.
- **d.** increasing oxygen content.

Chapter 36 **The Nervous System,** *continued*

Chapter Assessment

Understanding Main Ideas (Part B)

Answer the following questions.

1. How is a nerve impulse transmitted through a neuron?

2. How does a nerve impulse pass from neuron to neuron?

3. How is the eye adapted for vision in a dimly lit place?

4. How do the semicircular canals help you to keep your balance?

5. What is the role of the somatic nervous system in your body?

Thinking Critically

If you enter a darkened room from a lighted area, you cannot see well at first. The retina of the eye lacks the light-sensitive pigment, called rhodopsin, in the rods. However, as the graph at the right shows, the concentration of rhodopsin builds up quickly, and the eyes adapt to the change in the amount of light.

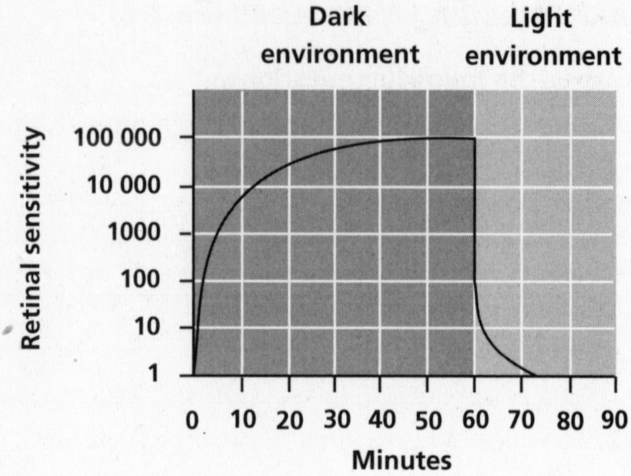

Use the graph to answer questions 1–4.

1. How long does it take for the sensitivity of the retina to improve from 1 to 10 000 arbitrary units?

____

____

2. After how many minutes does the retina have a sensitivity of 100 000 units?

____

3. How is the response of the retina to changes in light an adaptation?

____

____

____

____

4. Upon entering a bright room after being in the dark, what happens to the levels of rhodopsin in the rods?

____

____

The utricle and saccule are organs of the inner ear. Each of these organs contains a patch of epithelium called the *macula*. The macula is covered with tiny hairs, each of which is weighted by a small mineral grain. As the grains pull on the hairs, impulses are sent from the hair cells to the brain, alerting it to the head's position. The strength with which a mineral grain pulls a hair depends on the force of gravity.

5. In terms of the utricle and saccule, why might an astronaut in zero gravity experience space sickness?

____

____

____

____

Applying Scientific Methods

Scientists in western countries have been searching for a chemical that will help curb an alcoholic's appetite for alcohol. Recently, some scientists have been looking at a treatment used in China for over 2000 years. Chinese healers have given alcoholics an extract made from the root of the kudzu vine, which they claim is about 80 percent effective in reducing alcohol craving in patients who have been treated for two to four weeks. Dr. Wing-Ming Keung of Harvard Medical School in Boston visited China to find out what modern researchers thought of the herbal remedy. He spoke to physicians who claimed to have treated 300 human alcohol abusers with the extract. They were convinced that the chemicals in the extract effectively suppressed the patient's appetite for alcohol.

After returning to Harvard, Dr. Keung and Dr. Bert L. Vallee decided to try the drug on a group of Syrian golden hamsters in their laboratory. These hamsters were specifically selected because they are known to drink large amounts of alcohol when it is available to them. Suppose you are a member of the Harvard Medical School research team. Your job is to design an experiment that will demonstrate the effectiveness of the kudzu root extract to suppress the hamsters' craving for alcohol.

1. Describe the experimental procedure you will follow.

2. What will you use as your control?

3. What will be the variable in your experiment?

4. Predict the results of your experiment.

5. How might you follow up on your experiment?

Applying Scientific Methods *continued*

6. Dr. Keung and Dr. Vallee discovered two active ingredients in the root extract, each of which had the effect of lessening alcohol use in the hamsters by 50 percent. The two compounds appeared to interfere with the metabolism, or breakdown, of alcohol in the body. Hypothesize what this discovery may tell us about the nature of alcoholism.

7. How might Dr. Keung and Dr. Vallee's discovery help alcoholics overcome their addition?

Name ______________________ Date __________ Class __________

Chapter 36 Assessment
Student Recording Sheet

Chapter Assessment

Use with pages 968–969 of the Student Edition

Vocabulary Review

Write the word you chose and explain why it does not belong.

1. ______________________
2. ______________________
3. ______________________
4. ______________________
5. ______________________
6. ______________________

Understanding Key Concepts

Select the best answer from the choices given and fill in the corresponding oval.

7. Ⓐ Ⓑ Ⓒ Ⓓ
8. Ⓐ Ⓑ Ⓒ Ⓓ
9. Ⓐ Ⓑ Ⓒ Ⓓ
10. Ⓐ Ⓑ Ⓒ Ⓓ

11. Fill in the correct terms to complete the concept map.

1.______________ 4.______________

2.______________ 5.______________

3.______________

Constructed Response

Record your answers for Questions 12–14 on a separate sheet of paper.

Thinking Critically

15. **REAL WORLD BIOCHALLENGE** Follow your teacher's instructions for presenting your BioChallenge answer.

Record your answers for Questions 16–18 on a separate sheet of paper.

Standardized Test Practice

The Princeton Review

Part 1 Multiple Choice

Select the best answer from the choices given and fill in the corresponding oval.

19. Ⓐ Ⓑ Ⓒ Ⓓ
20. Ⓐ Ⓑ Ⓒ Ⓓ
21. Ⓐ Ⓑ Ⓒ Ⓓ
22. Ⓐ Ⓑ Ⓒ Ⓓ
23. Ⓐ Ⓑ Ⓒ Ⓓ
24. Ⓐ Ⓑ Ⓒ Ⓓ

Part 2 Constructed Response/Grid In

Record your answers for Questions 25 and 26 on a separate sheet of paper.

Contents

Chapter 37 Respiration, Circulation, and Excretion

Name Date Class

MiniLab 37.1

Experimenting

Checking Your Pulse

The heart speeds up when the blood volume reaching your right atrium increases. It also speeds up when the level of carbon dioxide in the blood rises. The number of heartbeats per minute is your heart rate, which can be measured by taking your pulse.

Procedure

1. Use the data table below.
2. Have a classmate take your resting pulse for 60 seconds while you are sitting at your lab table or desk. Use the photo on page 981 of your text as a guide to finding your radial pulse.
3. Record your pulse in the table.
4. Repeat steps 2 and 3 four more times, then calculate your average resting pulse rate. Switch roles and take your classmate's resting pulse.
5. Exercise by walking in place for one minute.
6. Have your classmate take your pulse for 60 seconds immediately after exercising and record the value in the data table.
7. Repeat steps 5 and 6 four more times, then calculate your average pulse after exercise. Switch roles again with your classmate.

Data Table

Heart rate (beats per minute)

Trial	Resting	After exercise
1		
2		
3		
4		
5		
Total		
Average		

MiniLab 37.1

Checking Your Pulse, *continued*

Analysis

1. Explain why your pulse is a means of indirectly measuring heart rate.

2. Use actual values from your data table to describe the changes that occur to your heart rate when exercising.

3. Suppose the amount of blood pumped by your left ventricle each time it contracts is 70 mL. Calculate your cardiac output (70 mL × heart rate per minute) while at rest and just after exercise.

MiniLab 37.2

Experimenting

Testing Simulated Urine for Glucose

Glucose is a sugar that is needed by the body and is normally not present in the urine. When the concentration of glucose becomes too high in the blood, as happens with diabetes, glucose is filtered out by the kidneys.

Procedure

1. Use the data table.
2. Using a grease pencil, draw two circles on a glass slide. Mark one circle N, the other A.
3. Use a clean dropper to add two drops of simulated "normal urine" to the circle marked N.
4. Use a clean dropper to add two drops of simulated "abnormal urine" to the circle marked A.
5. Hold a small strip of glucose test paper in a forceps and touch it to the liquid in the drop labeled N. Remove it, wait 30 seconds, and record the color. A green color means glucose is present. Use a new strip of glucose test paper to test drop A and record the color.
6. Test several simulated "unknown urine" samples for the presence of glucose. Use a clean slide for each test.

Data Table

Simulated Urine sample	Color of test paper	Glucose present?
Normal (N)		
Abnormal (A)		
Unknown X		
Unknown Y		
Unknown Z		

Analysis

1. Which of the "unknown" samples could be from a person who has diabetes?

2. Which part of the test procedure could be considered your control? Explain your answer.

INVESTIGATE BioLab

Chapter 37

Measuring Respiration

Preparation

Problem

How can you measure respiratory rate and estimate tidal volume?

Objectives

In this BioLab, you will:

- **Measure** resting breathing rate.
- **Estimate** tidal volume by exhaling into a balloon.
- **Calculate** the amount of air inhaled per minute.

Materials

round balloon
string (1 m)
metric ruler
clock or watch with second hand

Safety Precautions

CAUTION: *Always use laboratory materials appropriately.*

Skill Handbook

Use the **Skill Handbook** if you need additional help with this lab.

Procedure

Part A: Breathing Rate at Rest

1. Use Data Table 1.
2. Have your partner count the number of times you inhale in 30 s. Repeat step 2 two more times.
3. Calculate the average number of breaths. Multiply the average number of breaths by two to get the average resting breathing rate in breaths per minute.

Data Table 1

Resting breathing rate	
Trial	**Inhalations in 30 sec**
1	
2	
3	
Average number breaths	
Breaths/min	

Part B: Estimating Tidal Volume

1. Use Data Table 2.
2. Take a regular breath and exhale normally into the balloon. Pinch the balloon closed.
3. Have a partner fit the string around the balloon at the widest part.
4. Measure the length of the string, in centimeters, around the circumference of the balloon. Record this measurement.
5. Repeat steps 2–4 four more times.
6. Calculate the average circumference of the five measurements.
7. Calculate the average radius of the balloon by dividing the average circumference by 6.28 (which is approximately equal to 2π).
8. Calculate the average tidal volume using the formula for determining the volume of a sphere. Use the average balloon radius for r and 3.14 for π.

$$\text{Volume of a sphere} = \frac{4\pi r^3}{3}$$

where r = radius and $\pi = 3.14$.

INTERNET BioLab

Measuring Respiration, *continued*

Data Table 2

Tidal volume	
Trial	**String measurement**
1	
2	
3	
4	
5	
Avg. circumference	
Avg. radius	
Avg. tidal volume	

9. Your calculated volume will be in cubic centimeters: 1 cm^3 = 1 mL.

Part C: Amount of Air Inhaled

1. Use Data Table 3.
2. Multiply the average tidal volume by the average number of breaths per minute to calculate the amount of air you inhale per minute.
3. Divide the number of milliliters of air by 1000 to get the number of liters of air you inhale per minute.

Data Table 3

Amount of air inhaled	
mL/min	
L/min	

Analyze and Conclude

1. **Making Comparisons** Compare your average number of breaths per minute and tidal volume per minute with those of other students.

2. **Thinking Critically** An average adult inhales 6000 mL of air per minute. Compare your estimated average volume of air with this figure. What factors could account for any differences?

3. **Making Predictions** Predict what would happen to your resting breathing rate after exercise.

4. **Error Analysis** List reasons that explain why there are differences between your results and those of other students. What changes could you make to this experiment to obtain more accurate results?

Chapter 37

The Biology of a Hiccup

Real World BioApplications

You probably know the annoying feeling. You've just gulped down a cold drink after some vigorous exercise or perhaps eaten a large meal, when all of a sudden—"Hiccup!" Without any warning, your body is experiencing yet another bout of the hiccups. You decide to hold your breath and count to ten. It works. The hiccups vanish as quickly as they came.

Everyone has his or her own personal remedy for hiccups. But what causes hiccups and why do some remedies work better than others? In this activity, you will find the answers to these questions as you investigate the biology of hiccups.

Part A: The Biology of a Hiccup

When you breathe in and out, air moves into and out of your lungs due to the rhythmic contraction of the diaphragm, the tough sheet of muscle that separates the chest from the abdominal cavity. The epiglottis, the flap of tissue that prevents food from entering the respiratory passage, is in an open position during breathing and allows for a smooth flow of air. When a hiccup happens, this normal sequence of events is disturbed. Instead of contracting rhythmically, the diaphragm undergoes spasms and begins to twitch uncontrollably. As this occurs, air is gulped, and the epiglottis snaps shut. The typical hiccup sound is produced when air is forced past the vocal cords and then cut off by the epiglottis.

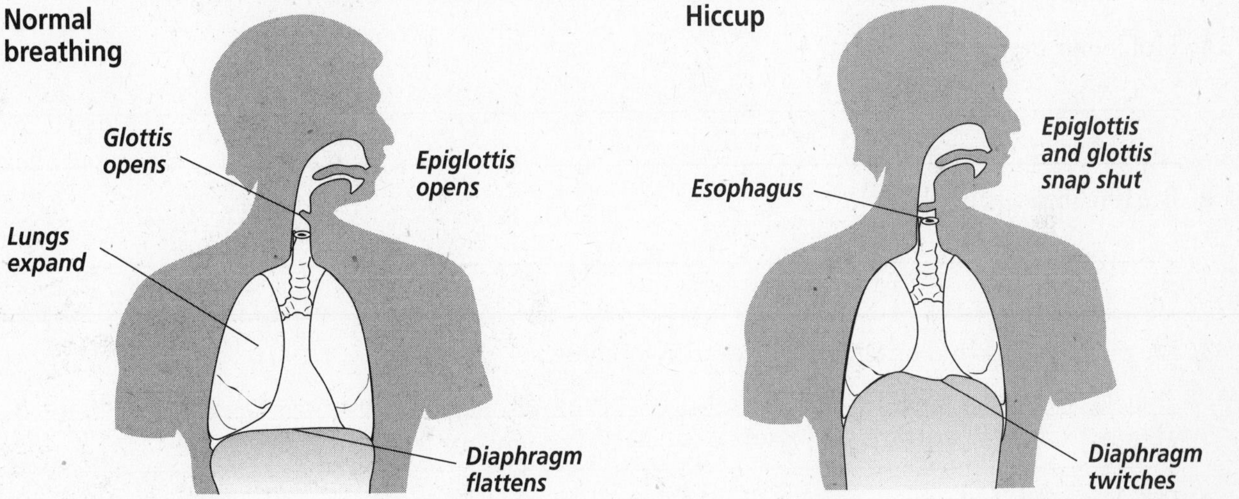

Figure 1 How Hiccups Happen

Thinking Critically

The precise cause of hiccups is not known; however, it is certain that one of two mechanisms, possibly both, is involved. Either there is a disturbance in the area of the brain that controls the contraction of the diaphragm, or an imprecise impulse is being sent out along one of the two phrenic nerves, the nerves that connect the diaphragm to the central nervous system. People get short-term hiccups for different reasons, but the most common reasons are eating or drinking too quickly, eating or drinking too much, eating spicy food, gulping air, or drinking alcohol. Long-term hiccups may be caused by lung diseases or diseases in the other tissues that surround the phrenic nerves.

Chapter 37

The Biology of a Hiccup

Real World BioApplications

1. Can you see any similarities in the reasons why people get the hiccups? If so, what are they? What might these similarities suggest about the cause of hiccups?

2. Based on what you know about the biology of hiccups, suggest a reason why eating or drinking too much can cause the hiccups.

Part B: Investigating Hiccup Remedies

People use a variety of cures for the hiccups, without actually knowing the reasons why these remedies work. Hiccups are muscle spasms caused by faulty signals from the brain. According to scientists, anything that interrupts these signals or influences the diaphragm to regain its rhythm can halt the hiccups. For each of the home remedies below, use your knowledge about the biology of hiccups to suggest a possible reason why it works. How might each remedy interrupt the signal from the brain to the diaphragm or help the diaphragm regain its rhythm?

1. Hold your breath.

2. Breathe into a paper bag.

3. Lie on your back and bring your knees to your chest.

4. Drink water rapidly.

5. Do you have another remedy you use for hiccups? Explain what it is and why you think it works.

Name Date Class

Chapter 37

Respiration, Circulation, and Excretion

Reinforcement and Study Guide

Section 37.1 The Respiratory System

In your textbook, read about air passageways and lungs.

Circle the letter of the choice that best completes the statement or answers the question.

1. During the process of respiration,
- **a.** oxygen is delivered to body cells.
- **b.** carbon dioxide is expelled from the body.
- **c.** oxygen is used in cells to produce ATP.
- **d.** all of these.

2. When you swallow, your epiglottis momentarily covers the top of the trachea so that
- **a.** you can swallow more easily.
- **b.** you can breathe more easily.
- **c.** you don't get food in your air passages.
- **d.** you can cough up foreign matter.

3. The cilia that line your trachea and bronchi
- **a.** produce dirt-trapping mucus.
- **b.** help in the exchange of oxygen and CO_2.
- **c.** move mucus and dirt upward.
- **d.** only beat when you inhale.

4. The first branches off the trachea are called
- **a.** bronchioles.
- **b.** bronchi.
- **c.** arterioles.
- **d.** alveoli.

5. Inside the alveoli, carbon dioxide and oxygen
- **a.** are exchanged between air and blood.
- **b.** are transported along microscopic tubules.
- **c.** are produced inside cells.
- **d.** are exchanged for other gases.

6. Which is the correct sequence for the path of oxygen through the respiratory system?
- **a.** nasal passages, bronchi, trachea, bronchioles, cells, blood, alveoli
- **b.** cells, blood, alveoli, bronchioles, bronchi, trachea, nasal passages
- **c.** nasal passages, blood, alveoli, bronchi, cells, trachea, bronchioles
- **d.** nasal passages, trachea, bronchi, bronchioles, alveoli, blood, cells

In your textbook, read about the mechanics of breathing and the control of respiration.

For each statement below, write true or false.

______________ **7.** Homeostasis in respiration is controlled by the cerebrum.

______________ **8.** As you exhale, the bronchioles in the lungs release most of their air.

______________ **9.** When you inhale, the muscles between your ribs contract.

______________ **10.** Relaxation of the diaphragm causes a slight vacuum in the lungs.

______________ **11.** Air rushes into the lungs because the air pressure outside the body is greater than the air pressure inside the lungs.

______________ **12.** Relaxation of the diaphragm causes it to flatten.

Chapter 37

Respiration, Circulation, and Excretion, *continued*

Reinforcement and Study Guide

Section 37.2 The Circulatory System

In your textbook, read about your blood, ABO blood types, and blood vessels.

Answer the following questions.

1. What cells and substances would you expect to find suspended or dissolved in plasma?

____

____

2. How is carbon dioxide transported in blood?

____

____

Complete the table below by checking the correct column for each description.

Description	Red Blood Cells	White Blood Cells	Platelets
3. Contain hemoglobin			
4. Fight infection			
5. Lack a nucleus			
6. Help clot blood			
7. Transport oxygen			
8. Comparatively large and nucleated			

For each statement below, write <u>true</u> or <u>false</u>.

______________ **9.** Your blood type can be changed with a blood transfusion.

______________ **10.** Different blood types result from different antibodies being present on the membranes of red blood cells.

______________ **11.** If you have type B blood, then you have anti-A antibodies in your plasma.

______________ **12.** Risks involving incompatible Rh factors are greatest for a woman's first child.

Chapter 37

Respiration, Circulation, and Excretion, *continued*

Reinforcement and Study Guide

Section 37.2 The Circulatory System

In your textbook, read about your heart, blood's path through the heart, and inside your heart.

Label the parts of the human heart in the diagram below. Use these choices:

aorta	left atrium	left ventricle	pulmonary arteries
pulmonary veins	right atrium	right ventricle	

13. ______________

14. ______________

15. ______________

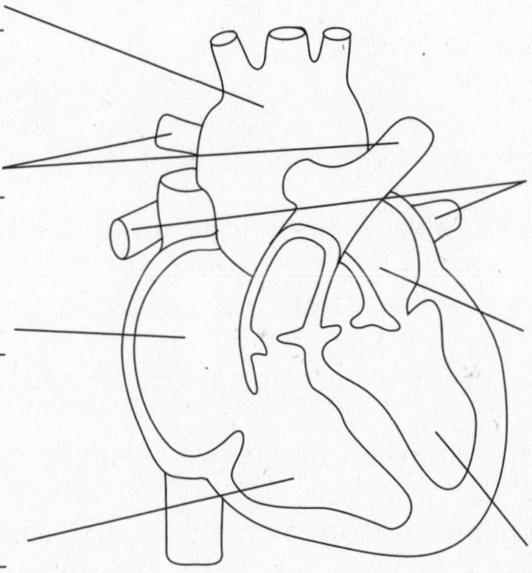

17. ______________

16. ______________

19. ______________

18. ______________

20. Where does blood go from the pulmonary veins? From the right ventricle? From the left ventricle?

____

21. What prevents blood from mixing between atria and ventricles?

____

In your textbook, read about heartbeat regulation, control of the heart, and blood pressure.

Determine if the statement is true. If it is not, rewrite the italicized part to make it true.

22. The surge of blood through an artery is called the *cardiac output*. ______________

23. The pacemaker initiates heartbeats *by generating electrical impulses*. ______________

24. An electrocardiogram is a record of *the strength of each heartbeat*. ______________

____

25. The *atrioventricular node*, along with sensory cells in arteries near the heart, regulates the pacemaker.

____

26. *Diastolic pressure* occurs when the heart's ventricles contract. ______________

Chapter 37

Respiration, Circulation, and Excretion, *continued*

Reinforcement and Study Guide

Section 37.3 The Urinary System

In your textbook, read about kidneys, nephrons, and the formation of urine.

Answer the following questions.

1. What is the major function of kidneys?

____

2. What role does the bladder play in the urinary system?

____

3. What are nephrons?

____

Order the following steps in the filtration of blood from 1 to 7.

__________ **4.** From the Bowman's capsule, fluid flows through a U-shaped tubule.

__________ **5.** Under high pressure, blood flows into capillaries that make up the glomerulus.

__________ **6.** After being stored in the bladder, urine exits the body via the urethra.

__________ **7.** Fluid moves from the end of the nephron's tubule to the ureter.

__________ **8.** Blood enters the nephron from a branch of the renal artery.

__________ **9.** Water, glucose, amino acids, and ions are reabsorbed into the blood.

__________ **10.** Water, glucose, amino acids, wastes, and other substances move from glomerular capillaries into a Bowman's capsule.

In your textbook, read about the urinary system and homeostasis.

Complete each statement.

11. __________________ and __________________ are two toxic nitrogenous wastes that your kidneys constantly remove from your bloodstream.

12. The kidneys also help regulate the blood's __________________ __________________, and __________________.

13. Individuals with diabetes have excess levels of __________________ in their blood.

Capítulo 37

Respiración celular, circulación y excreción

Refuerzo y Guía de estudio

Sección 37.1 El sistema respiratorio

En tu libro de texto, lee sobre los conductos para el paso del aire y los pulmones.

Haz un círculo alrededor de la letra de la opción que completa mejor o que contesta cada enunciado.

1. Durante el proceso de respiración celular
- **a.** se transporta oxígeno a las células.
- **b.** se expulsa dióxido de carbono del cuerpo.
- **c.** se usa oxígeno para producir ATP.
- **d.** todas las anteriores.

2. Cuando tragas alimentos, la epiglotis cubre momentáneamente la parte alta de la tráquea para que
- **a.** puedas tragar con mayor facilidad.
- **b.** puedas respirar con mayor facilidad.
- **c.** la comida no entre al tracto respiratorio.
- **d.** puedas toser cualquier sustancia extraña.

3. Los cilios que cubren la superficie interna de la tráquea y los bronquios
- **a.** producen una mucosidad que atrapa la suciedad del aire.
- **b.** ayudan durante el intercambio de oxígeno por CO_2.
- **c.** mueven la mucosidad y la suciedad del aire hacia la garganta.
- **d.** sólo se mueven cuando inhalas.

4. Las primeras ramas de la tráquea se conocen como
- **a.** bronquiolos.
- **b.** bronquios.
- **c.** arteriolas.
- **d.** alvéolos.

5. En el interior de los alvéolos, el oxígeno y el dióxido de carbono
- **a.** se intercambian entre el aire y la sangre.
- **b.** se transportan a través de túbulos microscópicos.
- **c.** se producen dentro de las células.
- **d.** se intercambian por otros gases.

6. ¿Cuál es la secuencia correcta de la ruta que sigue el oxígeno a través del sistema respiratorio?
- **a.** vías nasales, bronquios, tráquea, bronquiolos, células, sangre, alvéolos
- **b.** células, sangre, alvéolos, bronquiolos, bronquios, tráquea, vías nasales
- **c.** vías nasales, sangre, alvéolos, bronquios, células, tráquea, bronquiolos
- **d.** vías nasales, tráquea, bronquios, bronquiolos, alvéolos, sangre, células

En tu libro de texto, lee sobre la mecánica de la respiración y el control de la respiración celular.

Indica si cada uno de los enunciados es verdadero o falso.

________________ **7.** El cerebro controla la homeostasis de la respiración celular.

________________ **8.** Al exhalar, los bronquiolos de los pulmones liberan la mayoría del aire.

________________ **9.** Cuando inhalas, se contraen los músculos intercostales.

________________ **10.** La relajación del diafragma ocasiona un pequeño vacío en los pulmones.

________________ **11.** El aire entra a los pulmones porque la presión del aire fuera del cuerpo es mayor que la presión del aire dentro de los pulmones.

________________ **12.** La relajación del diafragma hace que este músculo se "aplane".

Capítulo 37

Respiración celular, circulación y excreción, *continuación*

Refuerzo y Guía de estudio

Sección 37.2 El sistema circulatorio

En tu libro de texto, lee sobre la sangre, los tipos de sangre ABO y los vasos sanguíneos.

Contesta las siguientes preguntas.

1. ¿Qué tipo de células y sustancias están disueltas o suspendidas en el plasma?

____

____

2. ¿Cómo se transporta el dióxido de carbono en la sangre?

____

____

Completa la tabla indicando la columna correspondiente a cada enunciado.

Enunciado	Glóbulos rojos	Glóbulos blancos	Plaquetas
3. Contienen hemoglobina			
4. Combaten infecciones			
5. Carecen de núcleo			
6. Participan en la formación de coágulos			
7. Transportan oxígeno			
8. Relativamente grandes y con núcleo			

Indica si cada uno de los enunciados es <u>verdadero</u> o <u>falso</u>.

__________ **9.** Se puede cambiar el tipo de sangre con una transfusión.

__________ **10.** Existen diferentes tipos de sangre porque las membranas de los glóbulos rojos tienen diferentes tipos de anticuerpos.

__________ **11.** Si tienes sangre tipo B, entonces tienes anticuerpos anti-A en tu plasma.

__________ **12.** Los riesgos de presentar un factor Rh incompatible son mayores durante el primer embarazo de una mujer.

Capítulo 37

Respiración celular, circulación y excreción, *continuación*

Refuerzo y Guía de estudio

Sección 37.2 El sistema circulatorio

En tu libro de texto, lee sobre el corazón humano, la circulación de la sangre a través del corazón y el interior del corazón.

Rotula las partes del corazón indicadas en el diagrama. Usa las siguientes opciones:

aorta **aurícula izquierda** **ventrículo izquierdo** **arterias pulmonares**
venas pulmonares **aurícula derecha** **ventrículo derecho**

13. ______________________

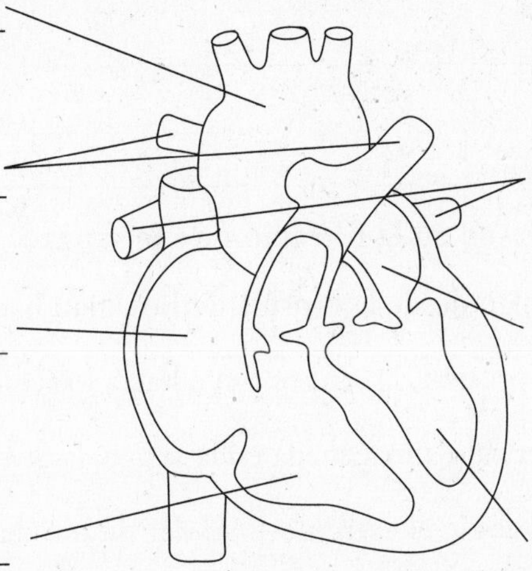

14. ______________________ **15.** ______________________

17. ______________________ **16.** ______________________

19. ______________________ **18.** ______________________

20. ¿Hacia dónde se dirige la sangre que llega a las venas pulmonares? ¿Hacia dónde es bombeada la que llega al ventrículo derecho? ¿Hacia dónde es bombeada la que llega al ventrículo izquierdo?

____

21. ¿Qué evita la mezcla de la sangre entre aurículas y ventrículos?

____

En tu texto, lee sobre la regulación de los latidos del corazón, el control del corazón y la presión sanguínea.

Si el enunciado es verdadero, escribe *verdadero*; de lo contrario, modifica la sección en itálicas para hacer verdadero el enunciado.

22. La oleada periódica de sangre que pasa por una arteria se conoce como *rendimiento cardiaco.*

____

23. El marcapasos inicia los latidos del corazón *al generar impulsos eléctricos.* ______________________

24. Un electrocardiograma es un registro de *la fuerza de cada latido.* ______________________

____

25. El *nódulo auriculoventricular,* junto con las células receptoras localizadas en las arterias cercanas al corazón, se encargan de regular el marcapasos.

____

26. La *presión diastólica* ocurre cuando se contraen los ventrículos del corazón. ______________________

Capítulo 37

Respiración celular, circulación y excreción, *continuación*

Refuerzo y Guía de estudio

Sección 37.3 El sistema urinario

En tu libro de texto, lee sobre los riñones, los nefrones y la formación de orina.

Contesta las siguientes preguntas.

1. ¿Cuál es la función más importante de los riñones?

____

2. ¿Cuál es la función de la vejiga en el sistema urinario?

____

3. ¿Qué son los nefrones?

____

Ordena del 1 al 7 los siguientes pasos en la filtración de la sangre.

__________ **4.** Los fluidos circulan desde la cápsula de Bowman hacia un túbulo en forma de "U".

__________ **5.** Debido a la alta presión, la sangre fluye hacia los capilares del glomérulo.

__________ **6.** Después de haber sido almacenada en la vejiga, la orina es excretada a través de la uretra.

__________ **7.** El fluido circula desde el extremo final del túbulo del nefrón hacia el uréter.

__________ **8.** La sangre entra al nefrón desde una ramificación de la arteria renal.

__________ **9.** Se reabsorben agua, glucosa, aminoácidos e iones hacia la sangre.

__________ **10.** Pasan agua, glucosa, aminoácidos, desechos y otras sustancias desde los capilares del glomérulo hacia la cápsula de Bowman.

En tu libro de texto, lee sobre la relación entre el sistema urinario y la homeostasis.

Completa cada enunciado.

11. El ____________________ y la ____________________ son dos desechos nitrogenados que los riñones eliminan constantemente del torrente sanguíneo.

12. Los riñones también ayudan a regular la ____________________ ____________________ y el ____________________ de la sangre.

13. Los individuos que padecen diabetes tienen un nivel excesivo de ____________________ en su sangre.

Chapter 37

Respiration, Circulation, and Excretion

Concept Mapping

Use with Chapter 37, Section 37.2

Circulation in Humans

Complete the concept map on human circulation and heart function. Use these words or phrases once: *high O_2, low O_2, venae cavae, left atrium, right ventricle, right atrium, high CO_2, low CO_2, pulmonary veins, left ventricle, aorta, lungs.*

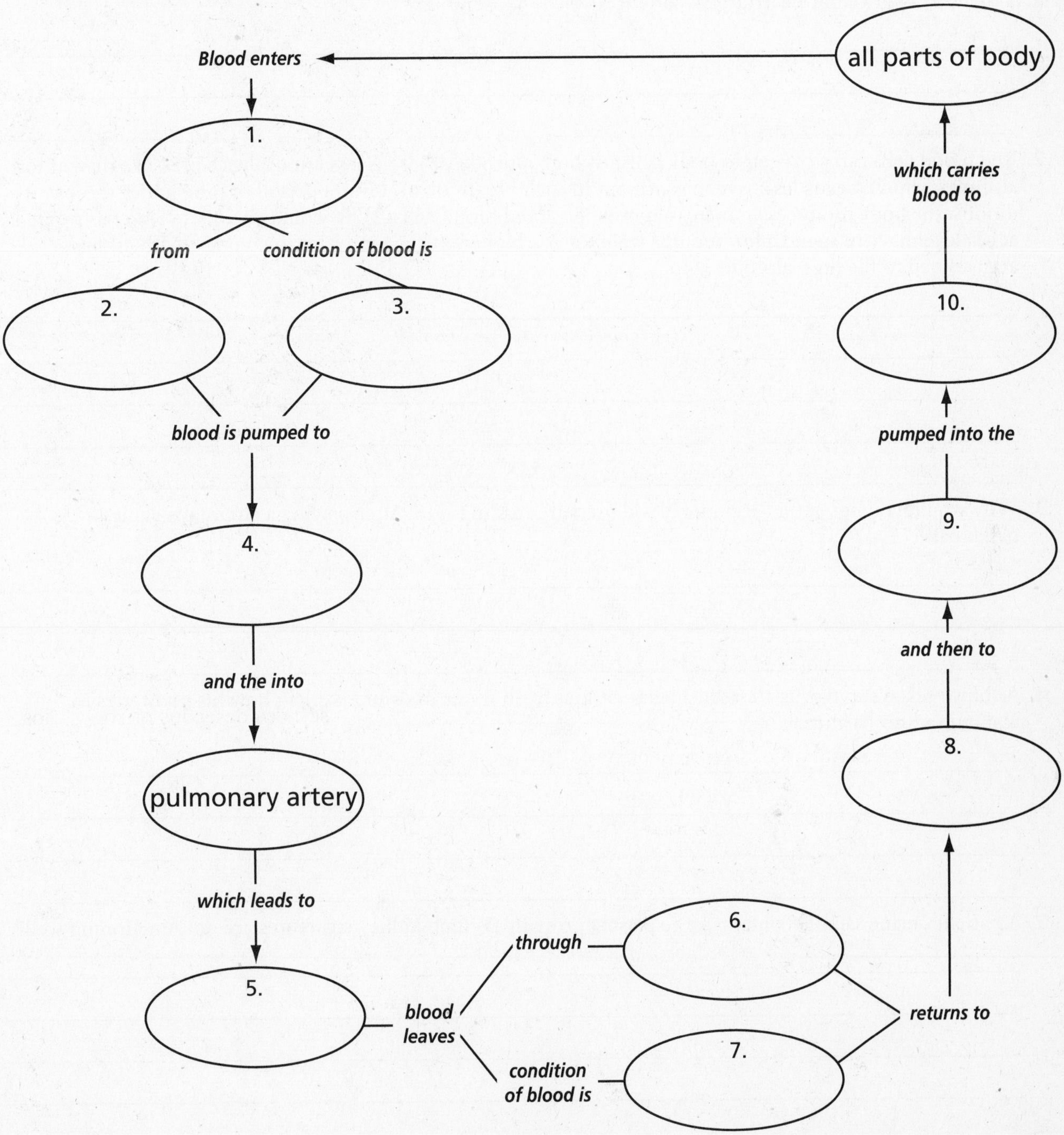

Name Date Class

Chapter 37

Respiration, Circulation, and Excretion

Critical Thinking

Use with Chapter 37, Sections 37.1, 37.2, 37.3

Solving Respiratory, Circulatory, and Excretory System Problems

In Chapter 37, you learned how the respiratory, circulatory, and excretory systems function in maintaining homeostasis in the body. The following questions relate to problems that affect these systems. Using what you have learned about these body systems, answer the questions.

1. Why is an overweight heart-attack patient advised to lose weight?

2. Red blood cells carry oxygen to body cells. At high altitudes, there is less atmospheric pressure than at low altitudes, which means less oxygen is present in each breath of air. Over a period of time under these conditions, the body produces an increased number of red blood cells. Why would an athlete who has trained at sea level have to spend a few months training at a higher altitude in order to compete with athletes accustomed to the high altitudes?

3. Why would you not get an accurate blood pressure reading right after playing a strenuous game of basketball?

4. A shipwrecked survivor is afloat in a boat without fresh water to drink. Explain how his body tries to maintain water balance.

5. A patient's urine sample contains large plasma proteins. Which kidney structures are not functioning well?

Name Date Class

Master 90

Take a Breath

Section Focus

Use with Chapter 37, Section 37.1

1. What happens when the sides of the bellows are pulled apart? Why does that happen?

2. What structures in the human body are comparable to the bellows and to the hands that push and pull on the bellows?

Master 91

The Blood Goes Around

Section Focus

Use with Chapter 37, Section 37.2

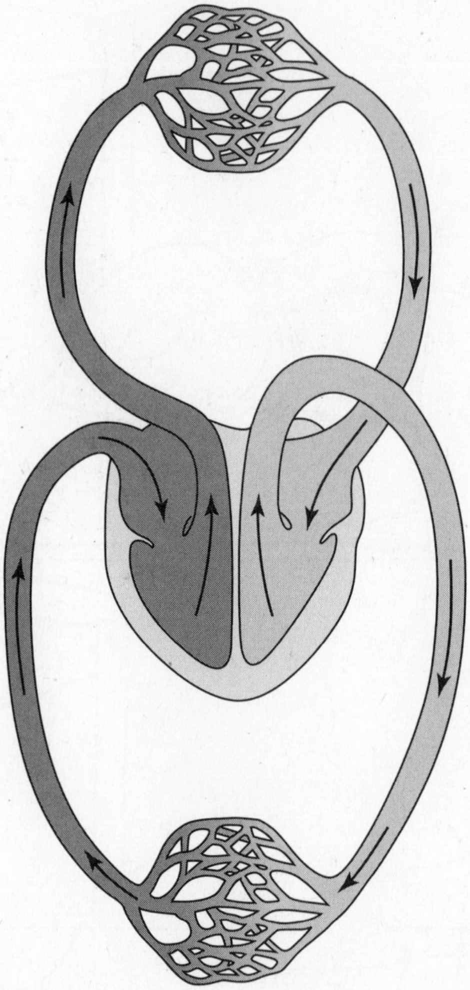

1. This is a simplified diagram of the blood circulation in humans. Why do you think two separate loops are necessary?
2. What do you think is represented by the network of capillaries at the top? The network of capillaries at the bottom?

Name Date Class

Master 92

Saving and Discarding

Section Focus

Use with Chapter 37, Section 37.3

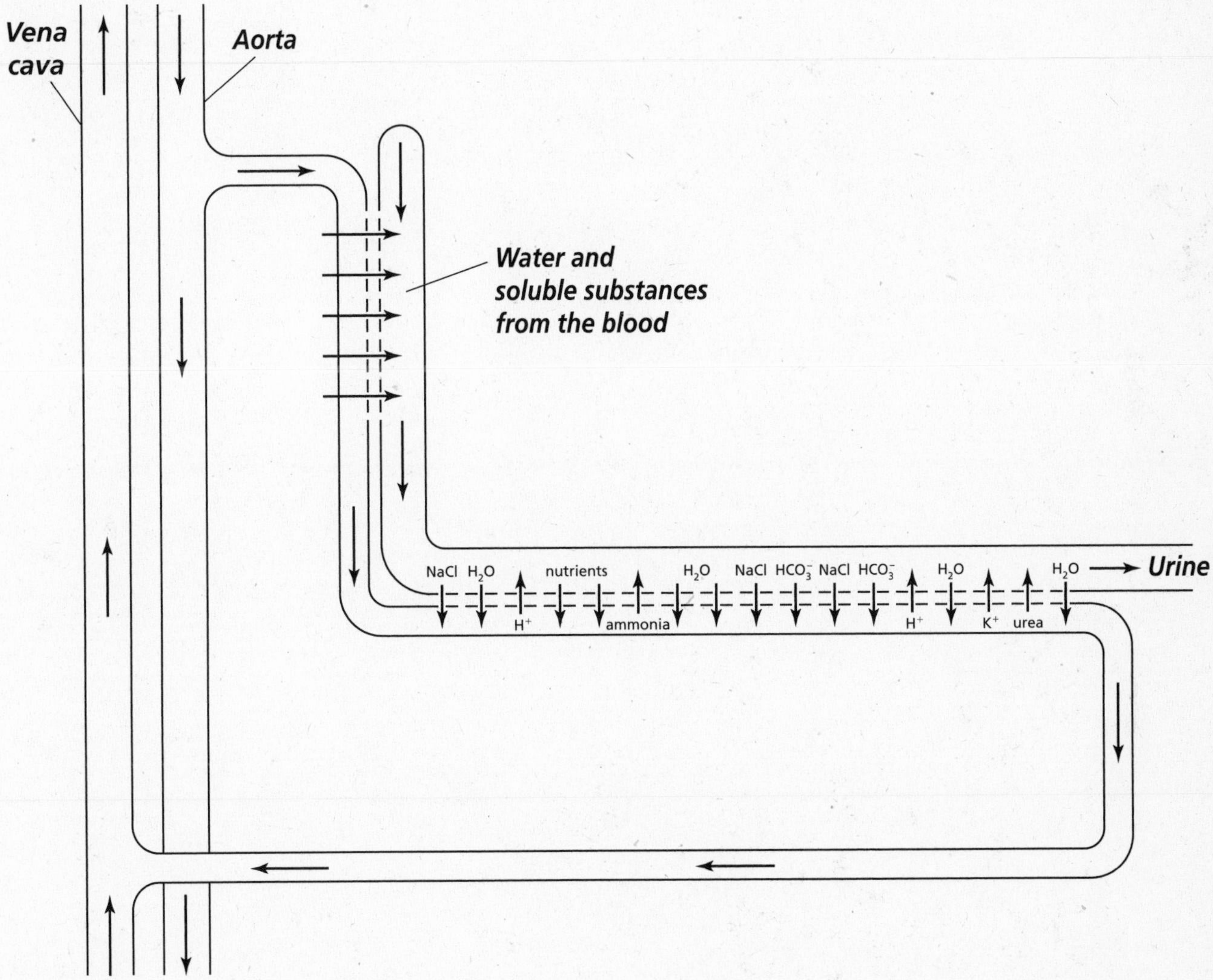

❶ Follow the flow of blood through this diagram of the operation of the kidney. What, in general, is happening along the horizontal part of the diagram?

❷ What substances are being conserved (saved) in the blood? What substances are being discarded?

Name Date Class

Master 70

Blood Types

Basic Concepts

Use with Chapter 37, Section 37.2

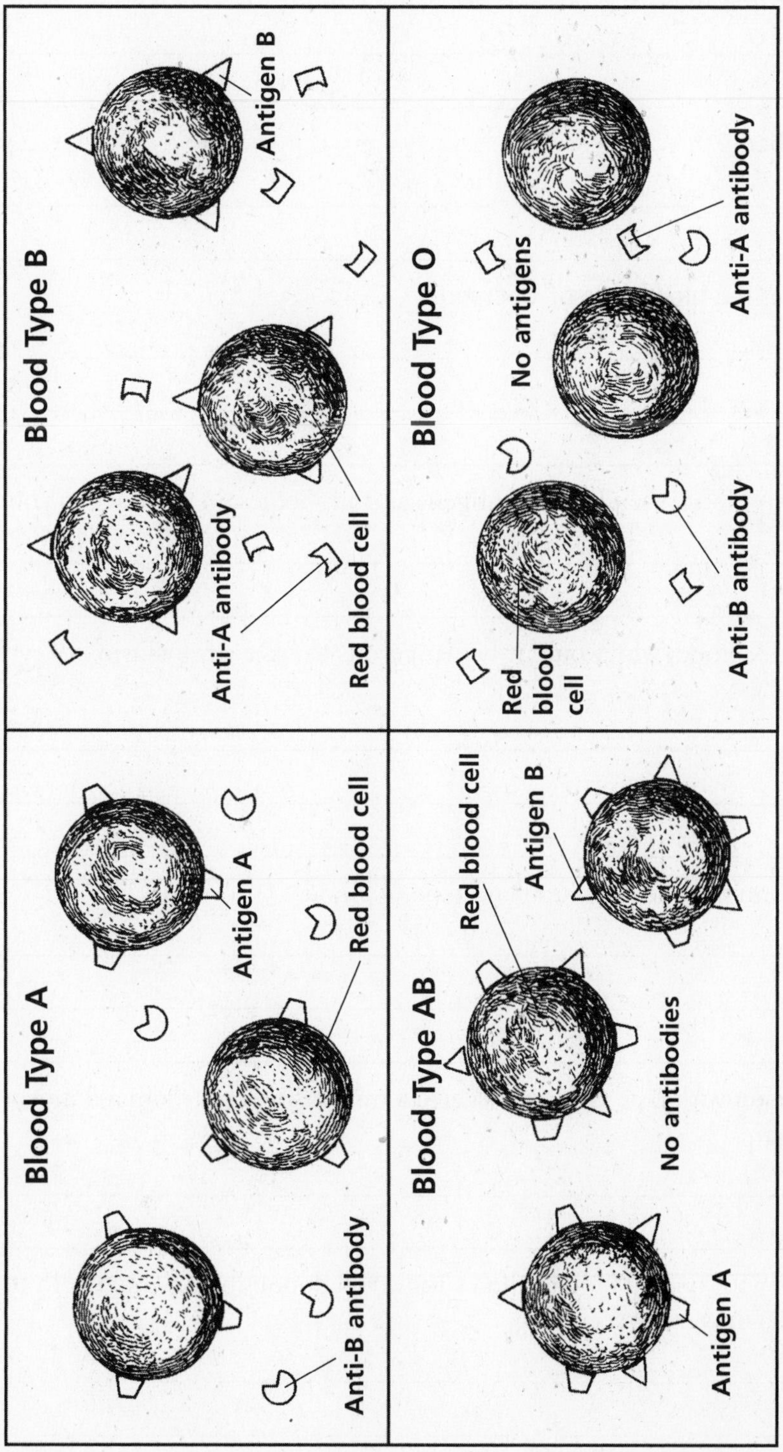

Name Date Class

Worksheet 70

Blood Types

Basic Concepts

Use with Chapter 37, Section 37.2

1. What is an antigen?

2. What is an antibody?

3. What determines the blood type of a person?

4. If you have type A blood, what kind of antigens and antibodies do you have in your blood?

5. If you have type A blood, why would it be dangerous to have a transfusion of type B blood?

6. Compare and contrast type AB blood and type O blood.

7. Why must a person with type O blood receive a transfusion only from a donor who also has type O blood?

8. Why is a person with type O blood called a universal donor and a person with type AB blood called a universal receiver?

Master 71

Your Blood Vessels

Basic Concepts

Use with Chapter 37, Section 37.2

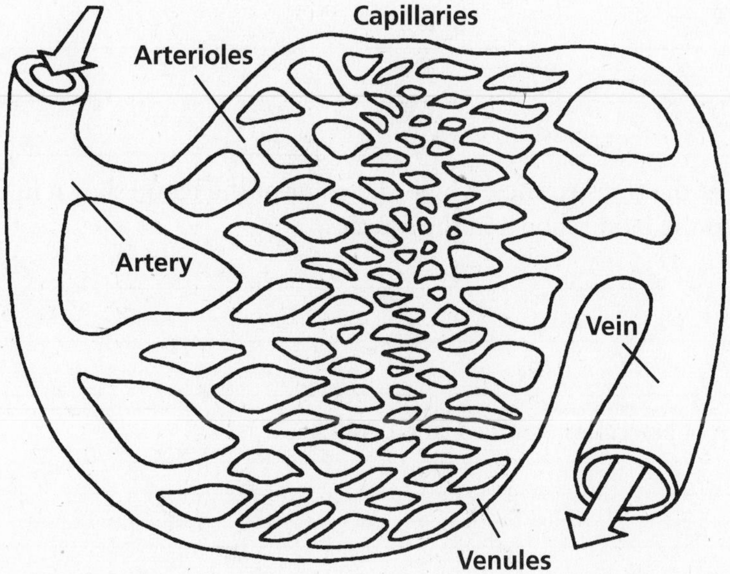

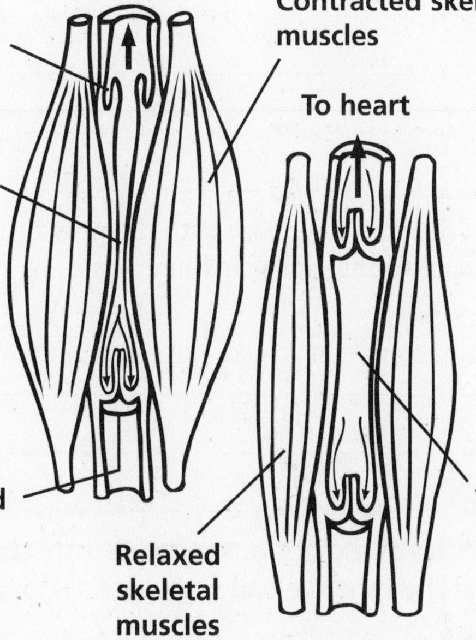

Worksheet 71

Your Blood Vessels

Basic Concepts

Use with Chapter 37, Section 37.2

1. Describe the structure and function of arteries.

2. In the top illustration of the transparency, why is the color of the blood shown in the veins much darker than the blood shown in the arteries?

3. Compare the structure of arterioles, venules, and capillaries.

4. How does the pressure of blood in the arteries affect the flow of blood from the heart to the tissues?

5. How does the pressure of blood in the veins compare with the pressure in the arteries? How does this difference in pressure relate to the fact that some veins are equipped with valves?

6. Study the drawing of skeletal muscles at the bottom of the transparency. Describe what happens to the valves in the veins when the skeletal muscles relax or contract.

Master 72

Your Heart

Basic Concepts

Use with Chapter 37, Section 37.2

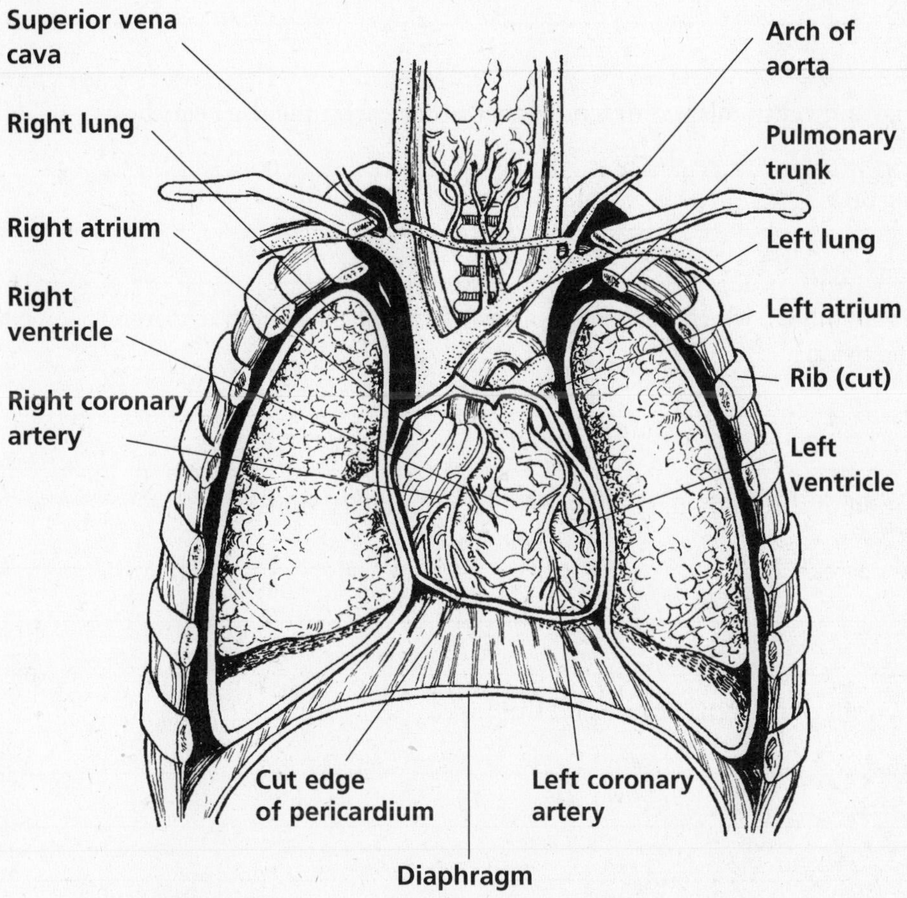

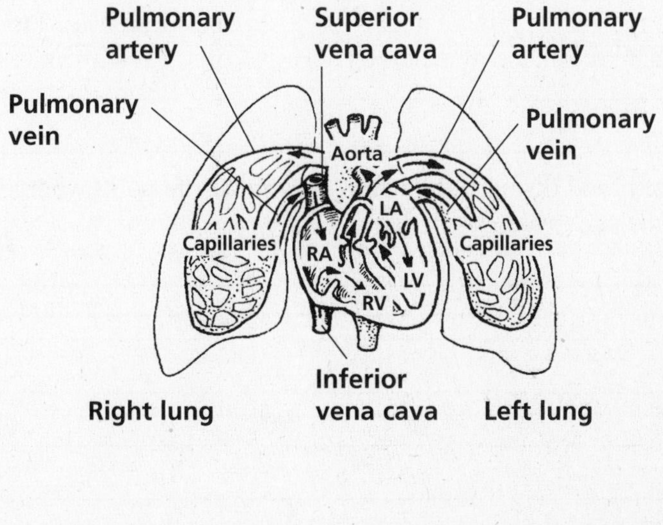

Name Date Class

Worksheet 72

Your Heart

Basic Concepts

Use with Chapter 37, Section 37.2

1. What is the function of the pericardium?

2. Describe the atrial and ventricular contractions that occur each time the heart beats.

3. Of the four heart chambers, which perform more work? How does the transparency support your conclusion?

4. What is the function of the pulmonary arteries? The pulmonary veins?

5. Contrast the functions of the venae cavae and the aorta.

6. Explain the function of a heart valve.

7. Briefly trace the path of a drop of blood through the heart, starting at the point where it returns from the body through a venae cavae.

Master 73

The Urinary System

Basic Concepts

Use with Chapter 37, Section 37.3

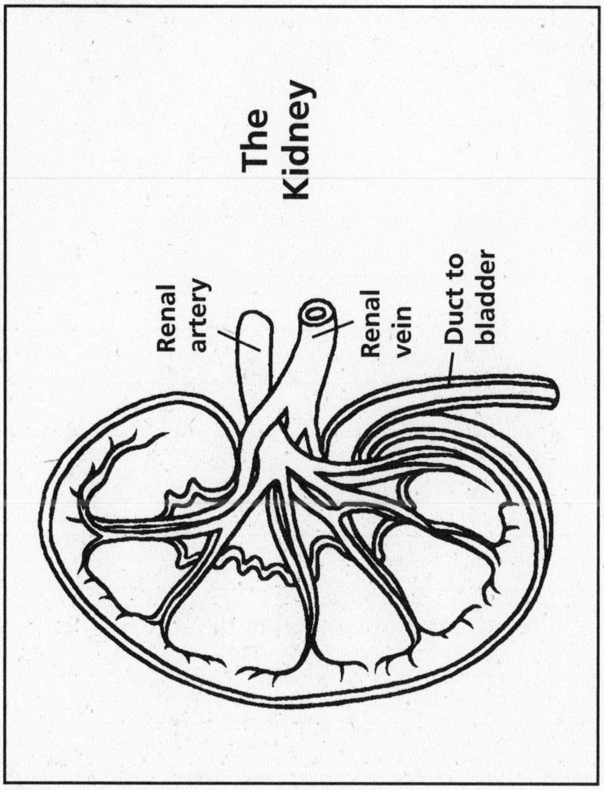

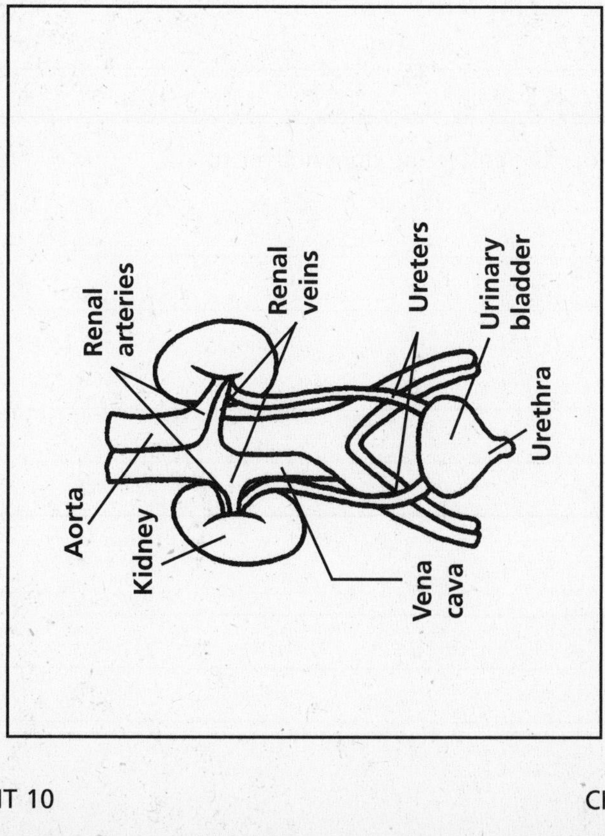

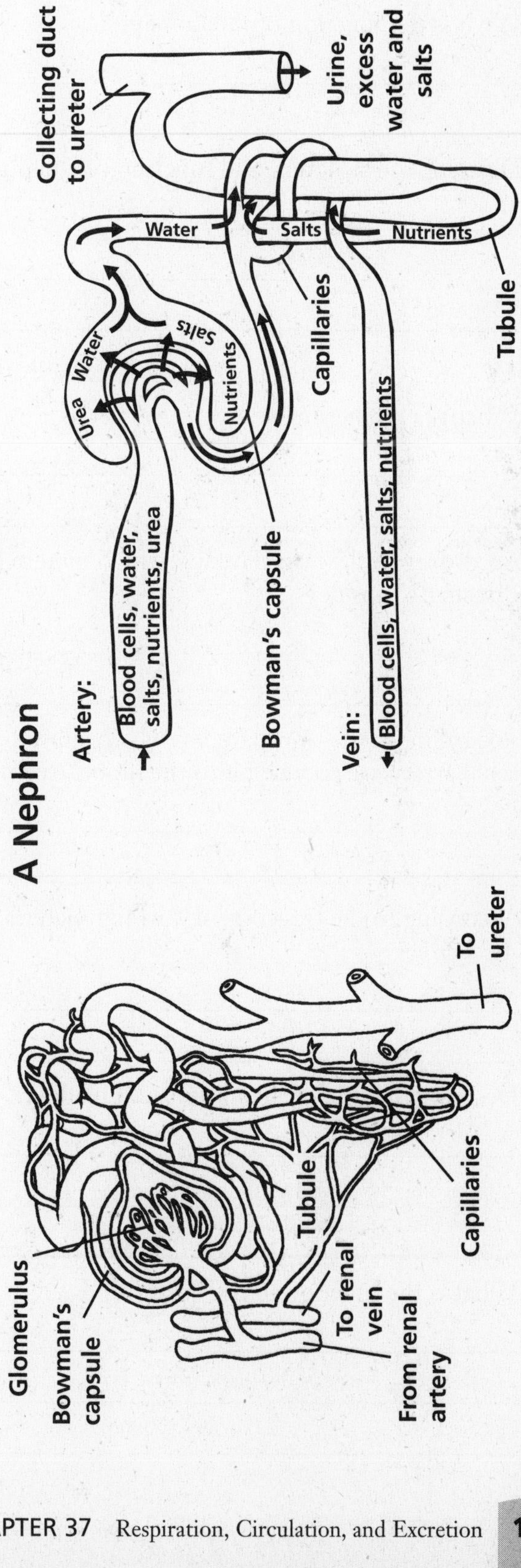

Worksheet **73**

The Urinary System

Basic Concepts

Use with Chapter 37, Section 37.3

1. What is the function of the kidneys?

2. Describe the structure and function of a nephron.

3. What is a glomerulus?

4. According to the transparency, which materials are filtered out of the blood in the Bowman's capsule?

5. According to the transparency, which substances that enter the kidney through the renal artery are recycled into the bloodstream through the renal vein?

6. According to the transparency, which materials does the collecting duct deliver to the ureter?

7. Describe the role of the ureters and bladder.

8. What is the function of the urethra?

Master 54

Circulatory Path Through the Heart

Reteaching Skills

Use with Chapter 37, Section 37.2

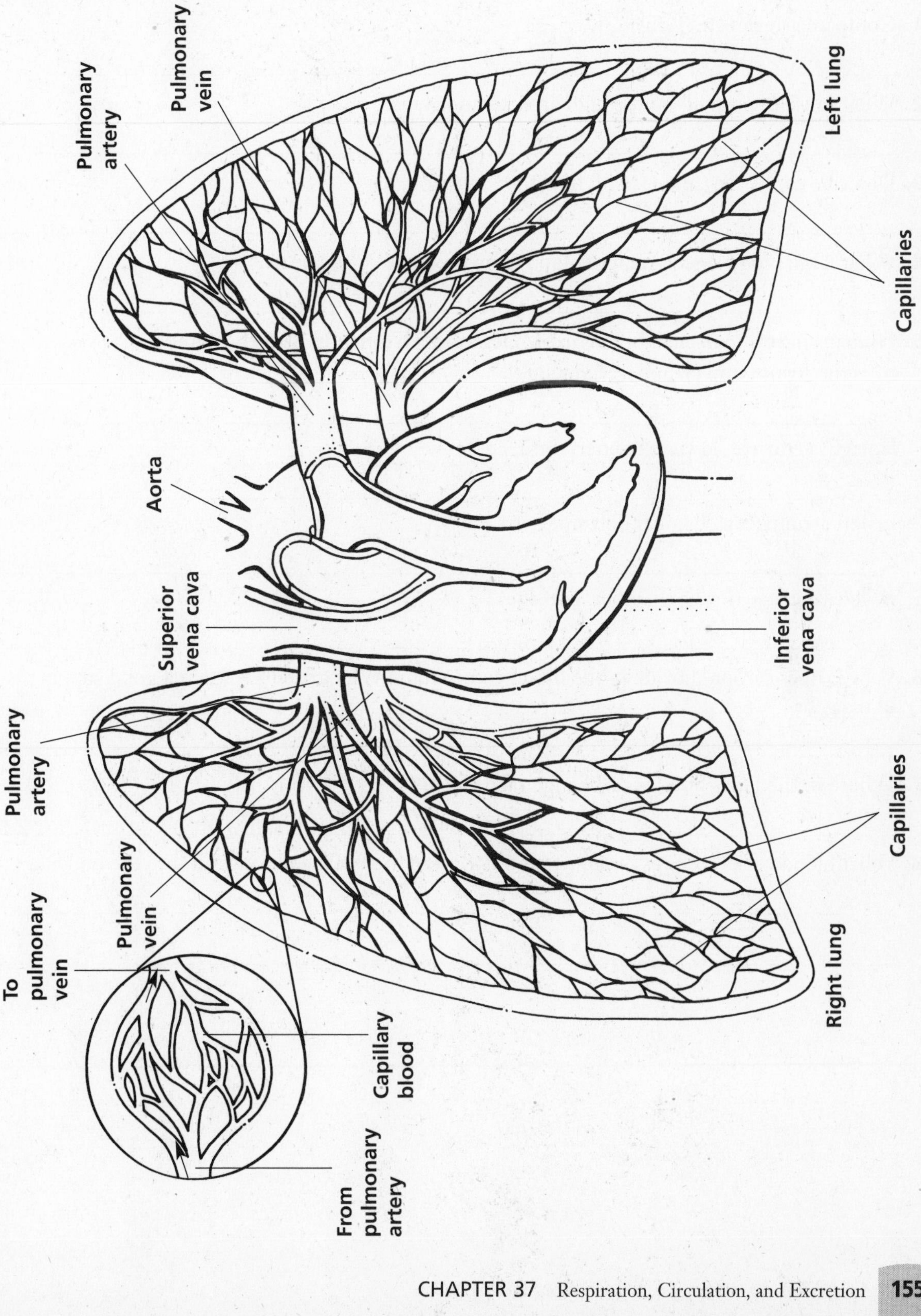

Name Date Class

Worksheet 54

Circulatory Path Through the Heart

Reteaching Skills

Use with Chapter 37, Section 37.2

1. Compare arteries and veins.

2. What muscles push blood through arteries and veins?

3. Describe capillaries, and explain how they function.

4. What large blood vessels deliver blood from the body to the heart?

5. Humans have a four-chambered heart. Describe the function of each chamber.

a. right atrium (top chamber, right side)

b. right ventricle (lower chamber, right side)

c. left atrium (top chamber, left side)

d. left ventricle (lower chamber, left side)

6. Where does carbon dioxide in the blood come from? Why do cells require a good supply of oxygen?

7. Where in the lungs does gas exchange take place?

8. What blood vessel receives oxygen-rich blood from the heart and moves it into the body?

Name Date Class

Chapter 37

Respiration, Circulation, and Excretion

Chapter Assessment

Reviewing Vocabulary

Match the definition in Column A with the term in Column B.

	Column A	Column B
______	**1.** Passageway leading from the larynx to the lungs	**a.** alveoli
______	**2.** Sacs of the lungs where exchange of oxygen and carbon dioxide takes place	**b.** antibody
______	**3.** Fluid portion of blood in which blood cells move	**c.** antigen
______	**4.** Iron-containing protein that picks up oxygen after it enters the blood vessels in the lungs	**d.** aorta
______	**5.** Cell fragments that help blood to clot after an injury	**e.** artery
______	**6.** A substance that stimulates an immune response in the body	**f.** atrium
______	**7.** Microscopic blood vessel	**g.** urine
______	**8.** Protein that reacts with an antigen	**h.** capillary
______	**9.** A kind of large, muscular, thick-walled elastic vessel that carries blood away from the heart	**i.** hemoglobin
______	**10.** A kind of large blood vessel that carries blood from the tissues to the heart	**j.** nephron
______	**11.** An upper chamber of the heart	**k.** plasma
______	**12.** A lower chamber of the heart	**l.** platelets
______	**13.** Largest blood vessel in the body	**m.** pulse
______	**14.** Regular surge of blood through an artery	**n.** trachea
______	**15.** Solution of body wastes consisting of excess water, waste molecules, and excess ions	**o.** vein
______	**16.** A filtering unit in the kidney	**p.** ventricle

Understanding Main Ideas (Part A)

In the space at the left, write true if the statement is true. If the statement is false, change the italicized word or phrase to make it true.

__________ **1.** Red blood cells are produced in the *spleen*.

__________ **2.** The blood in the veins is prevented from flowing backward because of *pressure* in these blood vessels.

__________ **3.** The only veins that carry oxygen-rich blood are the *venae cavae*.

__________ **4.** When blood first enters the heart, it passes into the *ventricles*.

__________ **5.** As the liquid passes through the *U-shaped tubule* in the nephron, most of the ions and water and all of the glucose and amino acids are reabsorbed into the bloodstream.

__________ **6.** The major waste products of the cells are ammonia and the wastes from the breakdown of *carbohydrates*.

__________ **7.** The urine of a person who has diabetes may contain excess *salts*.

__________ **8.** Carbon dioxide and *oxygen* are the waste products of cellular respiration.

__________ **9.** When your diaphragm *contracts*, the space in the chest cavity becomes larger.

__________ **10.** Breathing is controlled by changes in the chemistry of the blood, which cause the *medulla oblongata* to react.

__________ **11.** Your pulse represents the pressure that blood exerts as it pushes the walls of a(n) *vein*.

__________ **12.** If you have type A blood and *anti-A* is added during a transfusion, no clumps will form.

__________ **13.** *External respiration* uses oxygen in the breakdown of glucose in cells in order to provide energy in the form of ATP.

Chapter 37

Respiration, Circulation, and Excretion, *continued*

Chapter Assessment

Understanding Main Ideas (Part B)

Answer the following questions.

1. How does the respiratory system prevent most of the foreign matter in urban air from reaching your lungs?

2. Distinguish between systolic pressure and diastolic pressure.

3. What problem may arise when a woman with Rh^- blood is pregnant with an Rh^+ fetus?

4. How does a pacemaker set the heart rate?

5. How does the urinary system maintain homeostasis?

Chapter 37 **Respiration, Circulation, and Excretion,** *continued*

Chapter Assessment

Thinking Critically

A marathon runner is able to increase the amount of blood pumped by the heart (cardiac output) from 5 L/min while resting to 30 L/min while competing. The runner's stroke volume (pumping capacity per heart-beat) measured in mL/beat, and heart rate, measured in beats/min, are also increased.

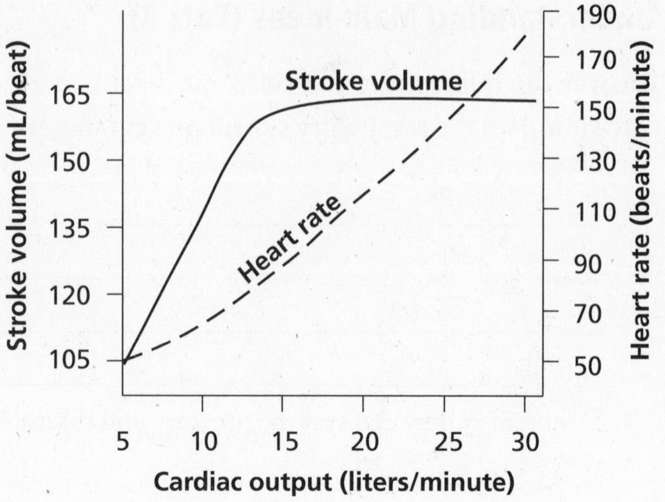

Use the graph to answer questions 1–3.

1. When the runner's cardiac output is 20 L/min, what is the heart rate?

____

2. What is the stroke volume when the cardiac output is 20 mL/min?

____

3. Which has the greater effect on cardiac output, stroke volume or heart rate?

____

Answer the following questions.

4. When a person has pneumonia, the alveoli become inflamed and the air spaces become clogged. What effect will these symptoms have on a pneumonia patient?

____

5. Arteriosclerosis slowly reduces blood flow through the arteries to the brain. Explain how this may affect a patient who has this condition.

____

6. The antidiuretic hormone (ADH) stimulates the reabsorption of water in the kidneys. Alcohol inhibits ADH secretion. Predict the effect of drinking alcoholic beverages on urine production.

____

Chapter 37 **Respiration, Circulation, and Excretion,** *continued*

Chapter Assessment

Applying Scientific Methods

The vertebrate heart can beat spontaneously. If the heart of a vertebrate is removed and placed in a balanced salt solution with nutrients, it will continue to beat for hours. In fact, the muscle from each part of the heart beats at its own rate if it is not under the control of the pacemaker.

In a physiology laboratory experiment, a frog is anaesthetized and the heart is exposed. Recall that the frog has a three-chambered heart, with right and left atria and a single ventricle. It also has a sinus venosus, which receives oxygen-depleted blood from all parts of the body except the lungs. The sinus venosus is where contraction begins. (This role is assumed by the pacemaker in the mammalian heart.) For this experiment, the nerve connections to the heart are blocked. The sinus venosus, the right atrium, and the ventricle are each attached to a stylus for marking on a kymograph (an instrument that records changes in pressure). In the graphs, rises represent contractions.

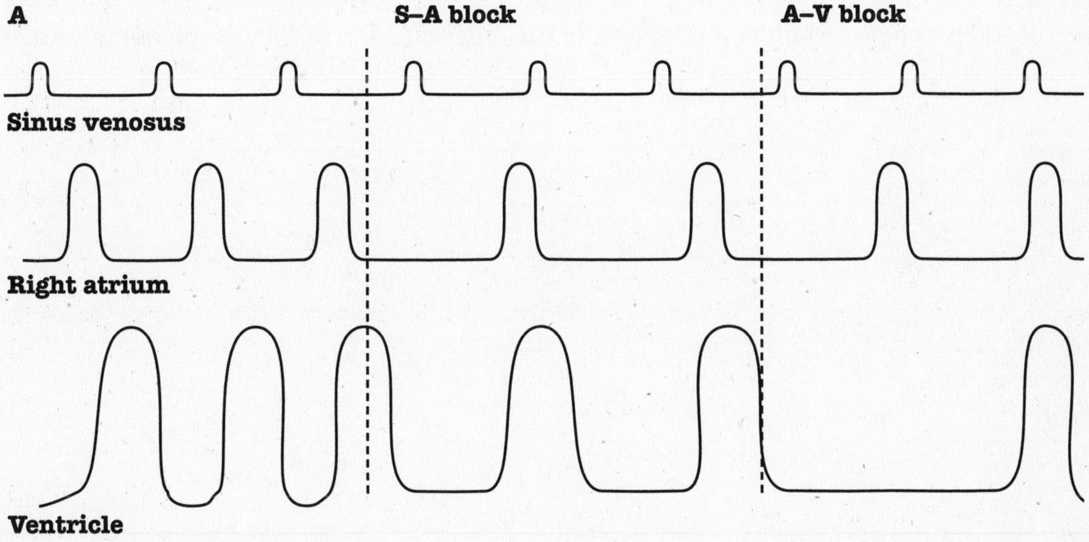

1. Interpret the data in A.

____

____

____

2. To understand how the heart beats when the impulse from the sinus is blocked, a string is tied tightly around the heart between the sinus and the atrium. This is called an "S-A block." How does the S-A block affect the rate of the beat of the sinus?

____

3. How does blocking the sinus affect the rate at which the atrium and ventricle beat?

____

Chapter 37

Respiration, Circulation, and Excretion, *continued*

Chapter Assessment

Applying Scientific Methods *continued*

4. What could you do to find out the effect of blocking the atrium?

____

____

5. How does blocking the action between the atrium and the ventricle, which is called an "A-V block," affect the beat of the sinus, the atrium, and the ventricle?

____

____

____

6. What can you conclude about the rate of beat of the different parts of the heart from this experiment?

____

____

____

____

____

Name Date Class

Chapter 37

Assessment
Student Recording Sheet

Chapter Assessment

Use with pages 992–993 of the Student Edition

Vocabulary Review

Explain the difference between the words in each pair.

1. ______________________________
2. ______________________________
3. ______________________________
4. ______________________________
5. ______________________________

Understanding Key Concepts

Select the best answer from the choices given and fill in the corresponding oval.

6. Ⓐ Ⓑ Ⓒ Ⓓ
7. Ⓐ Ⓑ Ⓒ Ⓓ
8. Ⓐ Ⓑ Ⓒ Ⓓ
9. Ⓐ Ⓑ Ⓒ Ⓓ
10. Fill in the correct terms to complete the concept map.
    1. ____________________
    2. ____________________
    3. ____________________
    4. ____________________

Constructed Response

Record your answers for Questions 11–13 on a separate sheet of paper.

Thinking Critically

Record your answers for Questions 14, 16, and 17 on a separate sheet of paper.

15. **REAL WORLD BIOCHALLENGE** Follow your teacher's instructions for presenting your BioChallenge answer.

Standardized Test Practice

The Princeton Review

Part 1 Multiple Choice

Select the best answer from the choices given and fill in the corresponding oval.

18. Ⓐ Ⓑ Ⓒ Ⓓ
19. Ⓐ Ⓑ Ⓒ Ⓓ
20. Ⓐ Ⓑ Ⓒ Ⓓ
21. Ⓐ Ⓑ Ⓒ Ⓓ
22. Ⓐ Ⓑ Ⓒ Ⓓ
23. Ⓐ Ⓑ Ⓒ Ⓓ
24. Ⓐ Ⓑ Ⓒ Ⓓ

Part 2 Constructed Response/Grid In

Record your answers for Questions 25 and 26 on a separate sheet of paper.

Contents

Chapter 38 Reproduction and Development

MiniLab 38.1

Observing and Inferring

Examining Sperm, Egg, and Early Embryonic Development

Sperm and egg cells are specialized for reproduction. The egg cell is produced with a large amount of cytoplasm and a special protective membrane. Sperm are specialized for their journey to join the egg. Once a sperm fertilizes the egg in the oviduct, the zygote begins to divide by repeated mitotic divisions to produce a blastocyst for implantation.

Procedure

Carefully examine the prepared slides of a human sperm, human egg, and a sea star blastula. Compare the human sperm to ***Figure 38.2***, the egg to ***Figure 38.6***, and the blastula to the figure above. **CAUTION:** ***Use care when working with a microscope and microscope slides.***

Analysis

1. Which structures labeled in ***Figure 38.2*** are visible on the sperm slide? What is the function of each structure?

____

____

2. What is the function of the cells of the follicle surrounding the egg?

____

____

3. Where did the cells of the blastula come from?

____

____

Name Date Class

MiniLab 38.2

Making and Using Graphs

Making a Graph of Fetal Size

You started out as a single cell. That cell divided by the process of mitosis to produce organ systems capable of maintaining an independent existence outside your mother's uterus. Growth in length is one of the many changes that occur as a fetus develops.

Growth of a Fetus

Source of sample	Time after fertilization	Size
First trimester	3 weeks	3 mm
	4 weeks	6 mm
	6 weeks	12 mm
	7 weeks	2 cm
	8 weeks	4 cm
	9 weeks	5 cm
	3 months	7.5 cm
Second trimester	4 months	15 cm
	5 months	25 cm
	6 months	30 cm
Third trimester	7 months	35 cm
	8 months	40 cm
	9 months	51 cm

Procedure

1. Prepare a graph that plots time on the horizontal axis and length in centimeters on the vertical axis. Equally divide the horizontal axis into nine months. Then equally divide each of the first three months into four weeks.
2. Plot the data in the table above on your graph.

Analysis

1. When is the fastest period of growth?

____

____

2. What structures are developing during this period of growth?

____

____

3. At what point does growth begin to slow down?

____

Name Date Class

INVESTIGATE BioLab

What hormone is produced by an embryo?

Chapter 38

Preparation

Problem
How can you test for the presence of hCG?

Objectives
In this BioLab, you will:
- **Model** the chemicals used to test for the presence of hCG.
- **Interpret** the results of chemical reactions involving hCG in a pregnant and nonpregnant female.

Materials
scissors
heavy paper
tracing paper

Safety Precautions
Handle scissors with caution.

Skill Handbook
Use the **Skill Handbook** if you need additional help with this lab.

Procedure

1. Use the data table below.
2. Copy models **A, B,** and **C** on page 1016 of your text onto tracing paper.
3. Copy the tracings onto heavy paper and cut them out. You will need 4 models of **A,** 4 models of **B,** and 1 model of **C.**
4. Model **A** represents a molecule of the hCG hormone. Model **B** represents a chemical called anti-hCG hormone. Model **C** represents a chemical that has four hCG molecules attached to it.
5. Note that the shapes of hCG and anti-hCG join together like puzzle pieces. These two chemicals react, or join together, when both are present in a solution. The shapes of anti-hCG and Chemical C also join, indicating that they chemically react when both are present. The combination of Chemical C and anti-hCG is green. Chemical C without anti-hCG attached is colorless.
6. Model the following events for the "Not pregnant" condition. Record them in the data table using drawings of the models.
   a. The hormone hCG is not present in the urine.
   b. Anti-hCG is added to a urine sample, then chemical C is added.
   c. Draw the resulting chemical in the data table and indicate the color that appears.

Data Table

Condition	hCG in urine?	+ Anti-hCG	= Joined hCG and anti-hCG?	+ Chemical C with anti-hCG?	Color
Not pregnant					
Pregnant					

INVESTIGATE BioLab

What hormone is produced by an embryo?, *continued*

Chapter 38

7. Model the following events for the "Pregnant" condition. Record them in the data table using drawings of the models.
   a. The hormone hCG is present.
   b. Anti-hCG is added to urine, then Chemical C is added.
   c. Draw the resulting chemical in the data table and indicate the color that appears.
8. **Cleanup and Disposal** Make wise choices about the disposal or recycling of materials used in this lab.

Analyze and Conclude

1. **Analyzing** Explain the origin of hCG in a pregnant female.

2. **Analyzing** Explain why hCG is absent in a nonpregnant female.

3. **Concluding** Describe the roles of anti-hCG and Chemical C in both tests.

4. **Observing and Inferring** Explain why anti-hCG is added to the sample before Chemical C is added.

Name Date Class

Real World BioApplications

Chapter 38 Tales from the Past

Have you ever heard the expression, "*Dead men tell no tales?*" Well, dead people *do* tell tales, especially to forensic anthropologists—scientists who specialize in the identification of individuals from skeletal and dental remains. During growth and development, individuals begin to take on traits that are characteristic of age, sex, and physical stature. Forensic anthropologists can take advantage of these developmental changes and by carefully examining and measuring bones and teeth can determine the age, sex, height, and ethnic background of a person from even the most meager remains. In this activity, you will solve a mystery by performing the work of a forensic anthropologist.

Part A: Techniques of Forensic Anthropology

Forensic anthropologists use a variety of techniques to determine the identity of a person. Some of the more common developmental features that they examine are shown below.

Age Estimation

Examine the inner surface of the pubic symphysis, the immovable joint between the two halves of the pelvis.

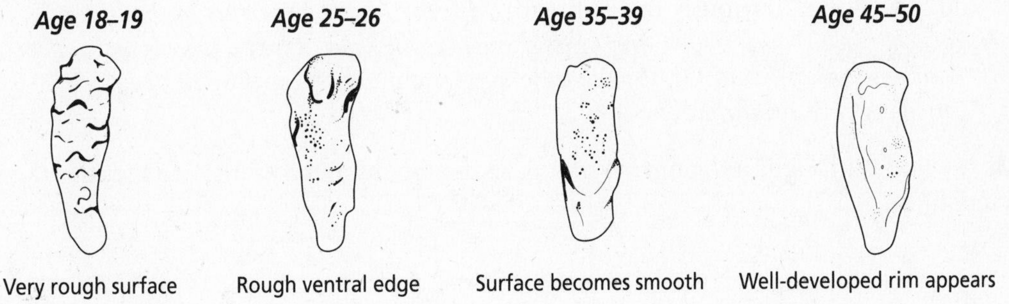

Figure 1

Sex Determination

Examine the shape of the pubic bone.

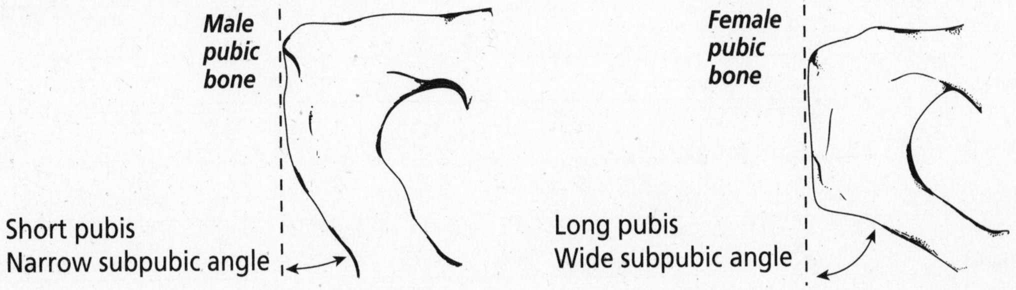

Figure 2

Measure the width of the knee joint.

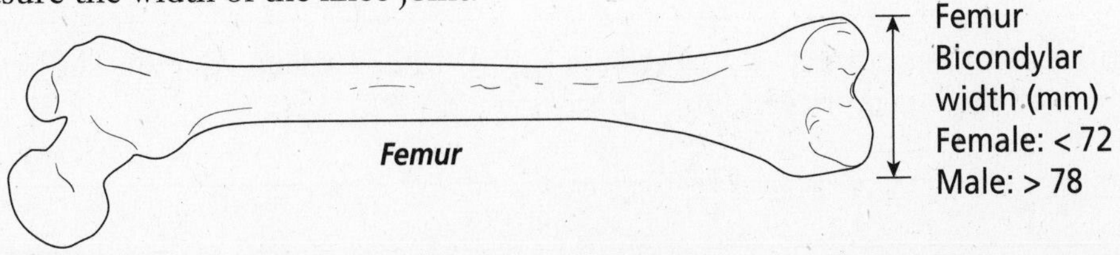

Figure 3

Chapter 38

Tales from the Past

Real World BioApplications

Stature Determination

Measure the length of long bones.

Table 1

Expected Height for Long-Bone Lengths			
Females		Males	
Femur (mm)	Height (cm)	Femur (mm)	Height (cm)
498	176	482	176
502	177	486	177
506	178	490	178
510	179	494	179

Part B: Identification of Skeletal and Dental Parts

Read the story and answer the questions below.

On a busy Monday morning, the door of Dr. Ojeda's crime lab suddenly burst open. It was Sgt. White. "*Hey Doc!*," said Sgt. White, obviously out of breath, "*I think I have some clues in that case about the missing guy. You know which one. Thirty-five years old, but really short. I found these bones buried in the woods.*" "*Wait one second!*," said Dr. Ojeda, quickly glancing at the specimen bags placed on her desk, "*I'm not so sure about that!*"

1. Figure 4 shows the bones brought in by Sgt. White. Use the techniques in Part A to identify the following characteristics.

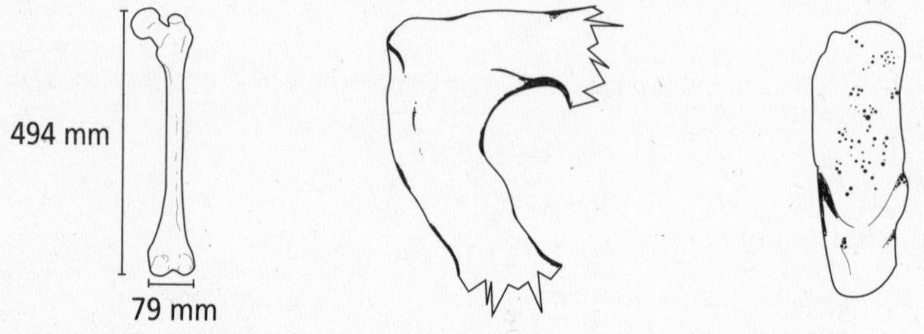

Figure 4

a. Probable sex __________

Evidence used __________

b. Estimated age __________

Evidence used __________

c. Estimated height __________

Evidence used __________

2. Based on your observations, who was correct—Dr. Ojeda or Sgt. White? Explain your answer by discussing the evidence you used in your investigation.

____

____

Name ______________________ Date __________ Class __________

Chapter 38

Reproduction and Development

Reinforcement and Study Guide

Section 38.1 Human Reproductive Systems

In your textbook, read about human male anatomy and hormonal control.

Answer the following questions.

1. What are the primary functions of the male reproductive system?

____

____

2. How does the location of the scrotum affect sperm?

____

____

3. How many sperm can the average mature male produce in one day?

____

Order the steps in the formation and transportation of sperm from 1 to 6.

__________ **4.** Mature sperm enter the vas deferens.

__________ **5.** Newly formed haploid sperm cells pass through a series of coiled ducts to the epididymis.

__________ **6.** Sperm leave the body via the urethra.

__________ **7.** Sperm mature in the epididymis.

__________ **8.** Cells lining tubules in the testes undergo meiosis.

__________ **9.** Sperm travel along the ejaculatory ducts and into the urethra.

Complete each sentence.

10. When a young man's voice "changes," he is probably entering ____________________, a time when he will develop other secondary ____________________ ____________________.

11. A hormone released by the ____________________ stimulates the ____________________ gland to release ____________________-____________________ and ____________________ hormones.

12. FSH regulates ____________________ production, while LH controls the production of the steroid hormone ____________________ by the testes.

Chapter 38 **Reproduction and Development,** *continued*

Reinforcement and Study Guide

Section 38.1 Human Reproductive Systems

In your textbook, read about human female anatomy and puberty in females.

If the statement is true, write *true*. If it is not, rewrite the italicized part to make it true.

13. When an egg cell is released from an ovary, it moves down the oviduct by *gravity*.

______

14. As is the case in human males, a woman's *hypothalamus* produces FSH and LH.

______

15. *FSH* stimulates follicle development and the release of estrogen from the ovary.

______

16. In females, *luteinizing hormone (LH)* is responsible for the development of the secondary sex characteristics.

______

17. Long before a woman is born, cells in her ovaries that are destined to become future eggs undergo several *mitotic divisions*.

______

In your textbook, read about the menstrual cycle.

Complete the table by checking the correct column for each event.

Event	Phase of Menstrual Cycle		
	Flow	Follicular	Luteal
18. LH stimulates the corpus luteum to develop from a ruptured follicle.			
19. Estrogen levels are at their peak.			
20. A cell inside a follicle resumes meiotic divisions.			
21. Progesterone levels are at their peak.			
22. The uterine lining is shed.			
23. LH levels rise abruptly.			
24. Ovulation occurs.			
25. The uterine lining becomes engorged with blood, fat, and tissue fluid.			
26. FSH begins to rise.			

Chapter 38

Reproduction and Development, *continued*

Reinforcement and Study Guide

Section 38.2 Development Before Birth

In your textbook, read about fertilization and implantation, and embryonic membranes.

Use each of the terms below just once to complete the passage.

amnion	**blastocyst**	**chorion**	**chorionic villi**	**embryo**
implants	**oviduct**	**placenta**	**umbilical cord**	**zygote**

Usually in the upper part of a(n) **(1)** ______________________, an egg and one sperm unite to form a(n) **(2)** ______________________. This single cell divides repeatedly to form a(n) **(3)** ______________________, which **(4)** ______________________ in the uterine wall. Part of the blastocyst becomes the **(5)** ______________________, which is surrounded by a fluid-filled, membranous sac called the **(6)** ______________________. The embryo is connected to the wall of the uterus by its **(7)** ______________________. The amniotic sac is enclosed by the **(8)** ______________________, which later forms the **(9)** ______________________. Nutrients and oxygen from the mother and wastes from the embryo are exchanged in the **(10)** ______________________.

In your textbook, read about fetal development and genetic counseling.

Complete the table by checking the correct column for each event or example.

Event/Example	Trimester		
	First	**Second**	**Third**
11. Fetus can survive outside the uterus with medical assistance.			
12. Fetus weighs more than 3000 grams.			
13. Embryo is most vulnerable to outside influences.			
14. Embryo becomes a fetus.			
15. Fetus can use its muscles to move spontaneously.			
16. Fetus becomes oriented head-down.			
17. Gender of fetus can be determined.			

Chapter 38

Reproduction and Development, *continued*

Reinforcement and Study Guide

Section 38.3 Birth, Growth, and Aging

In your textbook, read about birth.

Answer the following questions.

1. What are the three stages of birth? ______________________________

2. Describe the action of oxytocin. ______________________________

____

3. After the placenta is expelled from a woman's body, what effect do continued uterine contractions have? ______________________________

____

In your textbook, read about growth and aging.

Complete each sentence.

4. Your growth rate, as well as the type of growth you undergo, varies with both your ______________ and your ______________.

5. ______________ ______________ ______________, abbreviated ______________, regulates growth.

6. hGH exerts its effects primarily on ______________ and on ______________ ______________.

7. LGH works by increasing ______________ and ______________.

Complete the table by checking the correct column for each description.

Example	Childhood	Adolescence	Adulthood
8. Your growth rate continues at a steady rate.			
9. Lines develop on your face, especially around your eyes and mouth.			
10. You reach maximum physical stature.			
11. You begin to reason.			
12. You may have a sudden growth spurt.			

Capítulo 38

Reproducción y desarrollo

Refuerzo y Guía de estudio

Sección 38.1 Sistemas reproductores humanos

En tu libro de texto, lee sobre las estructuras y el control hormonal del aparato reproductor masculino.

Contesta las siguientes preguntas.

1. ¿Cuáles son las funciones primarias del sistema reproductor masculino?

____

____

2. ¿Cómo afecta a los espermatozoides la localización del escroto?

____

____

3. ¿Cuántos espermatozoides, en promedio, produce diariamente un hombre maduro?

____

Ordena del 1 al 6 los pasos en la formación y transporte de los espermatozoides.

__________ **4.** Los espermatozoides maduros entran a los conductos deferentes.

__________ **5.** Las células haploides recientemente formadas pasan a través de unos tubos enrollados y se dirigen hacia el epidídimo.

__________ **6.** Los espermatozoides salen del cuerpo a través de la uretra.

__________ **7.** Los espermatozoides maduran en el epidídimo.

__________ **8.** Las células que revisten los túbulos de los testículos se dividen mediante meiosis.

__________ **9.** Los espermatozoides se dirigen a la uretra a través de los conductos eyaculadores.

Completa cada enunciado.

10. Si a un adolescente le empieza a cambiar la voz, probablemente está entrando a la __________________, que es la etapa de su vida en que desarrollará otros __________________ __________________ secundarios.

11. Una hormona liberada por el __________________ estimula la glándula __________________ para que libere las hormonas __________________ y __________________.

12. La FSH regula la producción de __________________, mientras que la LH controla la producción en los testículos de la hormona esteroide llamada __________________.

Capítulo 38

Reproducción y desarrollo, *continuación*

Refuerzo y Guía de estudio

Sección 38.1 Sistemas reproductores humanos

En tu libro de texto, lee sobre la pubertad y la anatomía del cuerpo femenino.

Si el enunciado es verdadero, escribe *verdadero*; de lo contrario, modifica la sección en itálicas para hacer verdadero el enunciado.

13. Después de ser liberado por el ovario, el óvulo desciende al oviducto por *gravedad*.

____

14. Al igual que en los hombres, *el hipotálamo* de las mujeres produce FSH y LH.

____

15. La *FSH* estimula el desarrollo de los folículos y la liberación de estrógeno por el ovario.

____

16. En las mujeres, *la hormona luteinizante (LH)* es la responsable del desarrollo de los rasgos sexuales secundarios.

____

17. Antes de que nazca una niña, las células de sus ovarios que se van a convertir en óvulos sufren *varias divisiones mitóticas.*

____

En tu libro de texto, lee sobre el ciclo menstrual.

Completa la tabla indicando la columna correspondiente a cada evento.

Evento	**Fase del ciclo menstrual**		
	Flujo	**Folicular**	**Lútea**
18. La LH estimula la formación del cuerpo lúteo a partir del folículo roto.			
19. Los niveles de estrógeno están en su nivel más alto.			
20. Una célula dentro del folículo reinicia las divisiones mitóticas.			
21. Los niveles de progesterona están en su nivel más alto.			
22. Se desprende el revestimiento del útero.			
23. Aumentan abruptamente los niveles de LH.			
24. Ocurre la ovulación.			
25. El revestimiento del útero se llena de sangre, grasa, tejido y fluidos.			
26. Empieza a aumentar el nivel de FSH.			

Capítulo 38

Reproducción y desarrollo, *continuación*

Refuerzo y Guía de estudio

Sección 38.2 El desarrollo antes del nacimiento

En tu libro de texto, lee sobre la fecundación, la implantación y las membranas embriónicas.

Completa el párrafo usando cada término una sola vez.

amnios	**blastocisto**	**corión**	**vellosidades coriónicas**	**embrión**
implanta	**oviducto**	**placenta**	**cordón umbilical**	**cigoto**

Generalmente, el óvulo y el espermatozoide se unen en la parte alta del **(1)** ______________________ y forman un **(2)** ______________________. Esta célula individual se divide repetidas veces y forma un **(3)** ______________________ que se **(4)** ______________________ en la pared uterina. Parte del blastocisto se convierte en el **(5)** ______________________, el cual queda rodeado por el **(6)** ______________________ que es un saco membranoso lleno de fluido. El embrión está conectado a la pared uterina mediante el **(7)** ______________________. El saco amniótico está rodeado por el **(8)** ______________________, que más tarde se transforma en la **(9)** ______________________. Los nutrientes y el oxígeno proporcionados por la madre y los desechos del embrión se intercambian en las **(10)** ______________________.

En tu libro de texto, lee sobre el desarrollo fetal y el asesoramiento genético.

Completa la tabla indicando la columna correcta para cada evento.

	Trimestre		
Evento/Ejemplo	**Primero**	**Segundo**	**Tercero**
11. El feto puede sobrevivir fuera del útero con ayuda médica.			
12. El feto pesa más de 3000 gramos.			
13. El embrión es más vulnerable a las influencias externas.			
14. El embrión se convierte en feto.			
15. El feto puede usar sus músculos para moverse espontáneamente.			
16. El feto se acomoda con la cabeza hacia abajo.			
17. Se puede determinar el sexo del feto.			

Capítulo 38

Reproducción y desarrollo, *continuación*

Refuerzo y Guía de estudio

Sección 38.3 Nacimiento, crecimiento y envejecimiento

En tu libro de texto, lee acerca del nacimiento.

Contesta las siguientes preguntas.

1. ¿Cuáles son las tres etapas del nacimiento? ______________________________

2. Describe los efectos de la oxitocina. ______________________________

____

3. Después de que la placenta es expulsada del cuerpo de la mujer, ¿qué efecto tiene la continuación de las contracciones uterinas? ______________________________

____

En tu libro de texto, lee sobre el crecimiento y el envejecimiento.

Completa cada enunciado.

4. La tasa de crecimiento y el tipo de crecimiento varían de acuerdo con la

______________ y tu ______________ .

5. La ______________ ______________ ______________ ,

abreviada ______________ , regula el crecimiento.

6. La hGH ejerce sus efectos principalmente en los ______________ y en los

______________ ______________ .

7. La LGH aumenta la ______________ y el ______________ .

Completa la tabla indicando la columna correspondiente a cada enunciado.

Enunciado	Infancia	Adolescencia	Edad adulta
8. Tu tasa de crecimiento es continua.			
9. Se forman arrugas en tu cara, especialmente alrededor de los ojos y la boca.			
10. Alcanzas tu estatura máxima.			
11. Empiezas a razonar.			
12. Puedes presentar un estirón en el crecimiento.			

Chapter 38

Reproduction and Development

Concept Mapping

Use with Chapter 38, Section 38.1

Human Growth

Make a concept map showing the different stages of human growth and their characteristics. Use these words or phrases once: *puberty, human growth, two years, embryo, zygote, fetus, slower metabolism, teen years, physical and intellectual activity.*

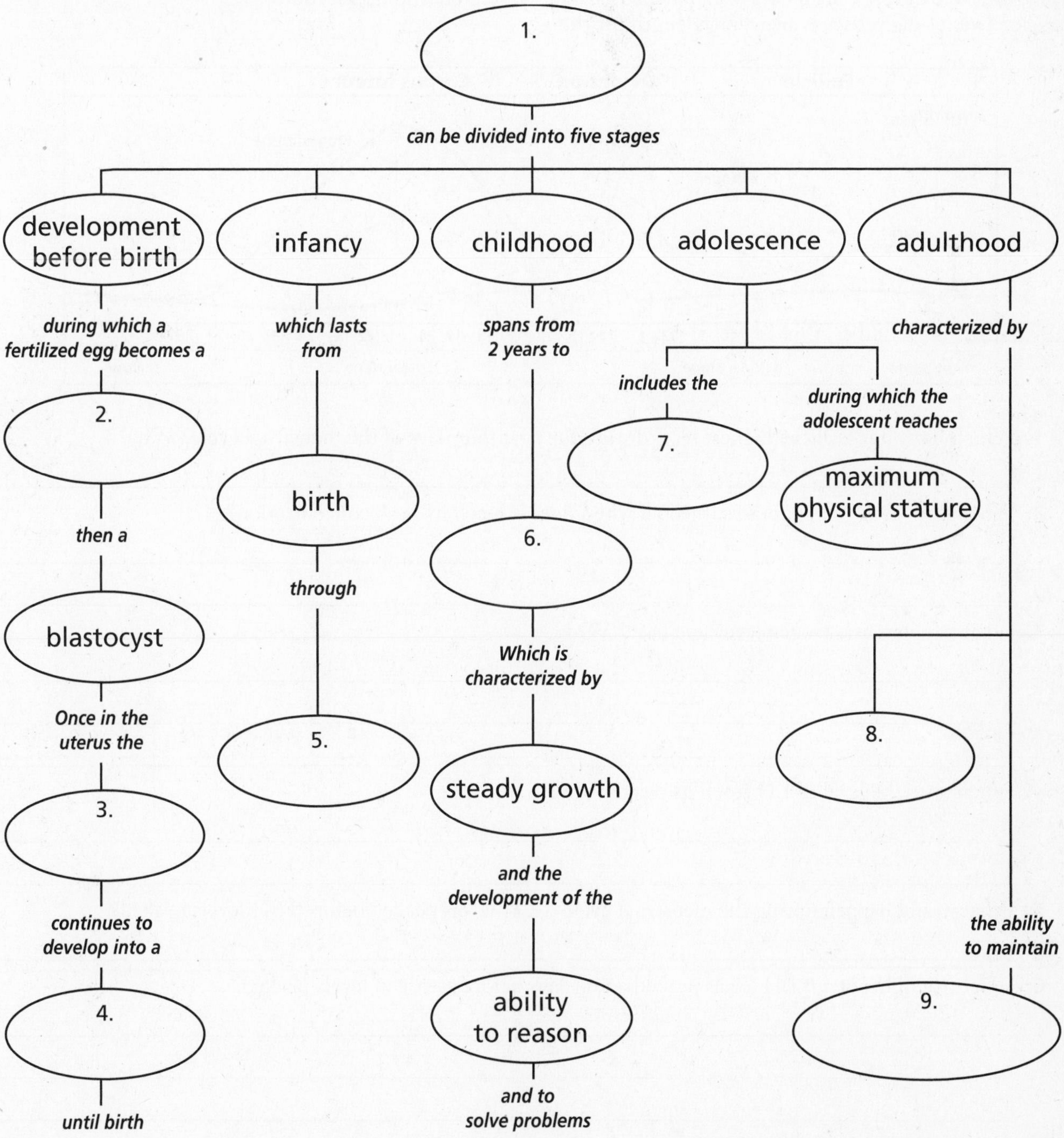

Name Date Class

Chapter 38

Reproduction and Development

Critical Thinking

Use with Chapter 38, Section 38.1

The Menstrual Cycle

The figure below shows simultaneous graphed curves for follicle-stimulating hormone (FSH), luteinizing hormone (LH), estrogen, and progesterone during the 28 days of the menstrual cycle. Twenty-eight days is an average length for the cycle, but for any individual female, variations can occur. Study the graphs and apply what you have already learned about the menstrual cycle to answer the questions that follow.

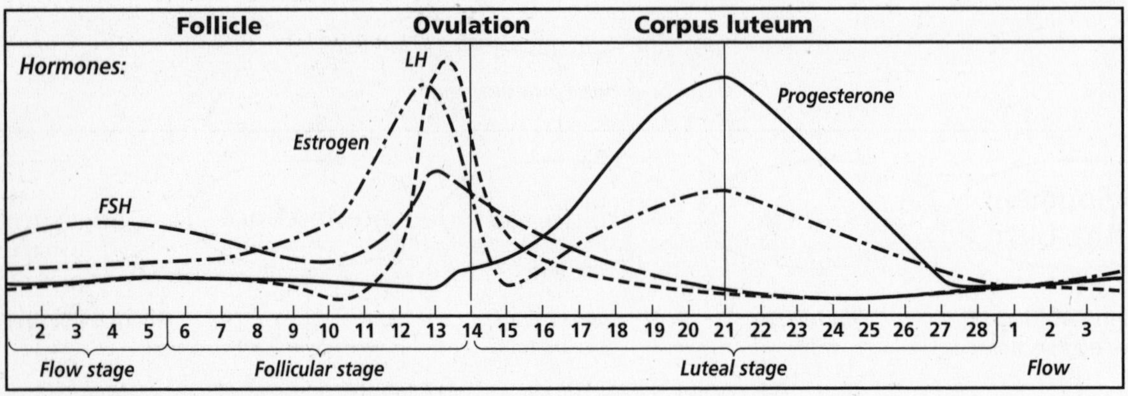

1. Which hormone is at the highest level during the first four days of the menstrual cycle? Why?

______

2. When does estrogen begin to surge and when does it reach its peak concentration?

______

______

3. What happens as estrogen levels increase? Why?

______

______

______

4. When does the level of LH reach its peak? Why?

______

______

5. What would happen during the menstrual cycle if LH levels peaked before FSH levels peaked?

______

6. What would happen if LH levels peaked a few days before estrogen levels peaked?

______

______

______

Name Date Class

Master 93

Beginning Again

Section Focus

Use with Chapter 38, Section 38.1

Human Brain

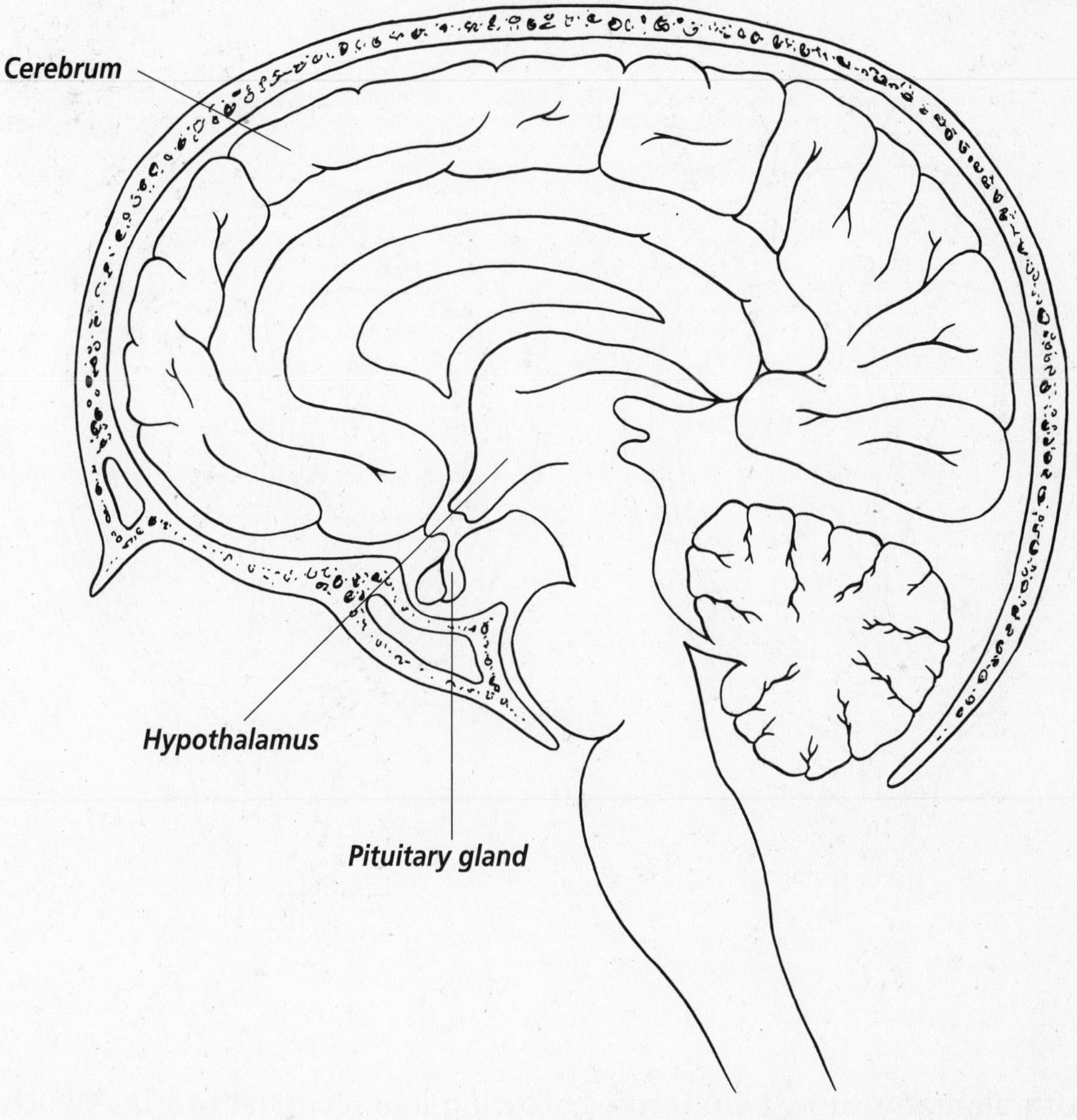

1. The labeled structures play major roles in human reproduction. What role does the cerebrum play?

2. What do you already know about the function of the pituitary gland?

Master 94

From a Cell to a Human

Section Focus

Use with Chapter 38, Section 38.2

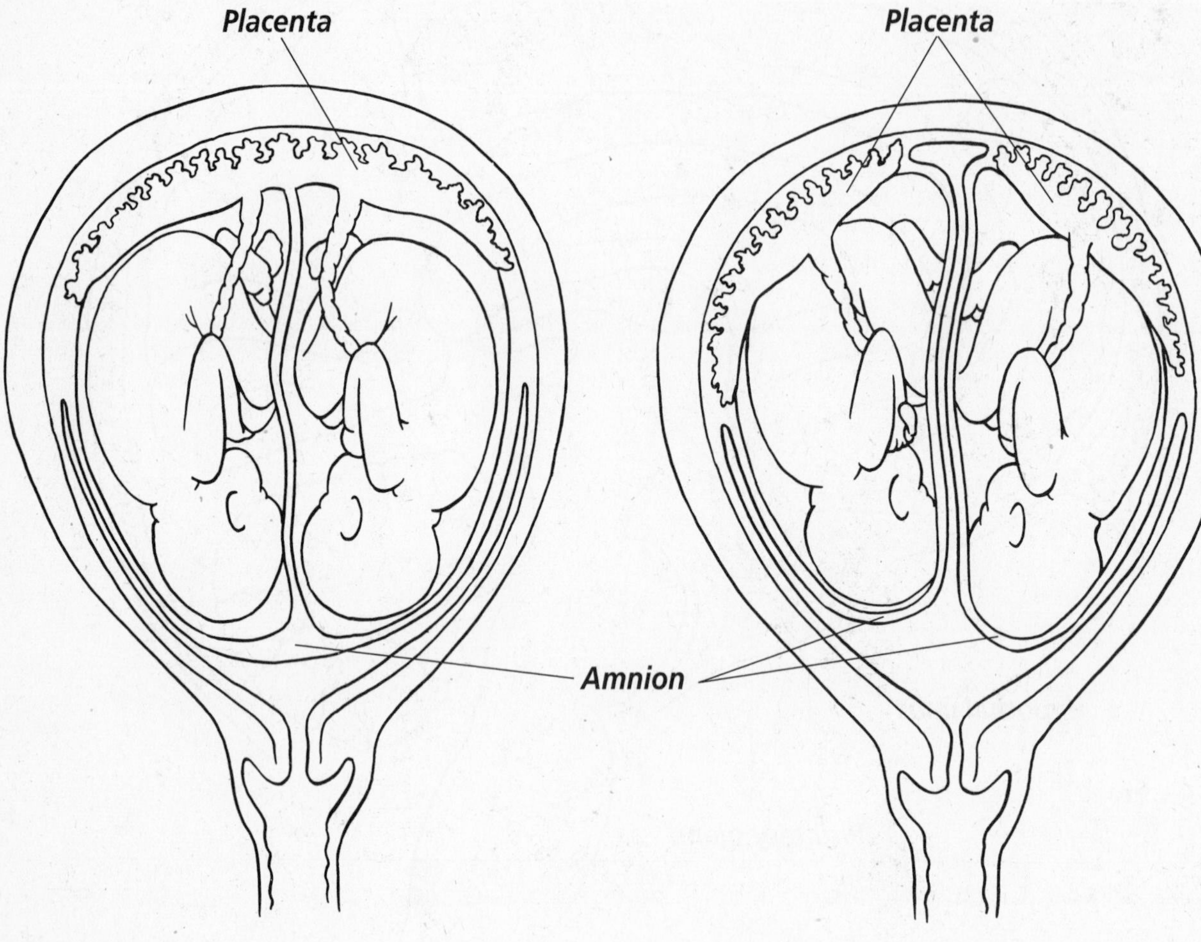

1. Both diagrams show twin fetuses growing in a woman's uterus. Which twins will be identical? Explain.

2. How do you think the embryos for each pair originated?

Master 95

Birth, Growth, and Age

Section Focus

Use with Chapter 38, Section 38.3

One month *6 years* *15 years* *25 years* *60 years* *85 years*

Age

1. How does height vary with age as this person grows up and ages?
2. How can you account for the changes in height from age 25 to age 85?

Name Date Class

Master 74

Female Reproductive System

Basic Concepts

Use with Chapter 38, Section 38.1

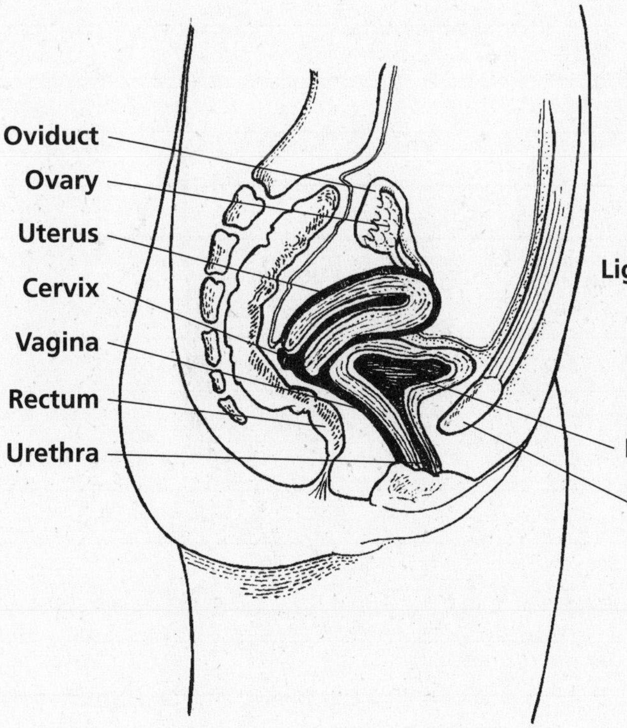

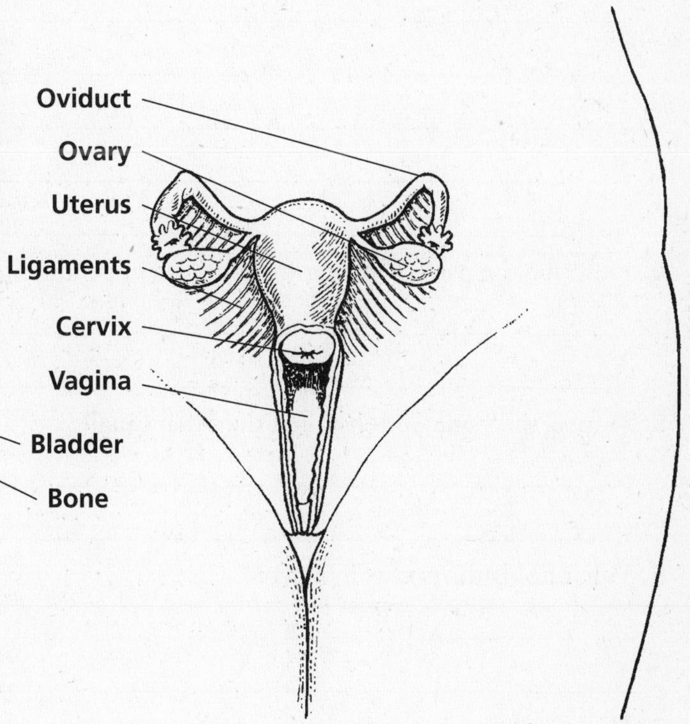

Worksheet 74

Female Reproductive System

Basic Concepts

Use with Chapter 38, Section 38.1

1. Which structures shown are *not* part of the female reproductive system?

2. In which organ are eggs produced?

3. Describe the structure and function of the uterus.

4. Describe the path of an egg from its site of production to its entry into the uterus.

5. Why is the vagina often called the birth canal?

6. What holds the uterus in place?

7. What is the entrance to the uterus?

8. How does egg production in a female differ from sperm production in a male?

Master 75

Basic Concepts

The Menstrual Cycle

Use with Chapter 38, Section 38.1

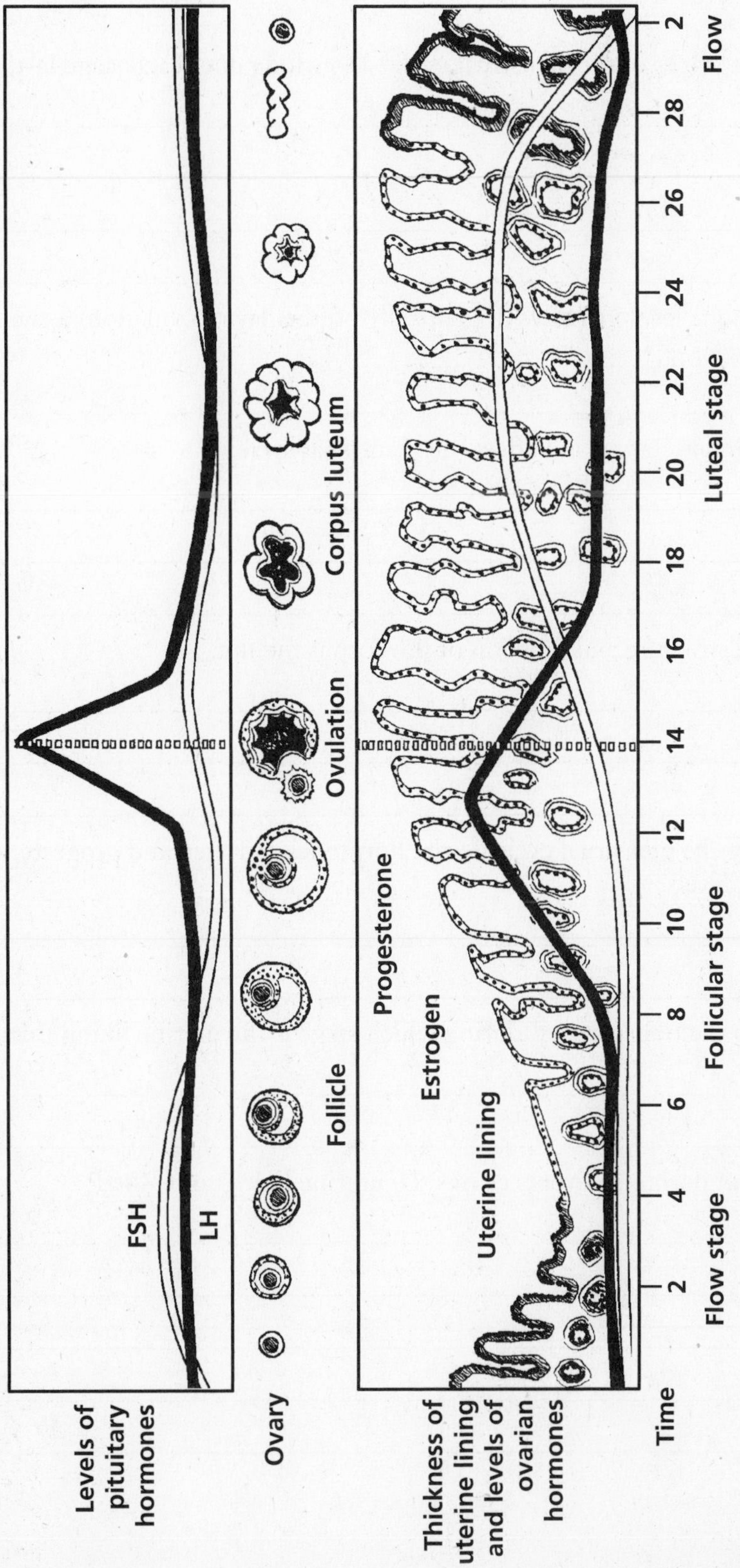

Worksheet 75

The Menstrual Cycle

Basic Concepts

Use with Chapter 38, Section 38.1

1. What are the stages of the menstrual cycle? How long does each stage last?

2. Which hormone level increases dramatically on the day of ovulation in the menstrual cycle?

3. How does the pituitary gland affect the menstrual cycle?

4. Describe the structure and function of the corpus luteum.

5. When during the menstrual cycle do the hormones estrogen and progesterone reach their highest levels?

6. According to the transparency, during which stage is the uterine lining thickest?

7. What series of hormonal events causes the uterine lining to be shed?

Master 55

Negative Feedback Systems

Reteaching Skills

Use with Chapter 38, Section 38.1

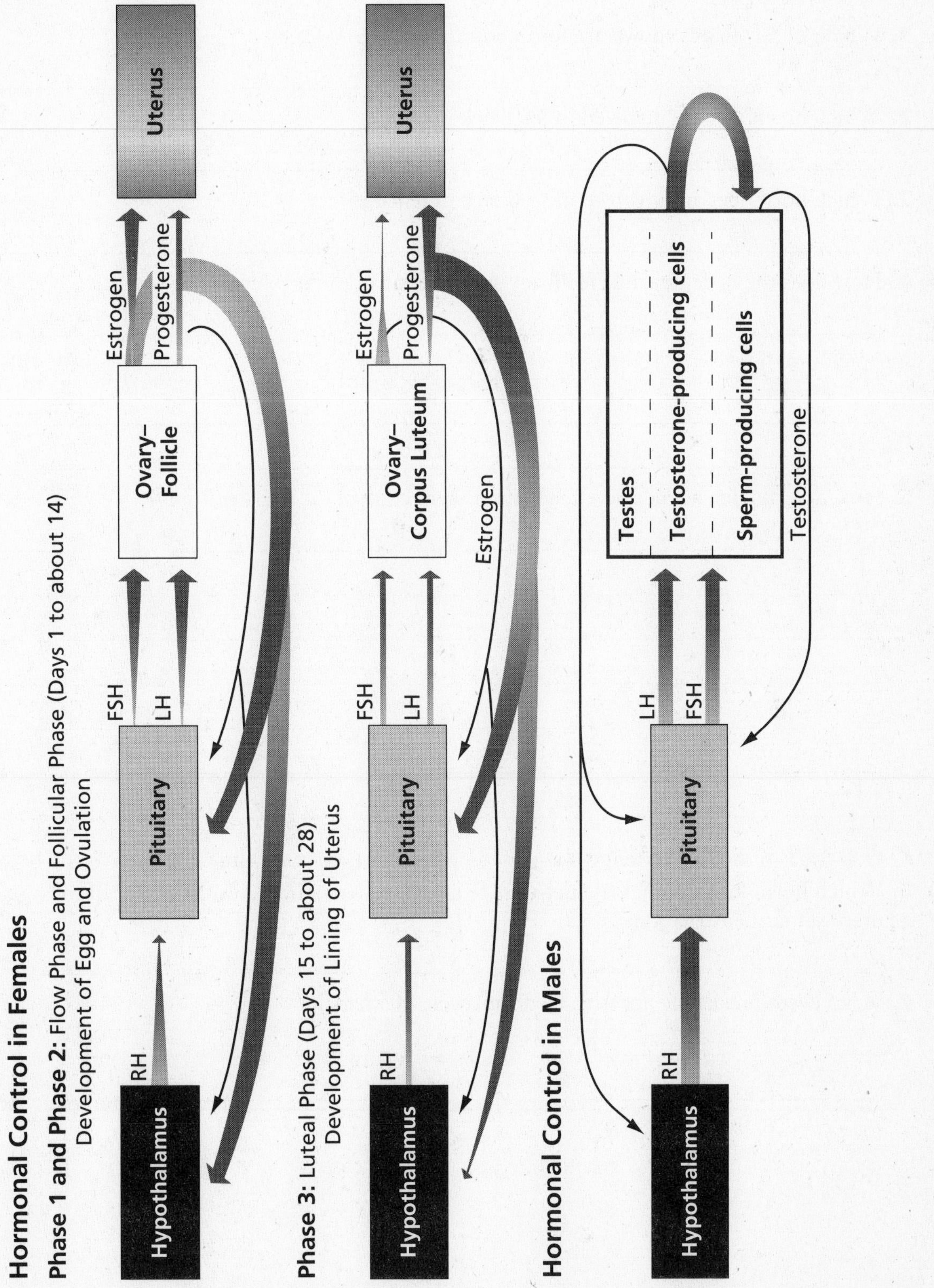

Worksheet 55

Negative Feedback Systems

Reteaching Skills

Use with Chapter 38, Section 38.1

1. Which of the glands shown are located in the brain?

2. Which hormones are involved in feedback in males?

3. Which hormones are involved in feedback in females?

4. How does the male negative feedback system control the production of sperm?

5. How does the female negative feedback system control the uterine lining?

6. Which hormone in the female negative feedback system stimulates the repair of the uterus after menstruation?

7. What event breaks the negative feedback cycle in a female?

Name Date Class

Master 56a

Fertilization

Reteaching Skills

Use with Chapter 38, Section 38.2

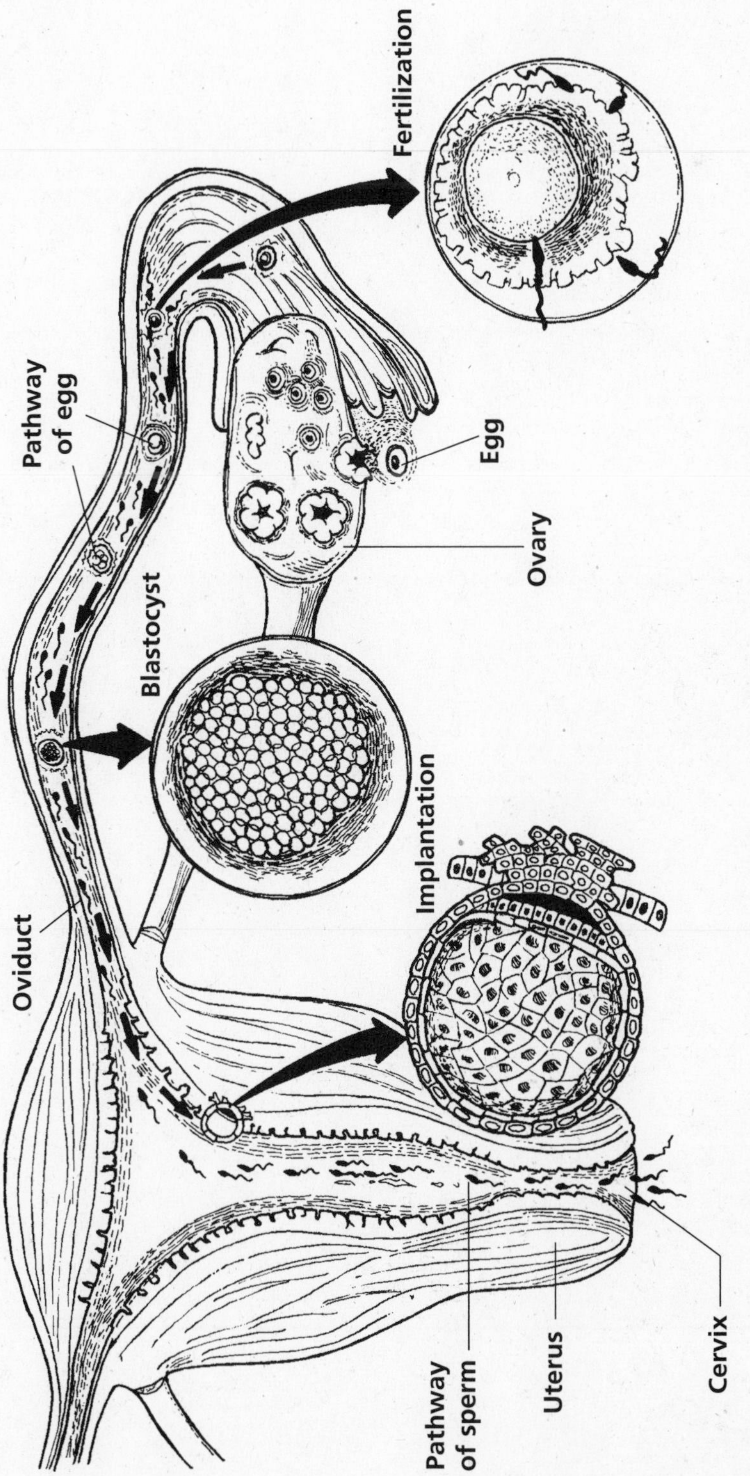

Master **56b**

Fetal Development

Reteaching Skills

Use with Chapter 38, Section 38.2

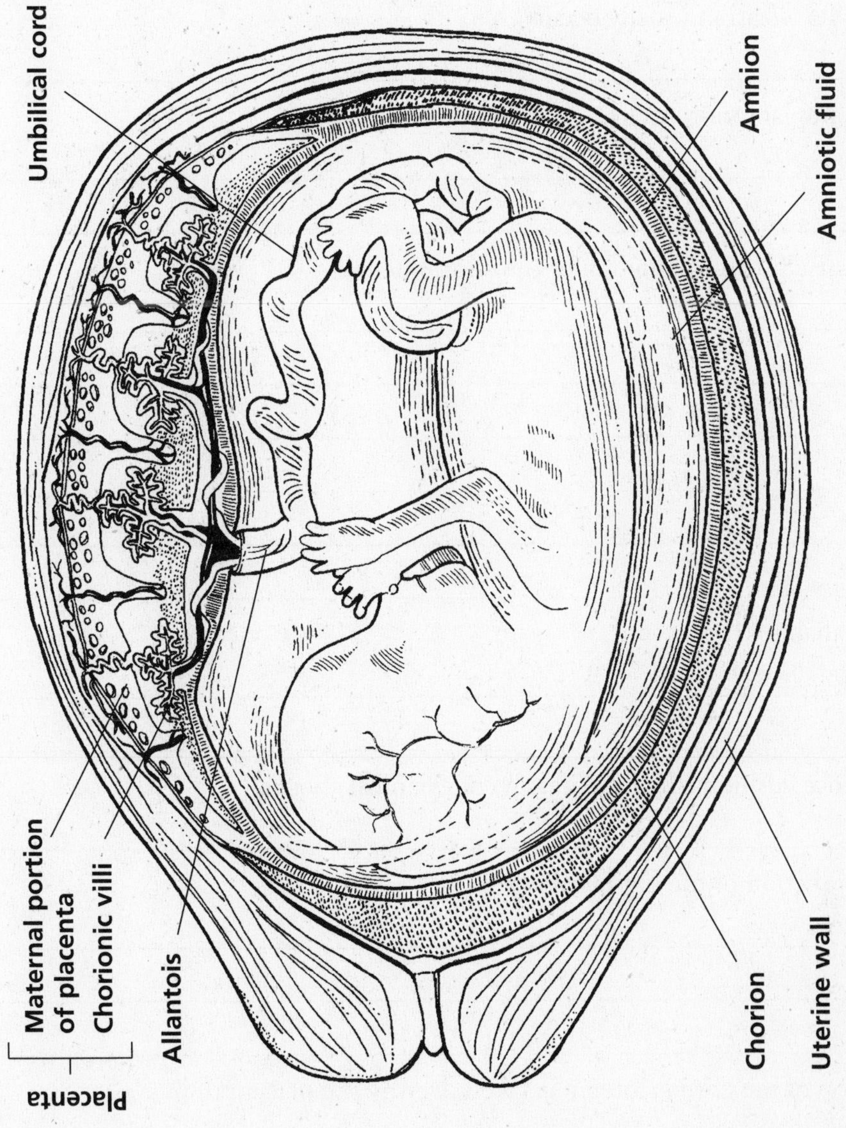

Worksheet 56

Fertilization and Fetal Development

Reteaching Skills

Use with Chapter 38, Section 38.2

1. What occurs at fertilization?

2. Where does fertilization usually occur?

3. Where does implantation occur?

4. Explain the structure and function of the chorionic villi.

5. What is the allantois?

6. What substance cushions the fetus against mechanical shocks?

7. What is the function of the umbilical cord?

8. What function of the corpus luteum is taken over by the placenta?

Name Date Class

Chapter 38

Reproduction and Development

Chapter Assessment

Reviewing Vocabulary

Match the definition in Column A with the term in Column B.

	Column A	Column B
______	**1.** Group of epithelial cells that surround a developing egg	**a.** semen
______	**2.** Information provided by trained professionals about the probabilities of hereditary disorders in a developing fetus	**b.** first trimester
______	**3.** Period of development in pregnancy during which all the organ systems of the embryo begin to form	**c.** puberty
______	**4.** Combination of sperm and fluids in which they are transported	**d.** pituitary
______	**5.** Refers to the time when secondary sex characteristics begin to develop	**e.** genetic counseling
______	**6.** Attachment of the blastocyst to the lining of the uterus	**f.** implantation
______	**7.** Ropelike structure that attaches the embryo to the wall of the uterus	**g.** umbilical cord
______	**8.** Gland that secretes hormones that influence many physiological processes of the body	**h.** follicle

Compare and contrast each pair of related terms.

9. bulbourethral gland, prostate gland

______

______

______

______

10. epididymis, vas deferens

______

______

______

______

Chapter 38 **Reproduction and Development,** *continued*

Chapter Assessment

Understanding Main Ideas (Part A)

Label the diagram. Use these choices: ovary, implantation, blastocyst, ovulation, fertilization, uterus, zygote, vagina, oviduct.

1. ______________

2. ______________

3. ______________

4. ______________

5. ______________

6. ______________

7. ______________

8. ______________

9. ______________

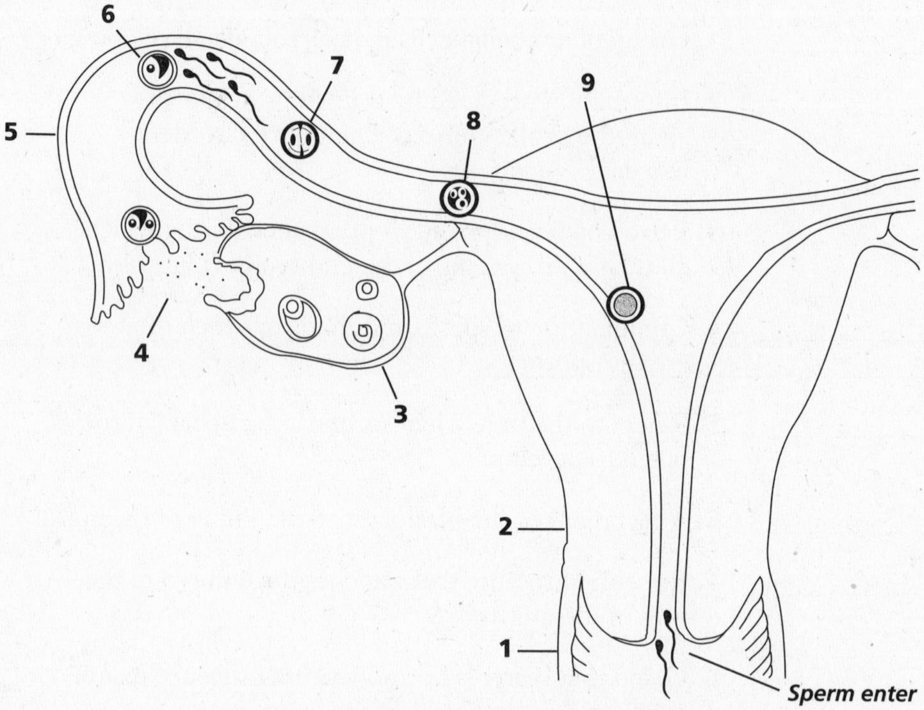

In the space at the left, write the letter of the word or phrase that best completes the statement.

______ **10.** The fluid that provides energy for the sperm cells comes from the
a. bulbourethral glands. **b.** seminal vesicles.
c. prostate gland. **d.** urethra.

______ **11.** When FSH reaches the testes, it causes the production of
a. testosterone. **b.** LH.
c. sperm cells. **d.** secondary sex characteristics.

______ **12.** In the female, FSH stimulates the
a. production of eggs. **b.** production of progesterone.
c. blastocyst. **d.** development of a follicle in the ovary.

______ **13.** All the body systems of the fetus are present by the
a. third week. **b.** sixth week. **c.** eighth week. **d.** first month.

Understanding Main Ideas (Part B)

Use the diagram of the negative feedback system in the male to complete the following statements.

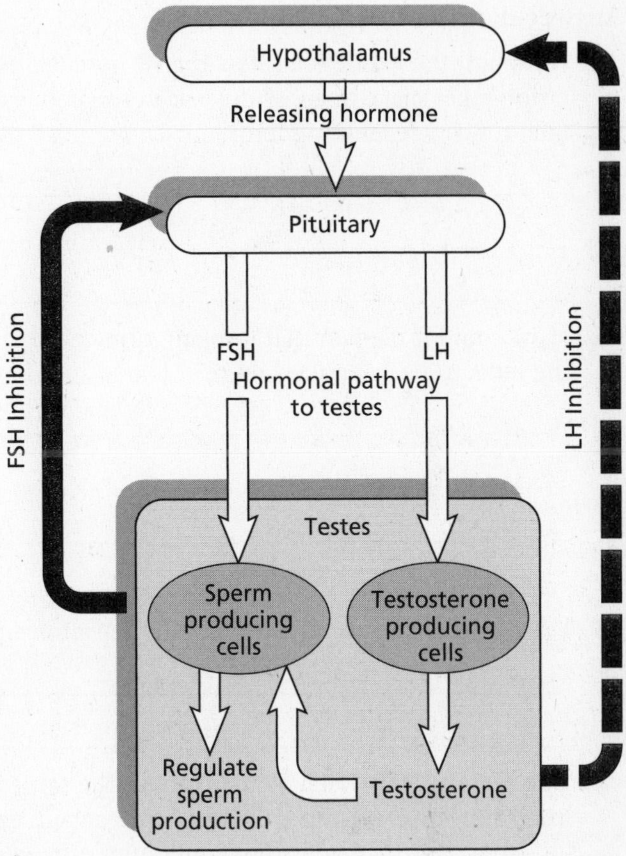

1. The release of LH by the pituitary is stimulated by a hormone secreted by the ______________________.

2. LH stimulates the production of ______________________.

3. ______________________ and testosterone affect sperm production.

4. An increase of testosterone inhibits ______________________ production.

5. Cells that produce sperm send signals to the pituitary and hypothalamus to stop releasing ______________________.

Answer the following questions.

6. Why is the scrotum located outside the male body?

____

____

7. What happens to the lining of the uterus if fertilization does not occur?

____

____

8. What is the function of the corpus luteum?

____

____

____

____

Chapter 38 **Reproduction and Development,** *continued*

Chapter Assessment

Thinking Critically

Answer the following questions.

1. Although the incidence is less than 1 percent, an ectopic pregnancy may occur, in which the implantation takes place in an oviduct or in the pelvic cavity. When would implantation in the oviduct be fatal for the developing fetus?

2. How could it happen that implantation could take place in the pelvic cavity? What must happen for the fetus to be nourished there?

3. Why would an ectopic fetus have to be removed by surgery, not by delivery through the birth canal?

4. Two groups of married women, about the same age and weight, participated in a test. The women in Group A were given a placebo, a sugar pill, each morning of their menstrual cycle. The women in Group B were given a pill containing estrogen and progesterone each morning of their menstrual cycle. The LH levels before, during, and after ovulation of both groups were recorded.

Group	Four Days Before	Day of Ovulation	Four Days After
A	17 mg/100mL	299 mg/100 mL	16 mg/100mL
B	20 mg/100mL	156 mg/100 mL	14 mg/100mL

The number of pregnancies during the year of the test in Group A was 25 times the number of pregnancies in Group B. What would you conclude, based on these data?

Applying Scientific Methods

The Smiths would like to have a baby. Mrs. Smith has begun to keep a record of her temperature readings during her menstrual cycle. She knows that she is fertile, or capable of beginning pregnancy, only for a period of about 24 hours from the time of ovulation. She also knows that her temperature rises about 0.3°C when she ovulates. She keeps a record of her temperature every day at the same time. The dates that are shaded on the calendars are the dates when Mr. Smith is away for National Guard duty. Use the temperature charts and the calendars to find out when Mrs. Smith has the best opportunity of becoming pregnant. (Note that sperm are able to survive inside the oviducts and uterus for several days.)

March

S	M	T	W	T	F	S
		1	2	3	4	5
6	7	8	9	10	11	12
13	14	15	16	17	18	19
20	21	22	23	24	25	26
27	28	29	30	31		

April

S	M	T	W	T	F	S
					1	2
3	4	5	6	7	8	9
10	11	12	13	14	15	16
17	18	19	20	21	22	23
24	25	26	27	28	29	30

May

S	M	T	W	T	F	S
1	2	3	4	5	6	7
8	9	10	11	12	13	14
15	16	17	18	19	20	21
22	23	24	25	26	27	28
29	30	31				

June

S	M	T	W	T	F	S
			1	2	3	4
5	6	7	8	9	10	11
12	13	14	15	16	17	18
19	20	21	22	23	24	25
26	27	28	29	30		

March Temp.

19	36.7 (°C)
20	37.0
21	37.0

April Temp.

16	36.7 (°C)
17	37.0
18	37.0

May Temp.

14	36.6 (°C)
15	36.9
16	37.0

June Temp.

11	36.7 (°C)
12	37.0
13	37.0

1. During which month or months do the Smiths have the best chance of producing a baby? Explain your answer.

Applying Scientific Methods *continued*

2. Would changing Mr. Smith's National Guard weekend to the second Saturday of every month have helped the Smiths in their efforts to have a baby?

3. Some researchers have noted slight physical variations in X and Y sperm. They postulate that because Y sperm are lighter than X sperm, the Y sperm travel more quickly. Hypothesize how this may affect the sex of the Smiths' baby, providing reasons on which your hypothesis is based.

4. What if the Smiths tried for their baby the day before ovulation. How might this affect the sex of their baby?

Name Date Class

Chapter 38

Assessment
Student Recording Sheet

Chapter Assessment

Use with pages 1020–1021 of the Student Edition

Vocabulary Review

Write the vocabulary words that match the definitions in your book.

1. ______________________
2. ______________________
3. ______________________

Understanding Key Concepts

Select the best answer from the choices given and fill in the corresponding oval.

4. Ⓐ Ⓑ Ⓒ Ⓓ
5. Ⓐ Ⓑ Ⓒ Ⓓ
6. Ⓐ Ⓑ Ⓒ Ⓓ
7. Ⓐ Ⓑ Ⓒ Ⓓ
8. Ⓐ Ⓑ Ⓒ Ⓓ
9. Ⓐ Ⓑ Ⓒ Ⓓ

10. Fill in the correct terms to complete the concept map.

 1. ______________________
 2. ______________________
 3. ______________________

Constructed Response

Record your answers for Questions 11–13 on a separate sheet of paper.

Thinking Critically

Record your answers for Questions 14, 16, and 17 on a separate sheet of paper.

15. **REAL WORLD BIOCHALLENGE** Follow your teacher's instructions for presenting your BioChallenge answer.

Standardized Test Practice

The Princeton Review

Part 1 Multiple Choice

Select the best answer from the choices given and fill in the corresponding oval.

18. Ⓐ Ⓑ Ⓒ Ⓓ
19. Ⓐ Ⓑ Ⓒ Ⓓ
20. Ⓐ Ⓑ Ⓒ Ⓓ
21. Ⓐ Ⓑ Ⓒ Ⓓ
22. Ⓐ Ⓑ Ⓒ Ⓓ
23. Ⓐ Ⓑ Ⓒ Ⓓ

Part 2 Constructed Response/Grid In

Record your answers for Questions 24 and 25 on a separate sheet of paper.

Contents

Chapter 39 Immunity from Disease

BioDigest 10 The Human Body

Name Date Class

MiniLab 39.1

Experimenting

Testing How Diseases are Spread

Microorganisms cannot travel over long distances by themselves. Unless they are somehow transferred from one animal or plant to another, infections will not spread. One method of transmission is by direct contact with an infected animal or plant.

Procedure

1 Label four plastic bags 1 to 4.

2 Put a fresh apple in bag 1 and seal the bag.

3 Rub a rotting apple over the entire surface of the remaining three apples. The rotting apple is your source of pathogens. **CAUTION:** ***Make sure to wash your hands with soap and water after handling the rotting apple.***

4 Put one of the apples in bag 2.

5 Put one of the apples in bag 3 and drop the bag to the floor from a height of about 2 m.

6 Use a cotton ball to spread alcohol over the last apple. Let the apple air-dry and then place it in bag 4.

7 Store all of the bags in a dark place for one week.

8 Compare the apples and record your observations. **CAUTION:** ***Give all apples to your teacher for proper disposal.***

Analysis

1. What was the purpose of the fresh apple in bag 1?

____

____

2. Explain what happened to the rest of the apples.

____

____

3. Why is it important to clean a wound with disinfectant?

____

____

Name Date Class

MiniLab 39.2

Observing and Inferring

Distinguishing Blood Cells

The human immune system includes five types of white blood cells found in the bloodstream: basophils, neutrophils, monocytes, eosinophils, and lymphocytes.

Procedure

1. Use the data table below.
2. Mount a prepared slide of blood cells on the microscope and focus on low power. Turn to high power and look for white blood cells. **CAUTION:** ***Use caution when working with microscope slides.***
3. Find a neutrophil, monocyte, eosinophil, and lymphocyte. You may see a basophil, although they are rare. Refer to ***Figure 39.9*** for photos of these cells.
4. Count a total of 50 white blood cells, and record how many of each type you see.
5. Calculate the percentage by multiplying the number of each cell type by two. Record the percentages. Diagram each cell type.

Data Table

Type of white blood cell	Number counted	Percent	Diagram
Neutrophil			
Monocyte			
Basophil			
Lymphocyte			
Eosinophil			

Analysis

1. Which type of white blood cell was most common? Second most common?

2. How do red and white blood cells differ?

INTERNET BioLab

Information on Emerging and Re-emerging Diseases

Chapter 39

Preparation

Problem

How can you obtain current research information on emerging and re-emerging diseases?

Objectives

In this BioLab, you will

- **Choose** five emerging and five re-emerging diseases for study.
- **Collect** data on the ten diseases and record in a table.

Materials

access to the Internet

Skill Handbook

Use the **Skill Handbook** if you need additional help with this lab.

Procedure

1. Copy the two data tables on the next page.
2. Go to **bdol.glencoe.com/internet_lab** to find links that will provide you with information for this BioLab.
3. Choose five emerging and five re-emerging diseases you wish to investigate.
4. List the diseases in your data tables and fill in the rest of the columns.
5. Be sure to complete the last two rows of your data table that ask for current research findings and your sources of information.

Data Table 1

Emerging diseases					
	1	2	3	4	5
Disease name					
Organism responsible					
Classification of organism					
Mode of transmission					
Symptoms					
Treatment					
Current research					
Source of information					

INTERNET BioLab

Getting Information on Emerging and Re-emerging Diseases, *continued*

Data Table 2

Re-emerging diseases					
	1	2	3	4	5
Disease name					
Organism responsible					
Classification of organism					
Mode of transmission					
Symptoms					
Treatment					
Current research					
Source of information					

Analyze and Conclude

1. **Define** What is a pathogen? Provide several examples.

2. **Contrast** Describe the difference between an emerging and a re-emerging disease. Provide several examples of each.

3. **Think Critically** Hypothesize why a disease that was once on the decline might re-emerge.

4. **Apply Concepts** Compared with travel in the 1800s, how would current worldwide travel affect the transmission of disease?

5. **Use the Internet** What are some advantages and disadvantages of getting information on disease research by way of the Internet rather than from textbooks or an encyclopedia?

Name Date Class

Chapter 39

Immunity from Disease

Reinforcement and Study Guide

Section 39.1 The Nature of Disease

In your textbook, read about what an infectious disease is, determining what causes a disease, and the spread of infectious diseases.

Answer the following questions.

1. Why is a disease like osteoarthritis not considered an infectious disease?

____

2. What is meant by Koch's postulates?

____

____

3. In terms of disease, what is a reservoir?

____

Complete the table by writing in the method of transmission for each example.

Example	Method of Transmission
4. While exploring a cave, a person breathes in fungal spores that cause a lung infection.	
5. A person contracts Rocky Mountain spotted fever after being bitten by a tick.	
6. After having unprotected sex, a person contracts syphilis.	

In your textbook, read about what causes the symptoms of a disease, patterns of disease, and treating diseases.

For each statement below, write true or false.

______________ **7.** The toxin produced by a particular microorganism might be far more destructive than the direct damage the microbe does to its host cells.

______________ **8.** Endemic diseases often disappear in a population, only to resurface unexpectedly many years later.

______________ **9.** If you catch the flu during an influenza epidemic, your best hope of recovery is to take antibiotics.

______________ **10.** It is important for researchers to try to discover new antibiotics because many types of bacteria are becoming resistant to the ones now being used.

Chapter 39 **Immunity from Disease,** *continued*

Reinforcement and Study Guide

Section 39.2 Defense Against Infectious Diseases

In your textbook, read about the innate immune system.

If the statement is true, write *true*. If it is not, rewrite the italicized part to make it true.

1. Healthy skin is a good defense against the invasion of pathogens because it is *free of bacteria*.

____

____

2. In your trachea, *saliva* traps microbes and prevents them from entering your lungs.

____

3. Macrophages migrate *into the bloodstream* when the body is challenged by a pathogen.

____

4. Phagocytes at the site of an infection or inflammation destroy pathogens by surrounding and engulfing them. ____

5. The third method of defense against infection is the consumption of pathogens by *neutrophils*.

____

6. Interferon is produced by cells infected by *pathogenic bacteria*.

____

In your textbook, read about acquired immunity.

Circle the letter of the choice that best completes the statement.

7. The human lymphatic system is important in

a. filtering pathogens from lymph.
b. keeping body fluids constant.
c. resistance to disease.
d. all of the above.

8. Tissue fluid is found

a. in lymph vessels.
b. in the bloodstream.
c. around body cells.
d. in lymph ducts.

9. The main function of lymph nodes is to

a. store red blood cells.
b. filter lymph.
c. filter excess fluid.
d. trigger an immune response.

10. A reservoir for lymphocytes that can be transformed into specific disease-fighting cells is the

a. thymus gland.
b. thyroid gland.
c. pituitary gland.
d. pancreas.

Section 39.2 Defense Against Infectious Diseases

In your textbook, read about antibody immunity and cellular immunity.

Complete each sentence.

11. ______________________ is the building up of a ______________________ to a specific pathogen.

12. Two types of immunity that involve different kinds of cells and cellular actions are ______________________ immunity and ______________________ immunity.

13. The presence of foreign ______________________ in the body triggers the production of ______________________ by plasma cells.

14. A ____________________ is a lymphocyte that, when activated by a ______________________, becomes a plasma cell and produces ______________________ .

15. Cellular immunity involves several different types of ______________________ cells.

16. A ____________________ releases enzymes directly into the ____________________ .

Complete the table by checking the correct columns for each example.

Example	**Type of Immunity**	
	Cellular	**Antibody**
17. Involves the protection of antibodies		
18. Simulated by antigens in the body		
19. Clones of killer T cells produced		
20. Memory cells produced so the body can respond quickly to a second attack		
21. Key role played by antigen-antibody complex		
22. T cells destroyed by pathogens directly		

Chapter 39 **Immunity from Disease,** *continued*

Reinforcement and Study Guide

Section 39.2 Defense Against Infectious Diseases

In your textbook, read about passive and active immunity to infectious diseases.

Answer the following questions.

23. Distinguish between active and passive immunity.

____

____

____

24. In what two ways can passive immunity develop?

____

____

25. What is a vaccine?

____

____

In your textbook, read about AIDS and the immune system.

For each statement below, write true or false.

__________ **26.** The virus that causes AIDS—Human Immunodeficiency Virus—is well-named because it attacks the immune system.

__________ **27.** HIV can be transmitted by air.

__________ **28.** A child born to a woman who is infected with HIV is at risk for being infected, too.

__________ **29.** HIV destroys a person's resistance to disease by attacking and destroying memory T cells.

__________ **30.** In a blood sample from an HIV-positive person, you would expect to find most of the viruses existing free in the blood, rather than being hidden inside cells.

__________ **31.** If a person is infected with HIV, he or she will usually develop AIDS within about a year.

__________ **32.** The cause of death for a person with AIDS usually is some type of infection that the body's weakened immune system can no longer fight off.

__________ **33.** The majority of untreated persons infected with HIV will develop AIDS.

Nombre Fecha Clase

Capítulo 39

Inmunidad contra las enfermedades

Refuerzo y Guía de estudio

Sección 39.1 La naturaleza de las enfermedades

En tu libro de texto, lee sobre lo que es una enfermedad infecciosa, cómo se determina qué causa una enfermedad y la propagación de enfermedades infecciosas.

Contesta las siguientes preguntas.

1. ¿Por qué una enfermedad como la osteoartritis no se considera como una enfermedad infecciosa?

____

2. ¿Qué significan los postulados de Koch?

____

____

3. En términos de una enfermedad, ¿que es un reservorio?

____

Completa la tabla indicando el método de transmisión de cada enfermedad.

Enfermedad	Método de transmisión
4. Durante la exploración de una caverna, una persona inhala esporas de un hongo que le ocasionan una infección en los pulmones.	
5. Una persona contrae la fiebre conocida como fiebre de las Montañas Rocosas, después de ser picada por un ácaro.	
6. Una persona contrae sífilis después de tener coito sin protección.	

En tu libro de texto, lee sobre los factores que causan los síntomas de una enfermedad, el patrón que sigue una enfermedad y cómo se trata una enfermedad.

Indica si cada uno de los enunciados es verdadero o falso.

______________ **7.** La toxina producida por un microorganismo puede ser más destructiva que el daño directo que causa el microbio en las células huéspedes.

______________ **8.** En general, las enfermedades endémicas desaparecen de una población y aparecen de repente, años después.

______________ **9.** Si contraes influenza durante una epidemia, la mejor manera de curarte es tomando antibióticos.

______________ **10.** Para los investigadores, es importante descubrir nuevos tipos de antibióticos porque muchas bacterias están adquiriendo resistencia a los antibióticos de uso actual.

Capítulo 39

Inmunidad contra las enfermedades, *continuación*

Refuerzo y Guía de estudio

Sección 39.2 Defensas contra las enfermedades infecciosas

En tu libro de texto, lee sobre la inmunidad innata.

Si el enunciado es verdadero, escribe *verdadero*; de lo contrario, modifica la sección en itálicas para hacer verdadero el enunciado.

1. Una piel saludable es una buena defensa contra la invasión de patógenos porque *está libre de bacterias*.

____

____

2. En la tráquea, *la saliva* se encarga de atrapar los microbios y evita que entren a los pulmones.

____

3. Los macrófagos emigran hacia *el torrente sanguíneo* cuando un patógeno invade el cuerpo.

____

4. Los fagocitos localizados en el sitio de una infección o de una inflamación destruyen los patógenos, rodeándolos con su membrana e incorporándolos al interior del fagocito.

____

5. El tercer método de defensa contra una infección es el consumo de patógenos por los *neutrófilos*.

____

6. Las células infectadas por *bacterias patógenas* producen interferón.

____

En tu libro de texto, lee sobre la inmunidad adquirida.

Haz un círculo alrededor de la letra de la opción que completa mejor cada enunciado.

7. El sistema linfático humano es importante porque

a. filtra los patógenos en la linfa.
b. ayuda a mantener el equilibrio de fluidos en el cuerpo.
c. ayuda en la resistencia contra enfermedades.
d. todas las anteriores.

8. El líquido tisular se encuentra

a. en los vasos linfáticos.
b. en el torrente sanguíneo.
c. alrededor de las células.
d. en los vasos linfáticos.

9. La función primaria de los ganglios linfáticos es

a. almacenar glóbulos rojos.
b. filtrar la linfa.
c. filtrar el exceso de fluidos.
d. iniciar una respuesta inmunológica.

10. El(La) ______________ es un depósito de linfocitos que se pueden transformar en células especializadas para combatir enfermedades.

a. timo
b. glándula tiroides
c. glándula pituitaria
d. páncreas

Capítulo 39

Inmunidad contra las enfermedades, *continuación*

Refuerzo y Guía de estudio

Sección 39.2 Defensa contra las enfermedades infecciosas

En tu libro de texto, lee sobre la inmunidad por anticuerpos y la inmunidad celular.

Completa cada enunciado.

11. La ______________________ es la adquisición de ______________________ a un patógeno específico.

12. Los dos tipos de inmunidad que incluyen diferentes actividades y diferentes tipos de células son la inmunidad ______________________ y la inmunidad ______________________ .

13. La presencia de ______________________ ajenos al cuerpo, inicia la producción de ______________________ por parte de las células plasmáticas.

14. Las ____________________ son linfocitos que al ser activados por las ____________________, se convierten en células plasmáticas y producen ______________________ .

15. La inmunidad celular incluye diferentes tipos de células ______________________ .

16. Las __________________ liberan enzimas directamente en el interior de los __________________ .

Completa la tabla indicando la columna correspondiente a cada ejemplo.

Ejemplo	Tipo de inmunidad	
	Celular	**Anticuerpo**
17. Incluye la protección por anticuerpos		
18. Es estimulada por la entrada de antígenos al cuerpo		
19. Se producen clones de células T asesinas		
20. Se producen células de memoria que ayudan a que el cuerpo responda rápidamente a un segundo ataque		
21. La función más importante la cumple el complejo antígeno-anticuerpo		
22. Las células T destruyen directamente los patógenos		

Capítulo 39

Inmunidad contra las enfermedades, *continuación*

Refuerzo y Guía de estudio

Sección 39.2 Defensas contra las enfermedades infecciosas

En tu libro de texto, lee sobre la inmunidad pasiva y activa contra enfermedades infecciosas.

Contesta las siguientes preguntas.

23. ¿Cuáles son las diferencias entre la inmunidad pasiva y la inmunidad activa.

____

____

____

24. ¿Cuáles son las dos maneras en que se puede adquirir inmunidad pasiva?

____

____

25. ¿Qué es una vacuna?

____

____

En tu libro de texto, lee acerca del SIDA y su relación con el sistema inmunológico.

Indica si cada uno de los enunciados es verdadero o falso.

__________ **26.** El virus que causa el SIDA, el virus de inmunodeficiencia humana, tiene un nombre adecuado porque ataca el sistema inmunológico.

__________ **27.** El SIDA se puede transmitir a través del aire.

__________ **28.** Un niño nacido de una madre infectada con VIH está expuesto a quedar infectado con el virus.

__________ **29.** El VIH destruye la capacidad de la persona para resistir las enfermedades porque ataca y destruye las células T de la memoria.

__________ **30.** En una muestra de sangre de una persona VIH positiva, la mayoría de los virus se encontrarán en la sangre, en lugar de estar escondidos en el interior de las células.

__________ **31.** Si una persona queda infectada con VIH, desarrollará SIDA en un período aproximado de un año.

__________ **32.** La causa de la muerte de una persona con SIDA es generalmente algún tipo de infección que el débil sistema inmunológico de la persona no puede combatir.

__________ **33.** La mayoría de las personas infectadas con VIH, y que no buscan tratamiento, desarrollarán SIDA.

Chapter 39

Immunity from Disease

Concept Mapping

Use with Chapter 39, Section 39.2

The Lymphatic System

Complete the concept map about the structure of the lymphatic system and how it defends the body against disease. Use these words or phrases one or more times: *foreign substances, two ducts, tissue fluid, lymph, white blood cells, lymph veins, protect body, nodes, bloodstream, lymphocytes, lymph capillaries.*

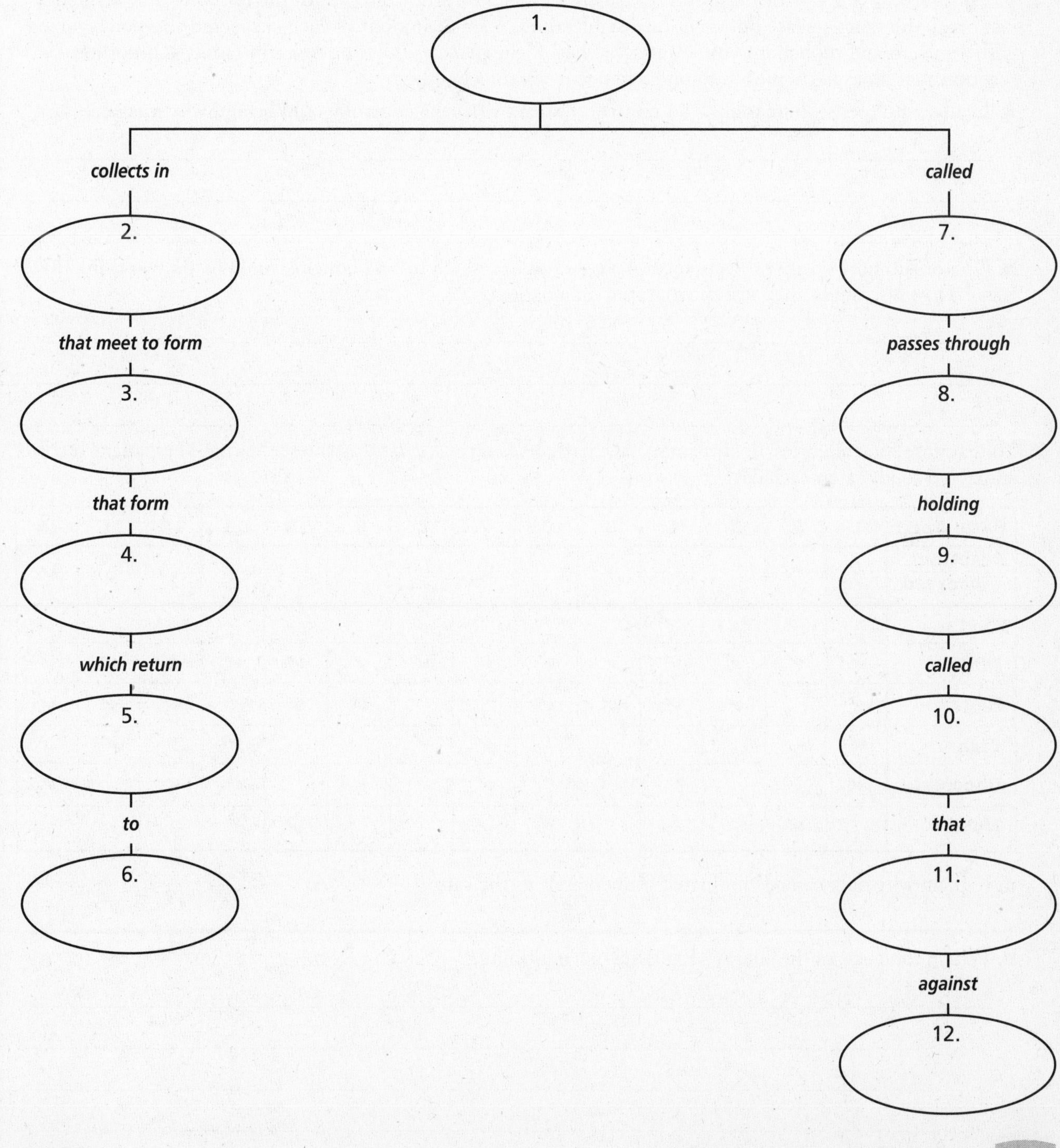

Name Date Class

Chapter 39

Immunity from Disease

Problem Solving

Use with Chapter 39, Section 39.2

Diagnosing Allergies

An allergy is the immune system's response to a foreign substance called an allergen. To treat allergy patients, doctors must first determine the cause of their allergies. Read about the different methods doctors use for diagnosing allergies and answer the following questions.

1. In *scratch testing*, the doctor makes several small scratches on sterilized skin of the forearm. The scratches just break the skin's surface but do not cause bleeding. A small amount of each suspected allergen is mixed with a solvent and rubbed into different scratches. If the person is allergic to a substance, a minor local reaction that looks like a mosquito bite will occur within a half hour.

a. In all scratch tests, there is always a control. Explain what the control would be and why it is necessary.

____

____

____

b. Doctors do not consider the absence of a reaction in scratch testing conclusive. Why do you think this is so? How else might they test the material on a patient?

____

____

____

2. To diagnose food allergies, doctors may have patients keep a *food diary* as shown below. The patient records suspected foods eaten each day.

Date: April	1	2	3	4	5	6	7	8	9	10	11	12	13	14
Reaction occurred	✔						✔							✔
Food														
Milk	✔	✔	✔	✔	✔	✔	✔	✔	✔	✔	✔	✔	✔	✔
Eggs	✔		✔	✔	✔	✔			✔	✔		✔	✔	✔
Fish	✔						✔	✔			✔		✔	
Chocolate	✔						✔							✔
Nuts		✔					✔			✔				

a. Explain why milk can be eliminated immediately as the cause.

____

b. Which food causes the allergy? Explain your reasoning.

____

____

____

____

Name Date Class

Master 96

Section Focus

Don't Spread It Around!

Use with Chapter 39, Section 39.1

1. How are the people in the first two pictures helping to prevent disease?

2. What do you think the person in the third picture is doing to prevent the spread of disease?

Master 97

Section Focus

Becoming Immune

Use with Chapter 39, Section 39.2

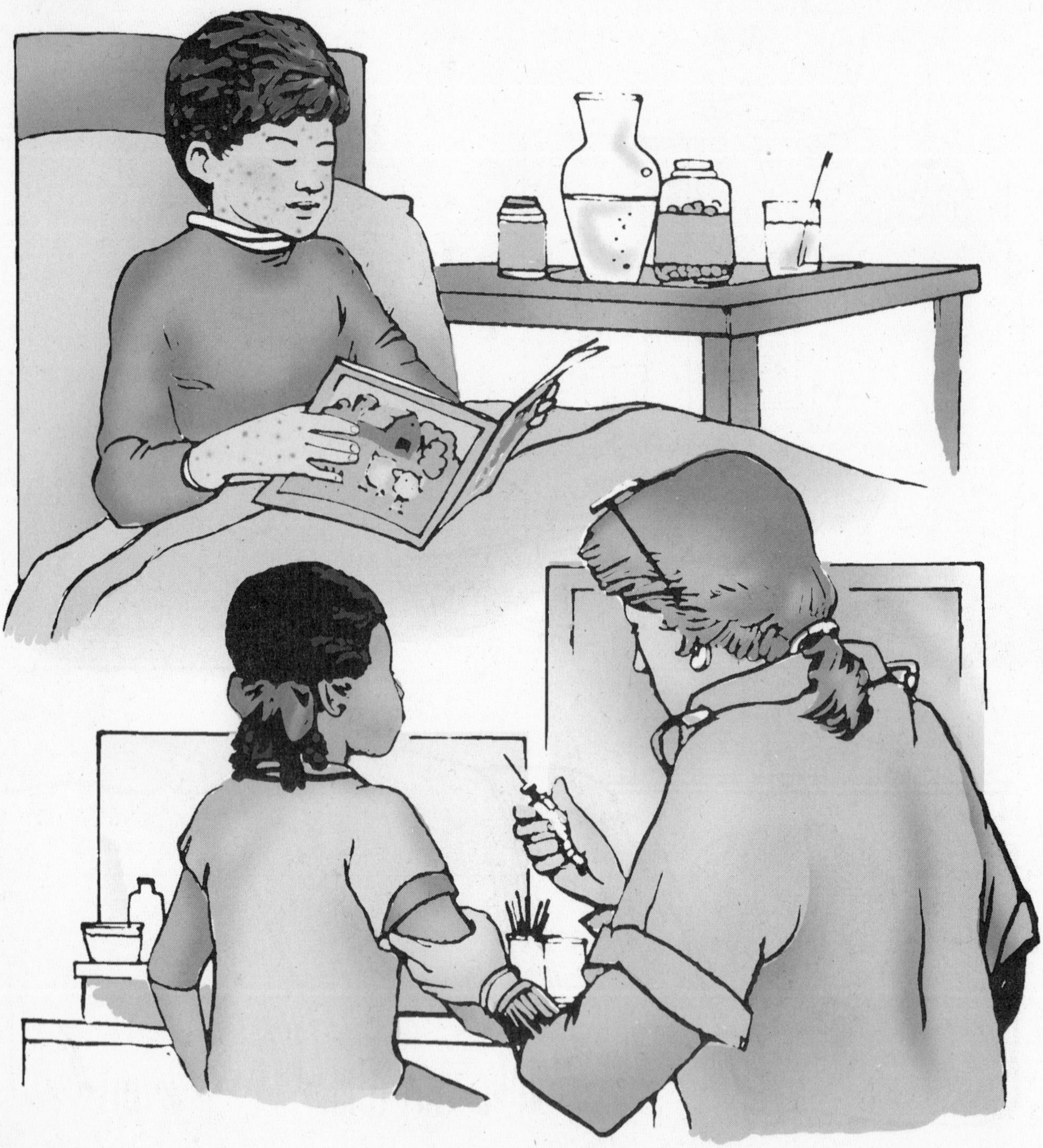

1. Do you think the first child will get the same disease again? Explain.

2. What is the second child doing to avoid getting the disease? How are the results the same for both?

Master 76

Identifying a Pathogen

Basic Concepts

Use with Chapter 39, Section 39.1

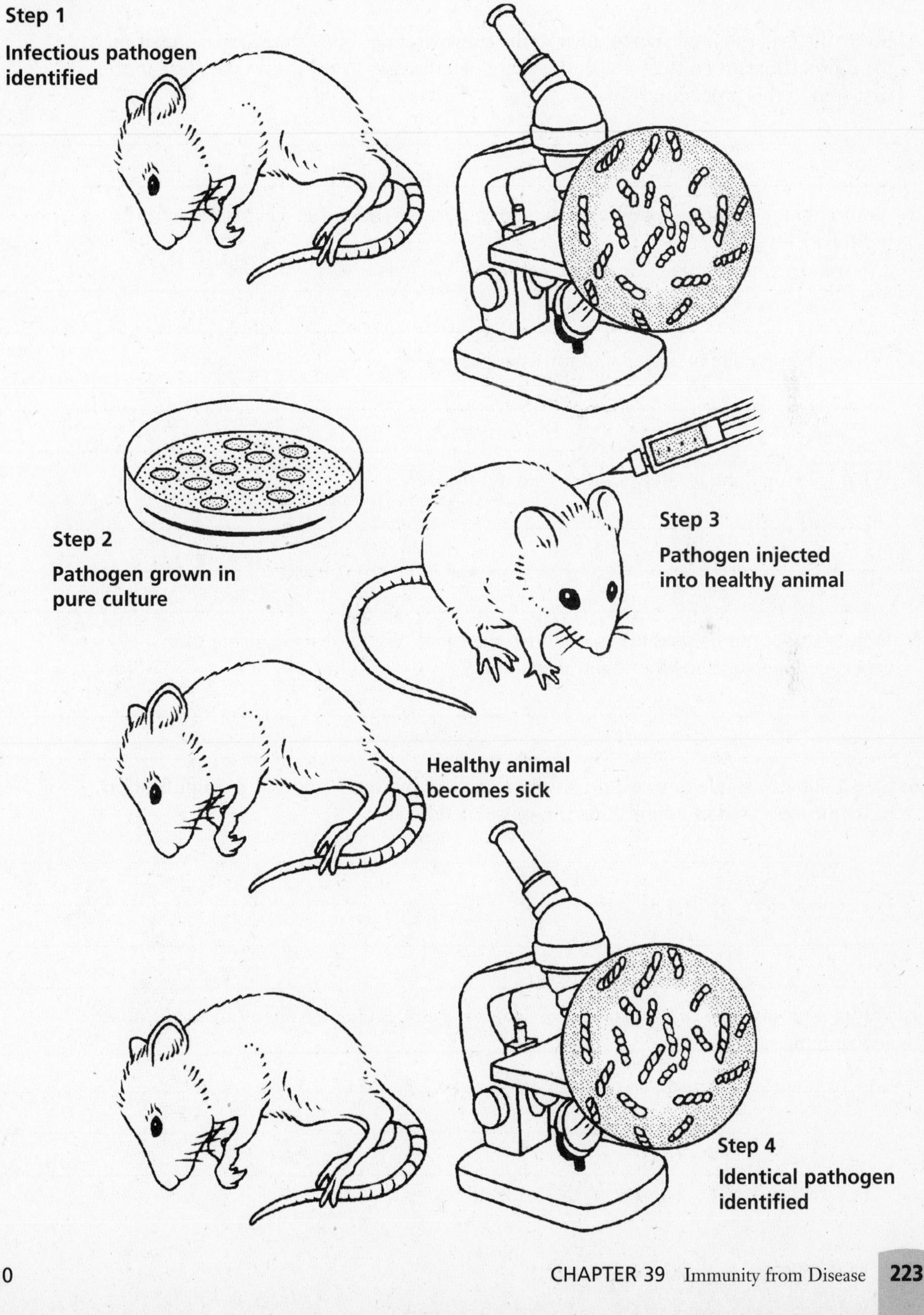
Step 1
Infectious pathogen identified
Step 2
Pathogen grown in pure culture
Step 3
Pathogen injected into healthy animal
Healthy animal becomes sick
Step 4
Identical pathogen identified

Name Date Class

Worksheet **76**

Identifying a Pathogen

Basic Concepts

Use with Chapter 39, Section 39.1

1. Study the experimental steps shown in the transparency. They summarize one of the main procedures used to establish the cause of a disease. What must take place in the first step of this procedure?

2. Assuming one or more potential pathogens are found in Step 1, what is the purpose of Step 2?

3. What is being done in Step 3 and for what purpose?

4. What is being done in Step 4 and for what purpose?

5. Why would it not be possible to establish the cause of viral disease, using the experimental steps shown in the transparency?

6. Step 1 shows a single diseased organism. Explain why this represents a simplification of the process used in establishing the cause of a disease.

7. Why isn't it possible to use Koch's postulates if a suspected pathogen causes a disease *only* in humans?

Master 77

Basic Concepts

Response to Injury

Use with Chapter 39, Section 39.2

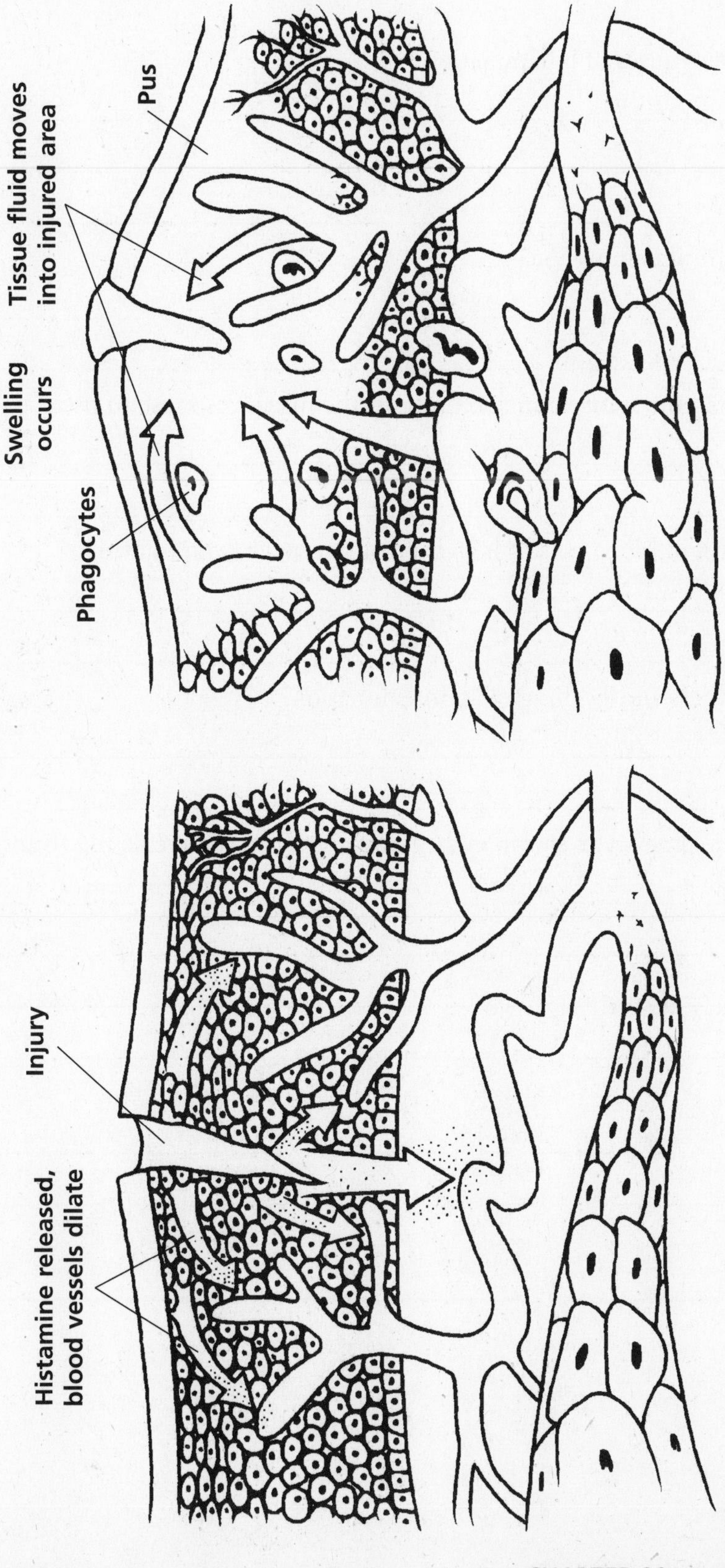

Name Date Class

Worksheet 77

Response to Injury

Basic Concepts

Use with Chapter 39, Section 39.2

1. What are five possible causes of inflammation?

2. What are four signs of inflammation?

3. Which event shown in the transparency represents the initial response to tissue damage?

4. How does the dilation of blood vessels help the body recover from injury?

5. What causes the redness and swelling of an inflammation?

6. What is the role of the phagocytes shown in the transparency and where do they come from?

7. What is pus?

Master 78a

Antibody Immunity

Basic Concepts

Use with Chapter 39, Section 39.2

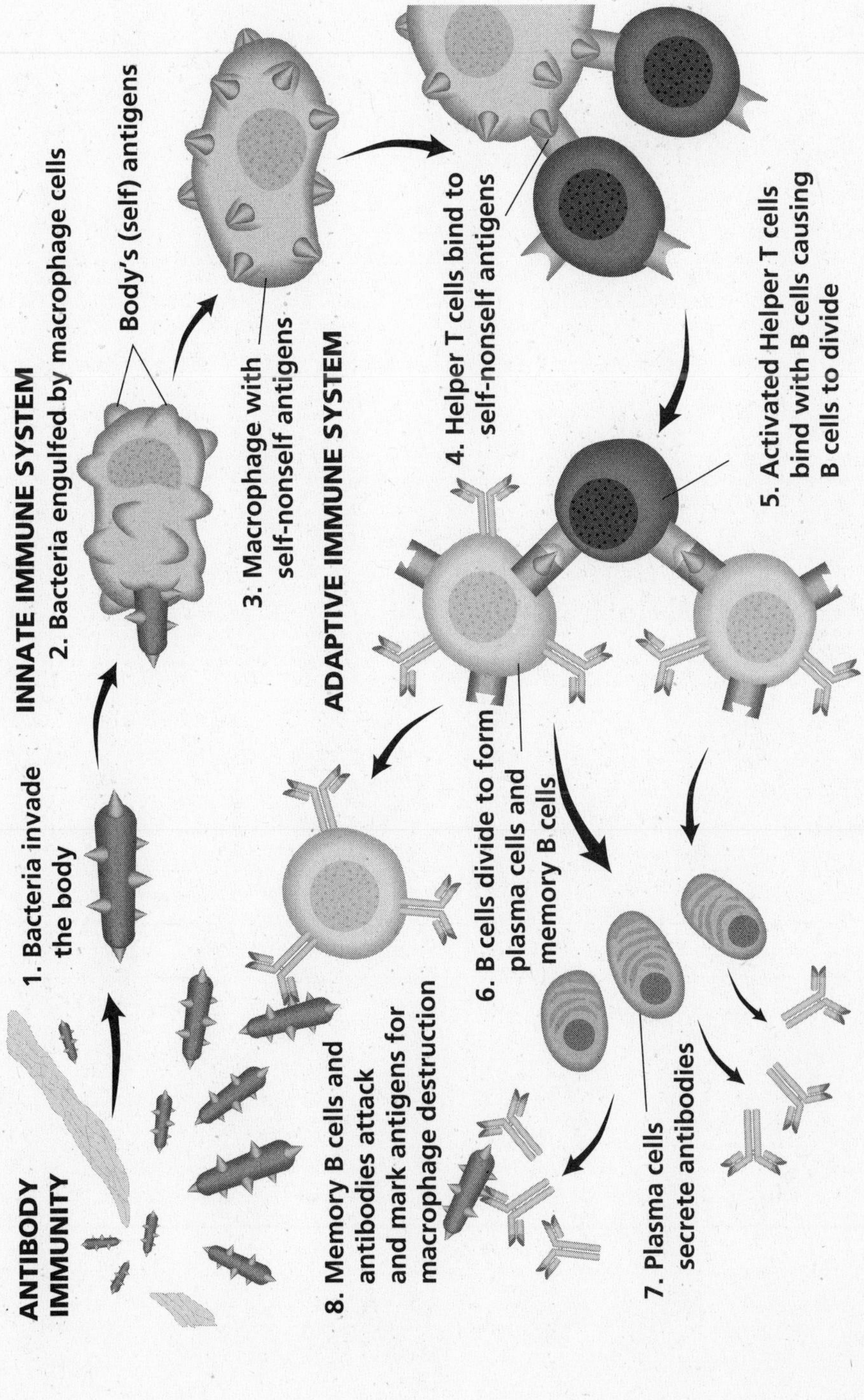
ANTIBODY IMMUNITY
1. Bacteria invade the body
INNATE IMMUNE SYSTEM
2. Bacteria engulfed by macrophage cells
Body's (self) antigens
3. Macrophage with self-nonself antigens
ADAPTIVE IMMUNE SYSTEM
4. Helper T cells bind to self-nonself antigens
5. Activated Helper T cells bind with B cells causing B cells to divide
6. B cells divide to form plasma cells and memory B cells
7. Plasma cells secrete antibodies
8. Memory B cells and antibodies attack and mark antigens for macrophage destruction

Master **78b**

Cellular Immunity

Basic Concepts

Use with Chapter 39, Section 39.2

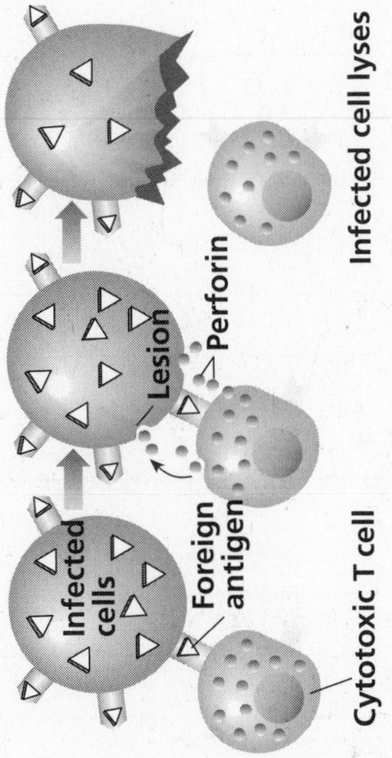

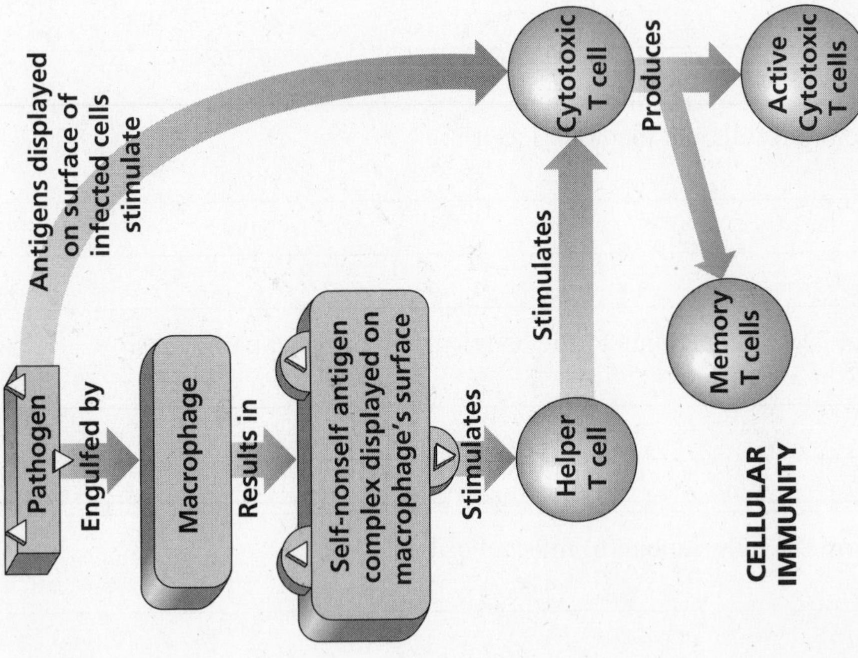

Name Date Class

Worksheet 78

Antibody and Cellular Immunity

Basic Concepts

Use with Chapter 39, Section 39.2

1. What are nonself antigens?

2. How does antibody immunity protect the body?

3. Compare T cells and B cells.

4. Which type of immune response involves direct contact between T cells and antigens?

5. What are memory B cells and memory T cells?

6. How do helper T cells contribute to the body's defense against pathogens?

7. How do cytotoxic T cells respond to infected cells?

Master 79

The AIDS Epidemic

Basic Concepts

Use with Chapter 39, Section 39.2

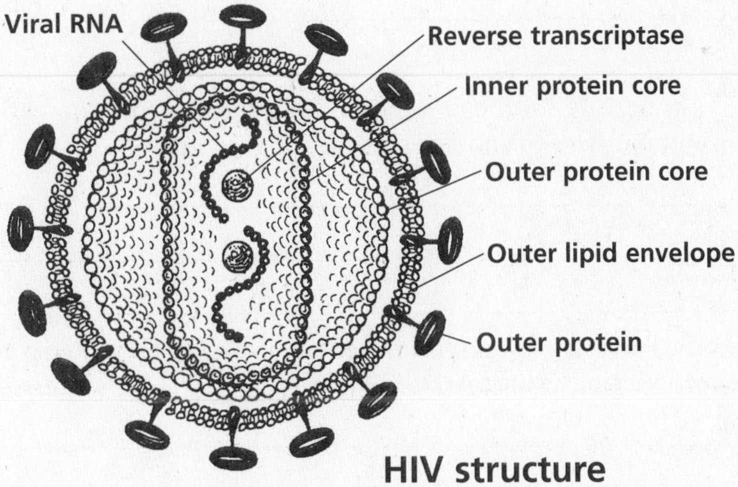

HIV structure

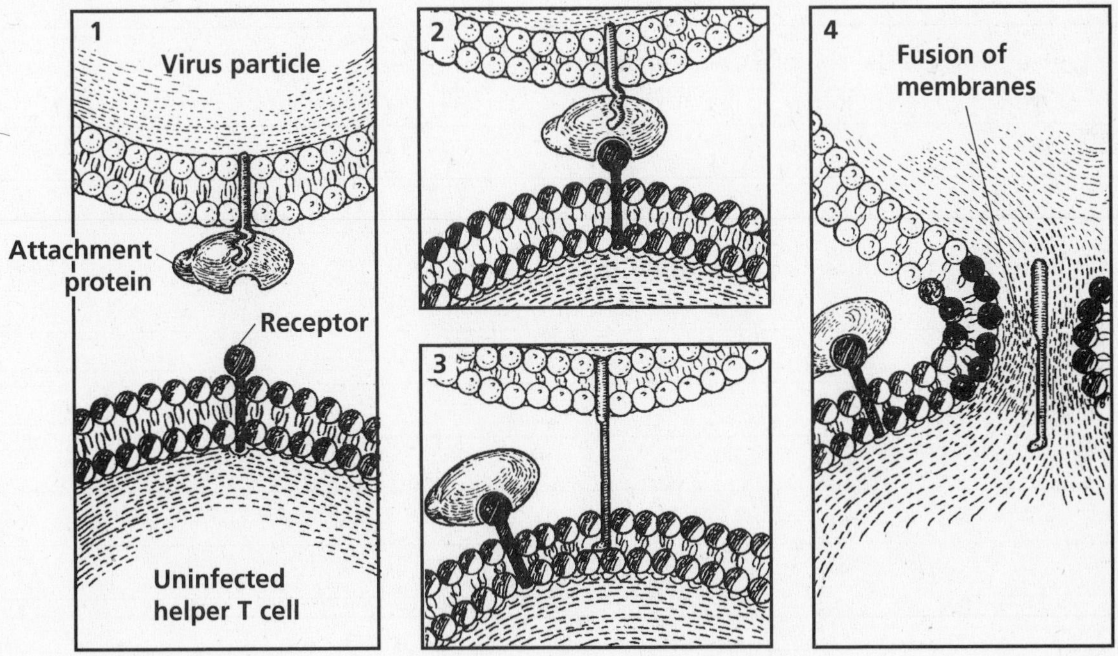

Name Date Class

Worksheet **79**

The AIDS Epidemic

Basic Concepts

Use with Chapter 39, Section 39.2

1. What is the full name of the pathogen that causes AIDS?

2. If a person tests positive for the presence of HIV, does that person have AIDS? Can that person transmit the virus to another person?

3. Why might the knoblike proteins on the outer surface of HIV hold a key to the production of a vaccine against AIDS?

4. What type of virus is HIV and what does it consist of?

5. What is happening in frames 2–4 of the transparency?

Name Date Class

Master 57

Reteaching Skills

Human Body Systems

Use with BioDigest 10, The Human Body

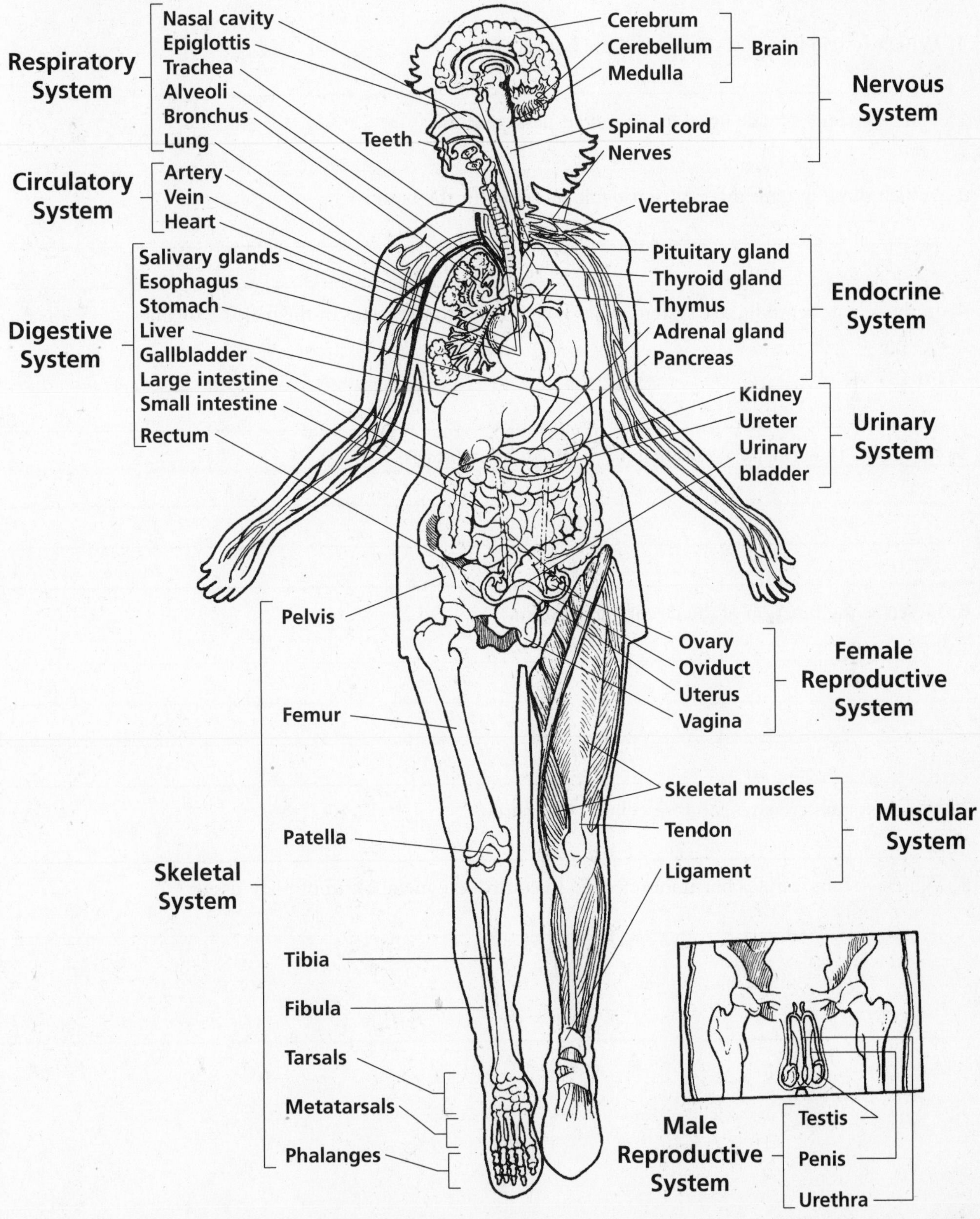

Worksheet 57

Human Body Systems

Reteaching Skills

Use with BioDigest 10, The Human Body

1. Which system provides support for the body?

2. Which system is made up of lungs and air passageways?

3. Which three systems interact to provide mobility for the body?

4. In the female reproductive system, what is analogous to the testes in the male? Explain your response.

5. How does the urinary system help to maintain homeostasis?

6. Describe the function of the circulatory system.

7. Which system prepares food for cellular utilization?

8. Which system secretes hormones needed to control the metabolism of body tissues?

Name Date Class

Master 58

Cells of the Immune Response

Reteaching Skills

Use with Chapter 39, Section 39.2

Type of Blood Cell or Structure	Innate/Adaptive Immune System	Function
Basophil 		
Eosinophil 		
Neutrophil 		
Macrophage 		
T cells 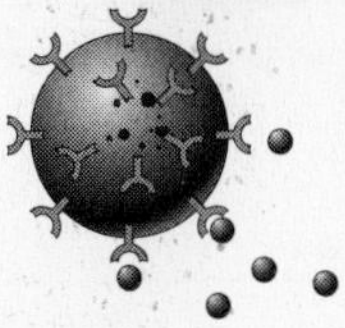 Helper T cell Killer T cell Memory T cell		
B cells 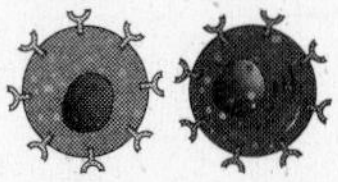 Memory B cell Plasma cell		
Antibodies 		

Name Date Class

Worksheet **58**

Cells of the Immune Response

Reteaching Skills

Use with Chapter 39, Section 39.2

1. Explain the difference between the innate immune system and the acquired immune system.

2. What is the role of skin in defending against infection?

3. Explain the role of secretions in the defense against infection.

4. Define these terms:

a. phagocyte

b. macrophage

c. pus

d. histamine

e. interferons

5. Define *vaccine* and discuss how it produces immunity to a disease.

Name ______________________ Date ______________ Class ______________

Chapter Assessment

Chapter 39 Immunity from Disease

Reviewing Vocabulary

Match the definition in Column A with the term in Column B.

	Column A	Column B
______	**1.** Disease caused by the presence of pathogens in the body	**a.** interferons
______	**2.** Substance produced by a microorganism, which kills or inhibits the growth and reproduction of other microorganisms	**b.** acquired immunity
______	**3.** Type of white blood cell that defends the body against foreign substances	**c.** lymph node
______	**4.** Disease-producing agents such as bacteria, protozoa, fungi, viruses	**d.** lymphocyte
______	**5.** Proteins that protect cells from viruses	**e.** pathogens
______	**6.** Defense against a specific pathogen by gradually building up resistance to it	**f.** vaccine
______	**7.** Small mass of tissue that filters pathogens from lymph	**g.** infectious disease
______	**8.** Procedure used to determine which pathogen causes a specific disease	**h.** Koch's postulates
______	**9.** Weakened, dead, or parts of pathogens or antigens that, when injected into the body, causes immunity	**i.** antibiotic

Contrast and compare each pair of related terms.

10. T cell, B cell

____

____

____

____

11. phagocyte, macrophage

____

Understanding Main Ideas (Part A)

In the space at the left, write the letter of the word or phrase that best completes the statement.

______ **1.** A bacterial disease becomes difficult to cure when the bacteria
- **a.** die off.
- **b.** make interferons.
- **c.** develop resistance to antibiotics.
- **d.** produce antibodies.

______ **2.** Toxins produced by invading bacteria
- **a.** are always harmless unless released in vary large amounts.
- **b.** can, in some cases, cause fever and cardiovascular disturbances.
- **c.** rarely attack the nervous or circulatory systems.
- **d.** are the same as those produced by HIV.

______ **3.** Interferons are a body cell's defense against
- **a.** all pathogens.
- **b.** bacteria.
- **c.** viruses.
- **d.** lymphocytes.

______ **4.** Immunity occurs when the system recognizes a foreign substance and responds by producing
- **a.** lymphocytes that make antibodies.
- **b.** antigens.
- **c.** toxins.
- **d.** all of these.

______ **5.** HIV can be transmitted by
- **a.** intimate sexual contact.
- **b.** contaminated food.
- **c.** air.
- **d.** shaking hands.

______ **6.** A person with AIDS is susceptible to all kinds of infectious diseases because HIV
- **a.** destroys pathogens.
- **b.** weakens the immune system.
- **c.** causes an increase of antigens.
- **d.** causes antibody production.

______ **7.** The symptoms of an infectious disease are caused by
- **a.** macrophages.
- **b.** toxins produced by pathogens.
- **c.** interferons.
- **d.** phagocytes.

______ **8.** Active immunity is obtained when a person is exposed to
- **a.** antigens.
- **b.** injected antibodies.
- **c.** macrophages.
- **d.** antibiotics.

______ **9.** Koch's postulates cannot be carried out on viral diseases because the viruses
- **a.** do not have hosts.
- **b.** are not pathogens.
- **c.** cannot be grown outside of cells.
- **d.** are too deadly.

Understanding Main Ideas (Part B)

Answer the following questions.

1. How do researchers identify the specific cause of an infectious disease?

2. How do interferons provide a defense against viruses?

3. How does a nonspecific defense mechanism differ from a specific defense mechanism?

4. What role do B cells play in immunity?

5. How does cellular immunity protect the body?

6. Why is AIDS considered a disease of the immune system?

Thinking Critically

Answer the following questions.

1. You get a splinter in your finger, which becomes sore and swollen. In a few days, pus forms around the splinter. Explain.

2. Antibodies produced by the body to combat the pathogen that causes rheumatic fever may begin to attack the patient's own cardiac muscle cells. How might such a mixup occur?

3. Organ-transplant patients are given a drug called cyclosporine to suppress the body's defenses against the transplanted organ. Why is this necessary?

4. Unlike earlier drugs that suppressed the entire immune system, cyclosporine does not significantly suppress the bone marrow where lymphocytes are formed. What was the danger of taking the earlier drugs?

5. Suppose parents hear that a neighbor's child has chicken pox, and they take their young child over to their neighbor's house. Why would they do this?

Applying Scientific Methods

Vincent Fischetti is a professor of bacterial pathogenesis and immunology at New York's Rockefeller University. His team of researchers has been studying why some Group A streptococcal bacteria manage to slip by the defenses of the human body. Group A streptococci cause strep throat, which often leads to acute rheumatic fever, a disease that damages heart valves.

First, Fischetti's team looked at Group A streptococci under an electron microscope. They noticed that some of these bacteria have long, hairlike filaments on their surfaces. The filaments were found to consist of a protein called M protein. They decided to find out if the M protein has anything to do with Group A's ability to resist ingestion by human phagocytes. They placed streptococci in a drop of human blood on a microscope slide. The phagocytes in the blood moved away from the bacteria that had M proteins on their surfaces. The phagocytes attacked any streptococci that lacked M-protein filaments.

Fischetti next wanted to know how the M protein resists the body's defenses. The team began a study of the protein sequence of M protein. Figure 1 shows what they found. Four different repeated amino acid sequences (A, B, C, and D) make up 80 percent of the protein.

Almost immediately a discovery slowed the study. Fischetti found that there are 80 different varieties of M protein! He realized that M-proteins must be affected by rapid mutations. Further study of different varieties of M protein showed that most of the mutations occur in the numbers of repeated A and B amino acid sequences, as shown in Figure 2. Mutated streptococci show deleted copies of the amino acid repeat blocks normally found in the parent.

Protein M6.1

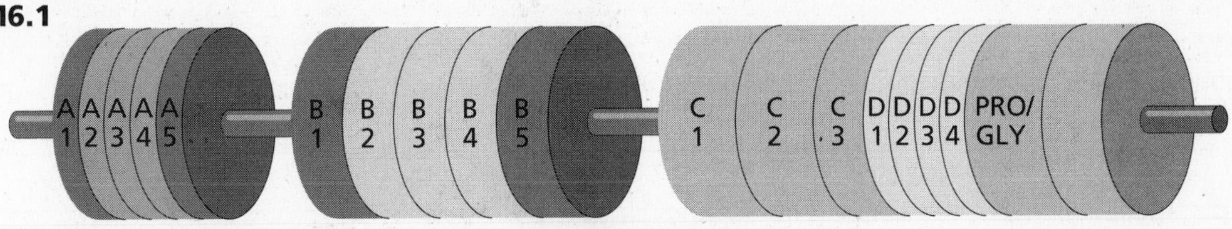

Figure 1

Protein M6.2

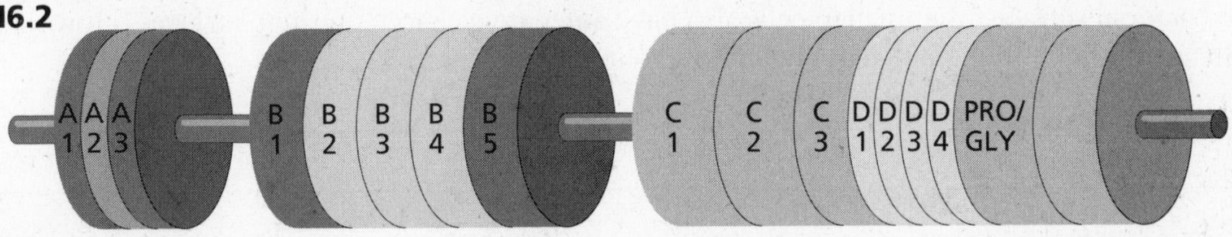

Protein M6.3

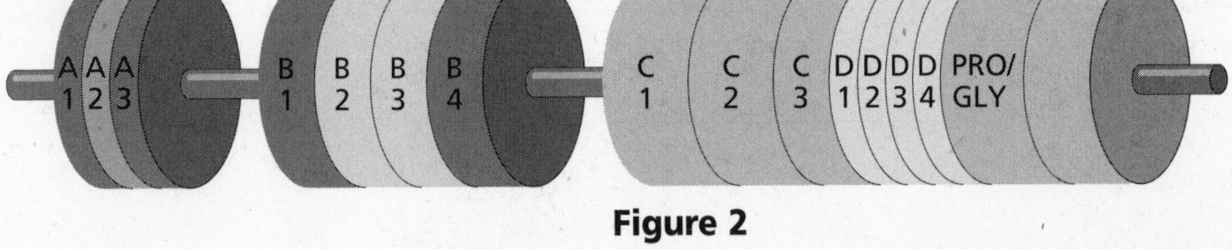

Figure 2

Applying Scientific Methods *continued*

Suppose that you are a new member of Fischetti's team. After observing the experiments just described, you are asked the following questions about the work being done.

1. Which experiment provided evidence that the M protein protects streptococci?

2. Having mutations in the numbers of repeated amino acid sequences in the M protein is extremely helpful to the bacteria. How might this adaptation help them to survive?

3. Figure 2 shows two mutations of the M protein. What differences do you observe between M6.1 and M6.2? Between M6.1 and M6.3?

4. How might rapid mutation thwart the human immune system?

5. The M protein has an excess of negatively charged amino acids. This results in a net negative charge on the bacterial surface. Mammalian cells also have a negative charge on their surfaces. How might this affect the ability of mammalian phagocytes to ingest the bacteria?

Chapter 39

Assessment
Student Recording Sheet

Chapter Assessment

Use with pages 1046–1047 of the Student Edition

Vocabulary Review

If the statement is true, write *true*. If the statement is false, replace the underlined word with the correct vocabulary word.

1. ______________________ 3. ______________________

2. ______________________ 4. ______________________

Understanding Key Concepts

Select the best answer from the choices given and fill in the corresponding oval.

5. Ⓐ Ⓑ Ⓒ Ⓓ 7. Ⓐ Ⓑ Ⓒ Ⓓ

6. Ⓐ Ⓑ Ⓒ Ⓓ 8. Ⓐ Ⓑ Ⓒ Ⓓ

9. Fill in the correct terms to complete the concept map.

 1. ______________________ 3. ______________________

 2. ______________________ 4. ______________________

Constructed Response

Record your answers for Questions 10–12 on a separate sheet of paper.

Thinking Critically

Record your answer for Questions 13, 15 and 16 on a separate sheet of paper.

14. **REAL WORLD BIOCHALLENGE** Follow your teacher's instructions for presenting your BioChallenge answer.

Standardized Test Practice

The Princeton Review

Part 1 Multiple Choice

Select the best answer from the choices given and fill in the corresponding oval.

17. Ⓐ Ⓑ Ⓒ Ⓓ 20. Ⓐ Ⓑ Ⓒ Ⓓ

18. Ⓐ Ⓑ Ⓒ Ⓓ 21. Ⓐ Ⓑ Ⓒ Ⓓ

19. Ⓐ Ⓑ Ⓒ Ⓓ

Part 2 Constructed Response/Grid In

Record your answers for Questions 22 and 23 on a separate sheet of paper.

BioDigest **10** Reinforcement and Study Guide

The Human Body

In your textbook, read about skin, bones, and muscles.

Skin has four functions: **(1)** ______________________, **(2)** ______________________, **(3)** ______________________, and **(4)** ______________________. These functions help maintain homeostasis in the body.

Complete the table to describe the role of bones.

Support for	**5.**
Place for	**6.**
Protects	**7.**
Manufacture of	**8.**
Storehouse of	**9.**

This diagram shows the various steps involved in the respiratory process. In the space provided, describe the steps as indicated.

Step 1: Oxygen enters the lungs when you inhale.

Step 7: Carbon dioxide leaves the lungs when you exhale.

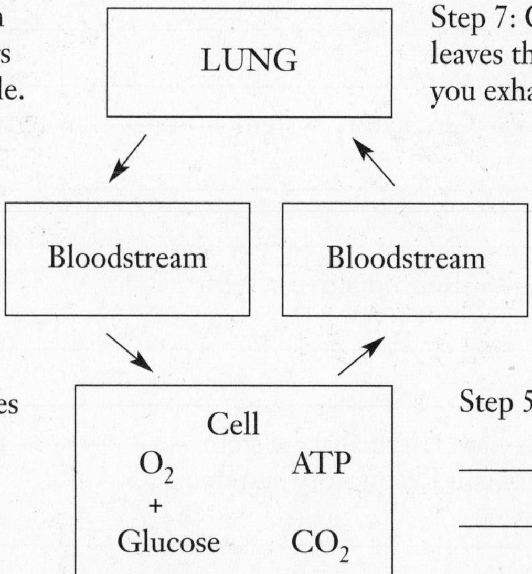

Step 2: **(10)** ______________________

Step 6: **(13)** ______________________

Step 3: Oxygen passes from blood to the cells.

Step 5: **(12)** ______________________

Step 4: **(11)** ______________________

BioDigest 10 **The Human Body,** *continued*

Reinforcement and Study Guide

In your textbook, read about reproductive, endocrine, and lymphatic systems.

14. The endocrine system is a communication system; its messages are hormones. They are produced by ______________________ and travel in the ______________________ to ______________ ______________. There they ______________________________________.

15. The structures of the male reproductive system—the scrotum, ______________________, epididymis, seminal vesicles, ______________________, bulbourethral gland, urethra, and ______________________—are involved in ______________________ and maintaining sperm cells and ______________________ into the female reproductive tract.

16. The structures of the female reproductive system—the ______________________, oviduct, ______________________, and vagina—produce and maintain ______________________, receive and transport ______________________, and support the development of the ______________________.

Explain how these systems of the body interact with each other.

17. Skeletal system ⟶ Circulatory system ⟶ Muscular system

____

____

18. Digestive system ⟶ Circulatory system ⟶ Urinary system

____

____

19. Endocrine system ⟶ Reproductive system

____

____

20. Respiratory System ⟶ Circulatory system ⟶ Cell ⟶ Circulatory system ⟶ Urinary and Respiratory systems

____

____

____

21. Circulatory system ⟶ Lymphatic system

____

____

Nombre Fecha Clase

BioCompendio **10**

El cuerpo humano

Refuerzo y Guía de estudio

En tu libro de texto, lee sobre la piel, los huesos y los músculos.

La piel cumple cuatro funciones: **(1)** ______________________________, **(2)** ____, **(3)** ______________________ y **(4)** ____. Estas funciones ayudan a mantener la homeostasis del cuerpo.

Describe las funciones de los huesos completando la tabla.

Sostén de	**5.**
Sitio para	**6.**
Protegen	**7.**
Formación de	**8.**
Almacenamiento de	**9.**

El siguiente diagrama muestra las diferentes etapas del proceso respiratorio. Describe los pasos indicados.

Etapa 1: Entra oxígeno a los pulmones, al inhalar aire.

Etapa 7: Sale dióxido de carbono de los pulmones, al exhalar el aire.

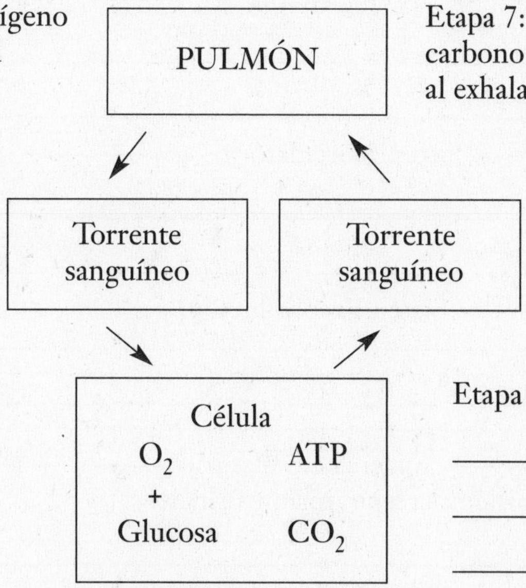

Etapa 2: **(10)** ______________________
____
____
____

Etapa 6: **(13)** ______________________
____
____
____

Etapa 3: El oxígeno pasa de la sangre a las células.

Etapa 5: **(12)** ______________________
____
____
____

Etapa 4: **(11)** ______________________
____
____
____

BioCompendio 10

Refuerzo y Guía de estudio

El cuerpo humano, *continuación*

En tu libro de texto, lee sobre los sistemas reproductor, endocrino y linfático.

14. El sistema endocrino es un sistema de comunicación y sus mensajes son las hormonas. Las ____________ producen las hormonas que son transportadas por la ____________ hacia los ____________. Al llegar a este punto, ____________.

15. Las estructuras del sistema reproductor masculino: el escroto, los ____________, el epidídimo, las vesículas seminales, la ____________, las glándulas bulbouretrales, la uretra y el ____________ se encargan de la ____________ y el mantenimiento de los espermatozoides, así como de la ____________ hacia el tracto reproductor femenino.

16. Las estructuras del sistema reproductor femenino: los ____________, los oviductos, el ____________ y la vagina se encargan de la producción y el mantenimiento de los ____________, de recibir y transportar los ____________ y del desarrollo del ____________.

Explica cómo interactúan los siguientes sistemas.

17. Sistema esquelético ⟶ Sistema circulatorio ⟶ Sistema muscular

____

____

18. Sistema digestivo ⟶ Sistema circulatorio ⟶ Sisitema urinario

____

____

19. Sistema endocrino ⟶ Sistema reproductor

____

____

20. Sistema respiratorio ⟶ Sistema circulatorio ⟶ Célula ⟶ Sistema circulatorio ⟶ Sistemas respiratorio y urinario

____

____

____

21. Sistema circulatorio ⟶ Sistema linfático

____

____

Unit 10

Assessment
Student Recording Sheet

Standardized Test Practice

Use with pages 1056–1057 of the Student Edition

Standardized Test Practice

The Princeton Review

Part 1 Multiple Choice

Select the best answer from the choices given and fill in the corresponding oval.

1. Ⓐ Ⓑ Ⓒ Ⓓ
2. Ⓐ Ⓑ Ⓒ Ⓓ
3. Ⓐ Ⓑ Ⓒ Ⓓ
4. Ⓐ Ⓑ Ⓒ Ⓓ
5. Ⓐ Ⓑ Ⓒ Ⓓ
6. Ⓐ Ⓑ Ⓒ Ⓓ
7. Ⓐ Ⓑ Ⓒ Ⓓ
8. Ⓐ Ⓑ Ⓒ Ⓓ
9. Ⓐ Ⓑ Ⓒ Ⓓ
10. Ⓐ Ⓑ Ⓒ Ⓓ
11. Ⓐ Ⓑ Ⓒ Ⓓ
12. Ⓐ Ⓑ Ⓒ Ⓓ
13. Ⓐ Ⓑ Ⓒ Ⓓ
14. Ⓐ Ⓑ Ⓒ Ⓓ

Part 2 Constructed Response/Grid In

Record your answers for Questions 15–18 on a separate sheet of paper.

Contents

Teacher Support and Planning

Protection, Support, and Locomotion

FOLDABLES™ Study Organizer

Use with Section 34.2

Identifying Parts of the Skeletal System

Have each student make a Foldable to identify the components of the skeletal system using the half book shown below.

How to Use the Foldable

Have students . . .

1. construct a half book. *If students need additional instructions to construct a half book, the bottom of this page can be reproduced and distributed to students.*
2. use a transparency marker (or colored pencil) to sketch and label a diagram of the appendicular skeleton on the inside of the Foldable.
3. sketch and label a diagram of the axial skeleton on the front of the Foldable. The two diagrams should match up when the Foldable is closed.
4. use their Foldables to review the skeletal system before the test.

Going Further

- Identify the joints in the skeleton and, with a different-colored label, indicate hinge joints, ball-and-socket joints, pivot joints, and gliding joints.
- Choose one bone of the skeleton. Draw it in detail and label the specific parts, such as the spongy bone, cartilage, and marrow cavity. Use ***Figure 34.8*** in the text as an example.

Half Book

STEP 1 **Fold** a transparency sheet or piece of tracing paper in half lengthwise.

STEP 2 **Label** as directed.

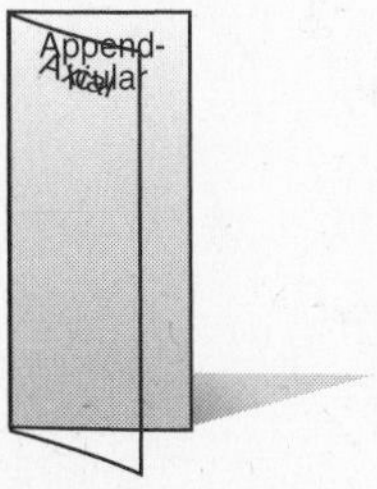

FOLDABLES™ Study Organizer

Use with Section 35.2

Chapter 35 The Digestive and Endocrine Systems

Classifying Nutrients

Have each student make a Foldable, using the accordion book shown below, to classify the different nutrients.

How to Use the Foldable

Have students . . .

1. construct an accordion book. *If students need additional instructions to construct an accordion book, the bottom of this page can be reproduced and distributed to students.*
2. label one side of each section of paper *Carbohydrates, Fats, Proteins, Minerals,* and *Vitamins.*
3. write a description of what each category of nutrients provides for the body on the other side of the same section of paper.
4. trade their Foldables with a friend and quiz each other on the contents.

Going Further

- Include an example of each type of nutrient.
- On a separate piece of colored paper, have students make a sketch of their favorite food in each category and then cut out their sketches and attach them to the appropriate section of paper.

Accordion Book

STEP 1 **Fold** three vertical sheets of paper in half from top to bottom.

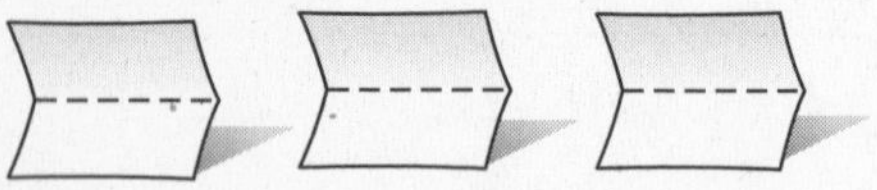

STEP 2 **Turn** the papers horizontally and **cut** the papers in half along the folds.

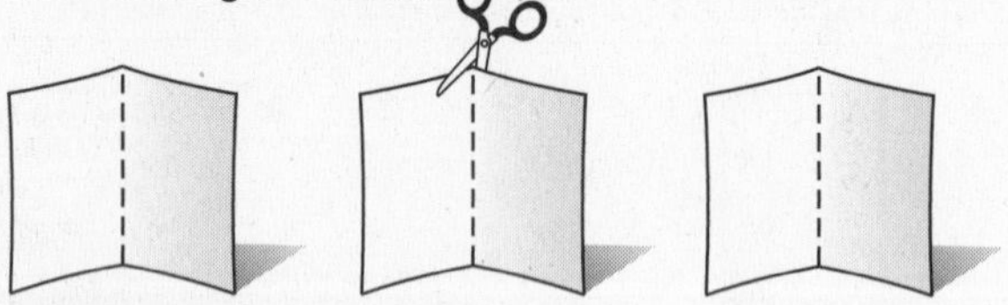

STEP 3 **Fold** five of the vertical pieces in half from top to bottom.

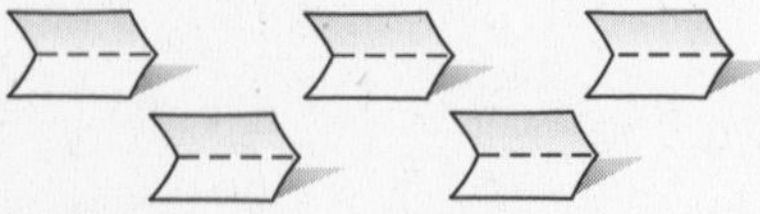

STEP 4 **Turn** the papers horizontally. **Tape** the short ends of the pieces together (overlapping the edges slightly) to make an accordion book.

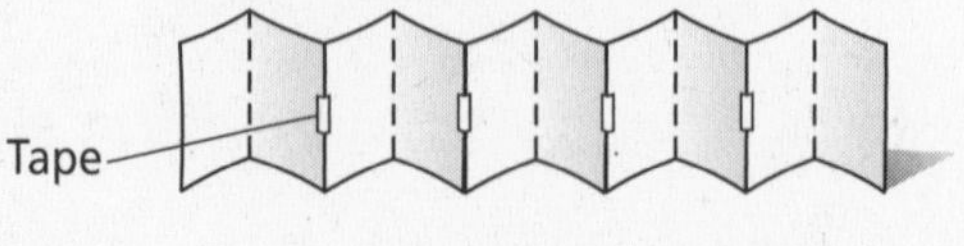

STEP 5 **Label** each section.

Chapter 36 The Nervous System

Use with Section 36.2

Relating Nervous System Components

Have each student make a Foldable to relate the components of the nervous system using the half book shown below.

How to Use the Foldable

Have students . . .

1. construct a half book. *If students need additional instructions to construct a half book, the bottom of this page can be reproduced and distributed to students.*
2. use a transparency marker (or colored pencil) to sketch and label a diagram of the central nervous system (CNS) on the front of the Foldable.
3. sketch and label a diagram of the peripheral nervous system (PNS) on the inside of the Foldable. The two diagrams should match up when the Foldable is closed.
4. use their Foldables to review what they have learned about the nervous system.

Going Further

Critical Thinking

- Distinguish the parts and functions of the CNS and indicate how it works with the PNS on the front of the Foldable.
- Distinguish the parts and functions of the PNS and how the somatic, autonomic, sympathetic, and parasympathetic nervous systems work on the inside of the Foldable.

Half Book

STEP 1 **Fold** a transparency sheet or piece of tracing paper in half lengthwise.

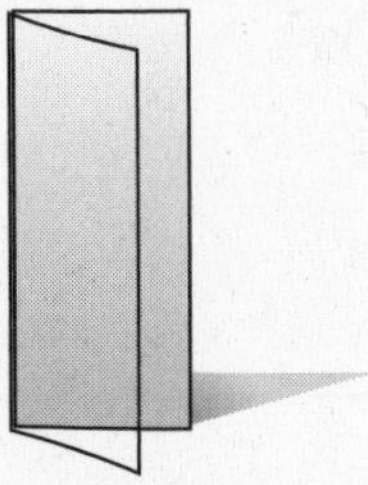

STEP 2 **Illustrate** and **label** as directed.

Respiration, Circulation, and Excretion

FOLDABLES™ Study Organizer

Use with Section 37.2

Sequencing Blood Flow

Have students make a Foldable to sequence the flow of blood through the circulatory system using the layered-look book shown below.

How to Use the Foldable

Have students . . .

1. construct a layered-look book. *If students need additional instructions to construct a layered-look book, the bottom of this page can be reproduced and distributed to students.*
2. draw an outline of a human body over the Foldable layers so that the head is on the top layer, the neck is second, the chest is third, etc.
3. draw the appropriate part of the circulatory system on the inside of each tab within the outline of the body. ***Figure 37.8*** in the text is one example. Try to include the aorta, the brachiocephalic, the carotid, the renal arteries, the external iliac, and the internal iliac.
4. use red to indicate arteries and the flow of blood away from the heart and blue to illustrate veins and the flow of blood to the heart.
5. use their Foldables to review the circulatory system before the test.

Going Further

Critical Thinking

- On the appropriate tabs, label and describe the functions of arteries, arterioles, capillaries, veins, and the heart and its parts. Use an anatomy and physiology text as an additional reference.
- Infer how the circulatory system is adapted to the force of gravity.

Layered-Look Book

STEP 1 **Collect** three sheets of paper and layer them about 2 cm apart vertically. Keep the edges level.

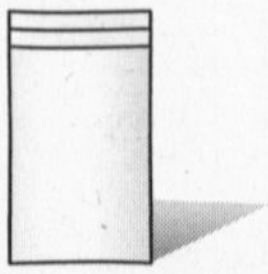

STEP 2 **Fold** up the bottom edges of the paper to form six equal tabs.

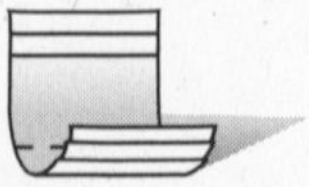

STEP 3 **Fold** the papers and crease well to hold the tabs in place. Staple along the fold. **Draw** and **label** each tab as instructed.

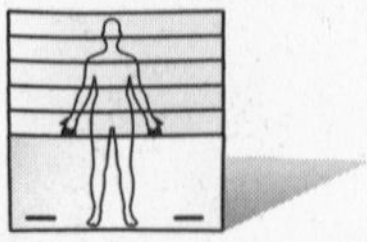

Chapter 38 Reproduction and Development

Use with Section 38.2

Sequencing Fetal Development

Have each student make a Foldable to sequence fetal development using the bound book shown below.

How to Use the Foldable

Have students . . .

1. construct a six-page bound book. *If students need additional instructions to construct a bound book, the bottom of this page can be reproduced and distributed to students.*
2. visit **bdol.glencoe.com** to find detailed illustrations of fetal development.
3. draw diagrams of developmental stages on each page, making sure to keep the sketch centered and indicate the increase in size as development progresses.
4. flip the pages of the book quickly to see the stages of development.
5. trade their Foldables with a friend and quiz each other on the contents.

Going Further

Critical Thinking

- Indicate the important changes that happen at each stage of fetal development on the back of the appropriate page.
- Research the problems that can occur in a developing fetus if it is exposed to drugs, such as alcohol or tobacco, and indicate on the diagrams where these problems can occur.

Bound Book

STEP 1 **Fold** three sheets of paper in half. **Mark** 2.5 cm from the edge of each sheet.

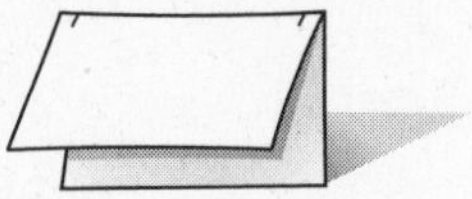

STEP 2 **Unfold** two sheets and cut them along the fold from each edge to each mark. **Cut** the third sheet along the fold between the marks to form a slot.

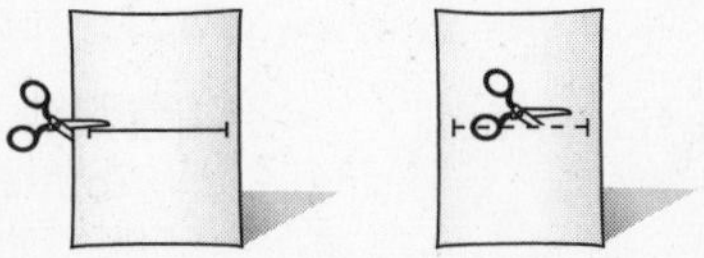

STEP 3 **Insert** the first two sheets into the second sheet and align folds.

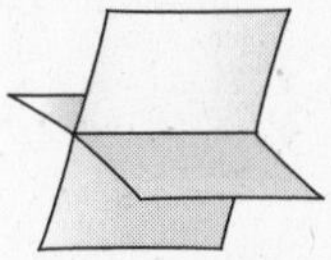

STEP 4 **Fold** the three sheets of paper to form a six-page bound book.

FOLDABLES™ Study Organizer

Use with Section 39.2

Chapter 39 Immunity from Disease

Describing Immunity

Have each student make a Foldable, using the accordion book shown below, to describe the different types of immunity.

How to Use the Foldable

Have students . . .

1. construct an accordion book. *If students need additional instructions to construct an accordion book, the bottom of this page can be reproduced and distributed to students.*
2. label one side of each sheet *Innate Immunity*, *Acquired Immunity*, *Antibody Immunity*, *Cellular Immunity*, *Passive Immunity*, and *Active Immunity*.
3. describe each type of immunity beneath the appropriate label.
4. use their Foldables to review what they have learned about immunity.

Going Further

- Infer the conditions under which each type of immunity would be used to deter pathogens.
- Illustrate each type of immunity at work in the body on the adjacent side of the appropriate fold.

Accordion Book

STEP 1 **Fold** three vertical sheets of paper in half from top to bottom.

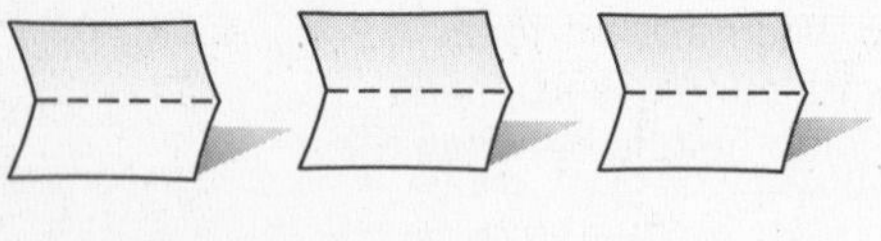

STEP 2 **Turn** the papers horizontally and **cut** the papers in half along the folds.

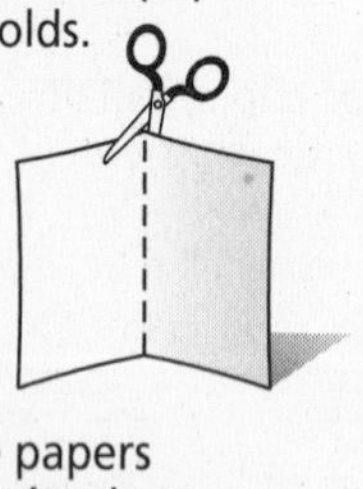

STEP 3 **Fold** the six vertical pieces in half from top to bottom.

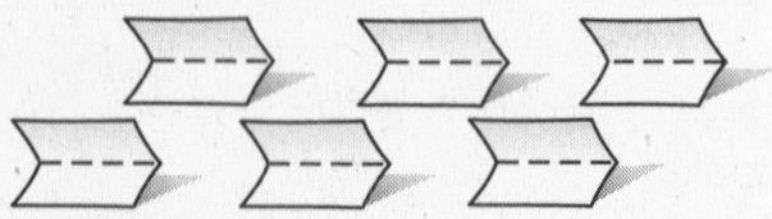

STEP 4 **Turn** the papers horizontally. **Tape** the short ends of the pieces together (overlapping the edges slightly) to make an accordion book.

Tape

STEP 5 **Label** each section.

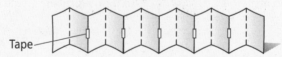

Chapter 34

MiniLab 34.1

Page 3 • Examine Your Fingerprints

Expected Results

Each finger has a unique fingerprint and each individual has a unique set of fingerprints.

Analysis

1. No; however, the general patterns may be the same on different fingers
2. It is possible that students may share patterns, but not identical fingerprints.
3. It is unique for each person.

MiniLab 34.2

Page 4 • Examining Muscle Contraction

Analysis

1. Students will learn that actin and myosin do not change in length.
2. Actin filaments slide over myosin filaments, shortening the sarcomere.

Design Your Own BioLab

Page 5 • Does fatigue affect the ability to perform an exercise?

Data and Observations

Student graphs should show that the number of exercise repetitions goes down over time as the muscles become tired.

Analyze and Conclude

1. The muscle groups became fatigued and the number of repetitions of the activity went down as more trials were run.
2. The muscles felt tired and may even have begun to hurt toward the end. It became harder to do the activity, and the strength of each contraction was reduced.
3. Cells are running out of oxygen and accumulating toxic products such as lactic acid and carbon dioxide as the muscles change to anaerobic processes.
4. Fatigued muscles should work as well after a rest of 30 minutes as they did before fatigue became a factor. The accumulated lactic acid has been broken down as the oxygen supply in the muscle cells has been replenished during the rest.
5. The greater the resistance, the more quickly fatigue will occur. One possible design would be to have a person do repetitions with increasing amounts of resistance with periods of rest in between each increment. The independent variable is the amount of resistance. The dependent variable is the number of repetitions completed in a certain time period.
6. Answers will vary. Differences may be explained by variations in types of activity and amount of individual exertion. Improvement answers will vary.

Real World BioApplications

Page 7 • Biceps Biomechanics

Planning the Activity

Have students complete this activity as they study the musculoskeletal system in Chapter 34. This activity can also be used to introduce students to the applications of biomechanics in medicine and other fields.

Purpose

Students investigate how lever mechanics are used to understand morphological adaptations of the human musculoskeletal system.

Career Applications

The relationship between physics, mechanics, and the human body presented in this activity has several implications in the field of biomechanics. Prosthetic and robotic design engineers rely on technicians to read blueprints, assemble, and test both prototype and manufactured devices. Technicians working in the prosthetics field evaluate devices for their replication of the strength and range of motion present in the human anatomy. Technicians evaluating robotic devices must consider how accurately, and with what touch sensitivity, the device performs.

Other fields that rely on a complete understanding of the musculoskeletal system include personal trainers and physical therapists. Physical therapist aids provide services designed to improve mobility, relieve pain, and prevent or limit permanent physical disabilities of patients suffering from injuries or disease. Personal trainers provide information and services designed to promote a healthy lifestyle, lose weight, and increase strength and mobility.

Teaching Strategies

- After students read the introduction, mention that the word *lever* is derived from the Latin root *levare* (to lift). Have students discuss how the meaning of the word reflects its root.

- Explain that a simple machine is a device that does work with only one movement. Have students suggest common examples of levers such as a seesaw, a crowbar, a nutcracker, or an arm swinging a tennis racket. You may wish to intorduce this activity by reviewing with students the basic principles of lever mechanics as well as the three types of levers. Emphasize that the lever classes are based on the positions of the effort force, resistance force, and fulcrum. The easiest way to identify the class of a lever is to concentrate on what is "in-between."
- Elaborate on the model of the skeletal system as a set of bony levers. Student understanding may be facilitated through manipulation of model skeletons. If biological models are not available, use cardboard Halloween skeletons to demonstrate bones that function as levers. Ask students to consider why it might be important to understand the skeleton on a mechanical level. Accept all reasonable responses, then relate student answers to the fields of prosthetics, robotics, sports medicine, and surgery.
- The equation in question 3 of Part B is often call the "law of the lever."

Answers to Student Worksheet

Part A

1. a. third-class lever
   b. first-class lever
   c. second-class lever

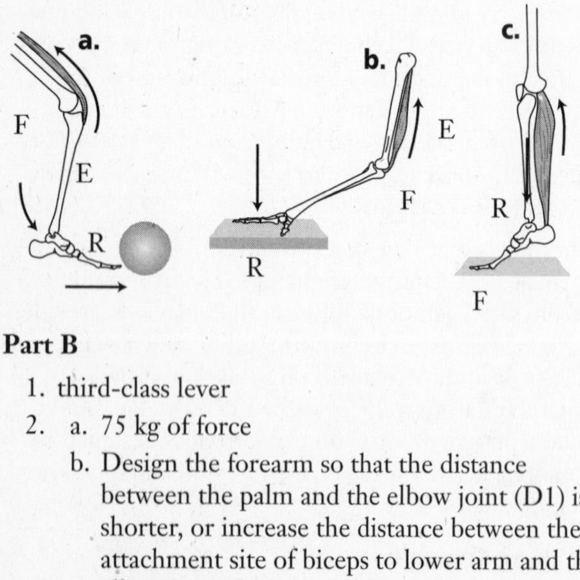

Part B

1. third-class lever
2. a. 75 kg of force
   b. Design the forearm so that the distance between the palm and the elbow joint (D1) is shorter, or increase the distance between the attachment site of biceps to lower arm and the elbow joint (D2).

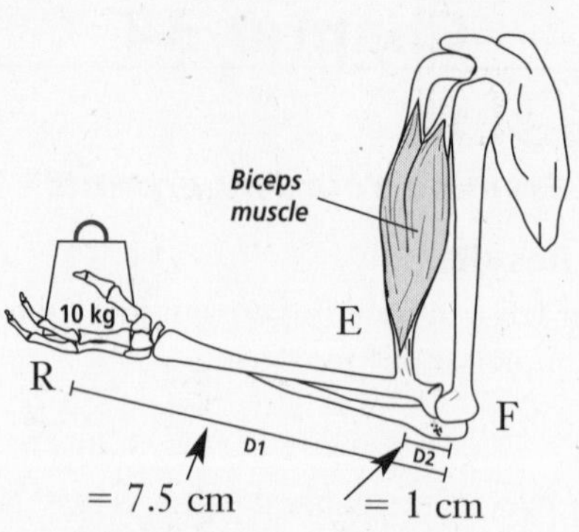

Real World BioApplications

Page 9 • Analyzing Dietary Fiber

Planning the Activity

This activity can be used to reinforce the importance of plants and plant products to humans. Alternatively, it can be used to review and extend the basic principles of digestion and nutrition. Student understanding of the physiological effects of dietary fiber will be facilitated if they have an understanding of intestinal function.

Purpose

Students learn about the importance of dietary fiber in a balanced diet and explore ways of increasing the fiber content of their meals.

Career Applications

Popular interest in nutrition has led to opportunities for dietitians and nutritionists in food manufacturing, advertising, and marketing. Dietitians working in these fields analyze foods, prepare literature for distribution, or report on issues such as the nutritional content of recipes, dietary fiber, or vitamin supplements.

Consultant dietitians may work under contract with health care facilities or in their own private practice, performing nutrition screening for their clients and offering advice on diet-related concerns such as weight loss or cholesterol reduction. Some dietitians work for wellness programs, sports teams, supermarkets, and other nutrition-related businesses.

Teaching Strategies

- Before students begin the activity, have them discuss the various health claims for fiber that have received much national publicity. You may wish to point out that fiber comes in two forms—water-soluble and water-insoluble. Water-insoluble fiber, such as that found in brown rice, legumes, and wheat bran cereals, provides the roughage that stimulates the muscles of the digestive tract and helps prevent constipation. Water-soluble fiber, such as that found in apples, carrots, and oat bran, appears to offer some cholesterol-lowering benefits.

- Table 1 lists only some of the foods that may be popular with students. Students will need to consult additional reference sources that give the fiber content of particular foods. Before students complete Part A, ask them to estimate what they think their daily fiber intake is. Then have them compare the actual number of grams from their list in question 2 with their estimates.
- When students prepare new, high-fiber menus in Part B, instruct them to replace or add to each of the foods in the old menu. For example, to increase fiber, students could replace the bowl of corn flakes with a bowl of toasted-oat cereal, or they could add a sliced banana to the cereal. Encourage students to be creative with their new menus, but make sure each student prepares a balanced diet.

Answers to Student Worksheet

Part A

1. Beans, such as lentils, pinto beans, and chick peas are the best source of dietary fiber.
2. Student answers will vary according to dietary preference.

Part B

Student menus will vary. Check to see that students replace low-fiber foods with high-fiber foods within the same food group. Also, make sure that menus provide a balanced diet.

Reinforcement and Study Guide

Page 11 • Section 34.1

1. Epidermis
2. Dermis
3. Dermis
4. Epidermis
5. Epidermis
6. Dermis
7. Epidermis
8. Dermis
9. Exposure to sunlight causes an increase in melanin production in epidermal pigment cells, in an attempt to protect cells from the damaging effects of ultraviolet light.
10. When capillaries dilate, blood flow to the skin increases, and excess heat is lost to the environment. When blood vessels constrict, body heat is conserved. Sweat produced by sweat glands in the dermis also helps cool the body by evaporation.
11. (1) serves as protective layer; (2) functions as a sense organ; (3) produces vitamin D

Page 12 • Section 34.2

1. appendicular
2. axial
3. axial
4. appendicular
5. axial
6. appendicular
7. What are tendons?
8. What are bursae?
9. What are ligaments?
10. How do a hinge joint and a ball-and-socket joint differ?
11. cartilage, bone, nose
12. osteoblasts, calcium, salts
13. ends
14. repair, maintenance
15. nerve and blood vessel-filled membrane; compact bone; spongy bone; marrow
16. through osteon systems
17. Red bone marrow produces red blood cells, some white blood cells, and cell fragments involved in clotting.
18. Calcium, phosphorus, and other minerals are stored in bone. Fat is also stored as yellow marrow.
19. false
20. true
21. false
22. true
23. false
24. false

Page 14 • Section 34.3

1. Skeletal
2. Skeletal, Cardiac
3. Smooth
4. Skeletal
5. Cardiac
6. Smooth, Cardiac
7. Smooth

8. the thickness of fibers and how many of them contract at one time
9. lactic acid fermentation
10. lactic acid
11. true

Refuerzo y Guía de estudio

Página 15 • Sección 34.1

1. epidermis
2. dermis
3. dermis
4. epidermis
5. epidermis
6. dermis
7. epidermis
8. dermis
9. La exposición a la luz solar causa un aumento en la producción de melanina en las células epidérmicas, para tratar de proteger las células de los efectos de la dañina luz ultravioleta.
10. Al dilatarse los capilares, el flujo de sangre hacia la piel aumenta y el exceso de calor se libera en el ambiente. Cuando se contraen los capilares, se conserva calor corporal. El sudor producido por las glándulas sudoríparas, localizadas en la dermis, también ayuda al cuerpo a enfriarse debido a la evaporación del sudor.
11. (1) Sirve como una capa de protección.
(2) Funciona como órgano de los sentidos.
(3) Produce vitamina D.

Página 16 • Sección 34.2

1. apendicular
2. axial
3. axial
4. apendicular
5. axial
6. apendicular
7. ¿Qué son los tendones?
8. ¿Qué es la bolsa?
9. ¿Qué son los ligamentos?
10. ¿En qué difieren una articulación de bisagra y una articulación de bola y receptáculo?
11. cartílago; hueso; nariz
12. osteoblastos; sales de calcio
13. extremos
14. reparación; mantenimiento
15. una membrana con nervios y vasos sanguíneos, hueso compacto, hueso esponjoso y médula ósea
16. a través de los sistemas de Havers
17. La médula ósea roja produce glóbulos rojos, algunos glóbulos blancos y fragmentos de célula que participan en la coagulación.
18. El hueso almacena calcio, fósforo y otros minerales. Además, la médula ósea almacena grasas
19. falso
20. verdadero
21. falso
22. verdadero
23. falso
24. falso

Página 18 • Sección 34.3

1. esquelético
2. esquelético; cardíaco
3. liso
4. esquelético
5. cardíaco
6. liso; cardíaco
7. liso
8. del grosor de las fibras y del número de fibras que se contraen a la vez
9. fermentación del ácido láctico
10. ácido láctico
11. verdadero

Concept Mapping

Page 19 • Section 34.2

1. ball-and-socket
2. rotational motion
3. hip, shoulder
4. pivot
5. elbow
6. hinge
7. back-and-forth motion
8. knee, fingers, toes
9. gliding
10. wrist, ankle

Critical Thinking

Page 20 • Section 34.2

1. abduction
2. the ability to grasp and hold things
3. Flexion increases the span of the hand. It allows us to grip large things.

4. Answers may vary. If the thumb were a hinge joint, one could not grasp things except by pinching them between the thumb and the hand. Also, the hand could not be "folded in" to narrow its girth in order to reach into small spaces.

Section Focus Transparency 81
Page 21 • To Cover, Contain, and Protect

Purpose

- To recognize that skin is not a passive container

Teaching Suggestions

- Before projecting the transparency, ask students what function skin has. Lead students to understand the active role that skin plays in maintaining homeostasis in the body. For example, remind students that the evaporation of sweat produced by the sweat glands of the skin helps the body lose excess heat.
- Project the transparency, and draw attention to the polyethylene bag.
- *Answers to questions on the transparency include:*
  1. Answers will vary but might include: The container covers because it seals against outside substances; it contains because the contents cannot leak out; it protects because it does not allow microorganisms to enter.
  2. Answers will vary, but most students will likely indicate that the polyethylene would not be a good substitute for skin. Reasons might include that it is not elastic enough, porous enough, or that it is passive.

Section Focus Transparency 82
Page 22 • Flexible Support

Purpose

- To recognize that different types of joints have different ranges of motion

Teaching Suggestions

- Project the transparency, and have students explain why the structure of each object is appropriate for its function.
- Have students move different parts of their bodies and describe the range of motion for the joints involved.
- *Answers to questions on the transparency include:*
  1. Shower head—can swivel up and down and in a rotational movement; strap hinge—allows door to move back and forth around the hinge pin; lamp—neck can bend into many different curves, shade can rotate around end of neck
  2. Shower head—hip or shoulder; strap hinge—elbow or knee; lamp—spine, neck

Section Focus Transparency 83
Page 23 • Built to Move

Purpose

- To relate the action of skeletal muscles to a mechanical model

Teaching Suggestions

- Project the transparency, and have students explain how the springs can be used to move the wood.
- Ask students how removing one of the springs would affect the movement of the board. (The board could only be moved in one direction.) Point out to students that in order for the piece of wood to move back and forth, two springs are necessary.
- *Answers to questions on the transparency include:*
  1. The joint will become straighter. The joint will become more bent.
  2. The elbow is similar. The muscles act like springs.

Basic Concepts Transparency 61
Page 25 • Skin Deep

Purpose

- To examine a cross section of human skin

Teaching Suggestions

- Ask students if they can explain why the skin is an organ. (It consists of tissues joined together to perform specific activities.) Then point out that the skin is the largest organ of the body.
- Explain that the skin acts as a barrier against injury and invasion by pathogenic organisms such as bacteria and viruses. The skin also contributes to homeostasis and maintenance of proper levels of fluid in the body.
- Discuss the function of each of the structures shown in the diagram of the skin.

Extension: Guest Speaker

- Invite a dermatologist to speak about the effects of ultraviolet radiation on skin function.

Answers to Student Worksheet

1. Skin oils keep hair from drying out, keep the skin soft and pliable, and inhibit the growth of some bacteria.

2. The primary function of sweat glands is to maintain normal body temperature during exercise or when ambient temperatures are high.
3. Sensory nerves are sensitive to external stimuli such as pressure, pain, heat, and cold. Motor nerves stimulate muscles such as those connected to hair follicles.
4. Differences in the pigmentation of the skin result from greater or lesser amounts of the pigment melanin in cells found in the epidermis. Exposure to sunlight increases melanin production.
5. The hair follicle is in the dermis, and the hair shaft emerges through an opening in the epidermis. Its function is to protect the skin from injury and sun and to provide an insulating layer of air on the surface of the skin when temperatures are cool.
6. They provide protection for the living cell layers beneath them.
7. The surfaces of these areas contain ridges and grooves that provide traction by increasing friction.
8. Fat provides insulation and protects against heat loss. It also cushions the body against mechanical injury and stores energy.

Basic Concepts Transparency 62

Page 27 • Skeleton and Joints

Purpose

- To show the structure and function of joints

Teaching Suggestions

- Project the transparency. Compare and contrast various types of joints.
- Discuss the functions of cartilage and tendons. Introduce the term tendonitis and ask students to speculate on its meaning. Tendonitis is a painful inflammation of a tendon that is often treated with anti-inflammatory medications such as cortisone.
- Discuss why an injury to the knee is more likely to occur than one to the hip when a football player is tackled from the side. (Unlike the hip joint, the knee joint does not allow movement to the side. Since the knee does not "give" in a sideways direction, tendons and ligaments tend to tear if the knee is struck forcefully from the side.)

Extension: Models

- Organize students into cooperative work groups. Have groups choose different joints for making models. The models should only allow movement typical of that joint.

Answers to Student Worksheet

1. Pivot joints, which can be found in the elbow and between neck vertebrae, allow bones to twist around each other.
2. Ligaments are tough bands of connective tissue that connect bone to bone, whereas tendons are thick bands of connective tissue that attach muscle to bone.
3. All the joints highlighted in separate boxes allow movement. The type of joint not shown is the fixed joint, such as the joints of the skull, which are not movable.
4. A gliding joint allows bones to slide past each other.
5. These joints experience considerable stress because they are constantly being used. The bursa, a fluid-filled sac, acts as a cushion to absorb shock and keep bones from rubbing together.
6. The knee, fingers, and toes are all hinge joints.
7. A ball-and-socket joint allows rotational movements.
8. Joint injuries, such as sprains, tend to occur most often at places such as the wrist, ankle, and knee because each of these joints involves a large range of motion and therefore a greater potential for injury to the bursa, ligaments, and tendons.

Basic Concepts Transparency 63

Page 29 • Structure of Bone

Purpose

- To review the structures and functions of bones

Teaching Suggestions

- Use the transparency as a departure point for the discussion of bone formation.
- Point out that the structures shown in the transparency are typical of long bones such as those of the appendicular skeleton.
- Discuss the fact that bones consist of living tissue and nonliving substances. The living tissue includes blood vessels, nerves, bone cells, blood cells, cartilage, and fat cells. The nonliving materials include water and minerals, mainly calcium and phosphates.

Extension: Research Report

- Have students investigate the nature, causes, consequences, treatment, and prevention of osteoporosis. Students should illustrate their reports.

Answers to Student Worksheet

1. The osteon systems are located within compact bone. Nerves running through the canals carry impulses to and from bone cells. Blood vessels within the canals carry oxygen and nutrients to bone cells.
2. The membrane is filled with nerve cells and blood vessels needed for the proper functioning of bone cells.
3. Bone marrow fills the cavities of the ribs, sternum, vertebrae, skull, and the long bones of the arms and legs.
4. The cartilage skeleton of the embryo is covered by a membrane. Blood vessels penetrate the membrane and stimulate cartilage cells to enlarge and become osteoblasts. These potential bone cells then secrete a substance in which calcium salts and other minerals are deposited, thereby hardening the cartilage and changing it to bone.
5. Bones grow in diameter on their outer surface. Growth in length occurs in the cartilage plates at the ends of bones.
6. Red bone marrow produces red blood cells, some white blood cells, and certain cell fragments that are involved in blood clotting.
7. Yellow bone marrow stores fats.
8. spongy bone
9. Bone cells, or osteoblasts, secrete such a substance.
10. Many bones produce red and white blood cells as well as cell fragments. These materials are produced in the marrow. Bones also store minerals such as calcium and phosphates.

Extension: Challenge

- Have students find out how the dart poison curare paralyzes muscles and how curare has been used medicinally. Encourage students to find information on the natural, social, and scientific history of curare.

Answers to Student Worksheet

1. Each muscle fiber is composed of smaller fibers, called myofibrils, which are composed in turn of even smaller filaments that can be thick or thin. The arrangement of the thick filaments, made of the protein myosin, and the thin filaments, made of the protein actin, are what give skeletal muscle its striated appearance.
2. A sarcomere is a section of a myofibril. It is the functional unit of muscle.
3. Calcium is released inside the muscle fibers.
4. Calcium causes the myosin and actin filaments to form attachments. The actin filaments are pulled inward toward the center of each sarcomere. This causes the sarcomere to shorten, or contract.
5. Molecules of ATP are necessary for muscle contraction.
6. the sliding filament theory
7. Smooth muscle and cardiac muscle are called involuntary muscles because their contraction is not under conscious control. The contraction of skeletal muscle, on the other hand, is under conscious control. Therefore, skeletal muscle is called voluntary muscle.
8. Both cardiac muscle and skeletal muscle are striated in appearance.

Basic Concepts Transparency 64

Page 31 • Muscle Contraction

Purpose

- To show how the structure of muscles enables them to contract

Teaching Suggestions

- Make sure that students understand that the schematic drawing in the lower part of the transparency shows what is happening inside two sarcomeres.
- Point out that, according to the sliding filament theory, only the actin filaments move; the myosin filaments do not move.
- Explain that, with the exception of reflex movements, skeletal muscles are consciously controlled by the brain.

Reteaching Skills Transparency 49

Page 33 • The Muscular System

Purpose

- To review the structures and functions of the muscular system
- Skill: Interpreting scientific illustrations

Teaching Suggestions

- Project the transparency and discuss the functions of skeletal muscles in general.
- Elaborate on the answer to Question 1. Many students might respond to this question with the answer: "They all move bones." Point out that some skeletal muscles do not move bones, but all are connected to bones. Skeletal muscles that do not move bones include those that move the eyes, eyelids, tongue, lips, cheeks, and scalp.

- Emphasize that muscles move in response to nerve impulses coming from the brain or spinal cord.

Extension: Research Report

- Have students research and report on a common sports injury and the techniques used to rehabilitate the muscles. For example, to treat a twisted ankle, one must strengthen the tibialis anterior and the gastrocnemius.

Answers to Student Worksheet

1. They all connect to bones and are therefore skeletal muscles.
2. The arm is drawn upward at the shoulder.
3. Your brain must order your quadriceps femoris to contract.
4. You must contract the tibialis anterior muscle.
5. The biceps would contract.
6. rectus abdominis
7. The gastrocnemius contracts.
8. the external oblique muscles
9. pectoralis major
10. frontalis

Chapter Assessment

Page 35 • Reviewing Vocabulary

1. h
2. e
3. d
4. b
5. g
6. c
7. a
8. i
9. f
10. Compact bone is the outer layer of hard bone. The inner spongy bone is less dense and has holes like a sponge.
11. The axial skeleton includes the skull, the vertebral column, ribs, and sternum. The appendicular skeleton includes the bones of the arms, legs, shoulders, and pelvic girdle.
12. Voluntary muscle is under conscious control, whereas involuntary muscle is not under conscious control.
13. The epidermis is the outer, thinner portion of the skin. The dermis is the inner, thicker portion of the skin.

Page 36 • Understanding Main Ideas (Part A)

1. skin cells
2. Red marrow
3. calcium
4. smooth
5. ends, outer
6. thickness, contract
7. lactic acid fermentation
8. The skin is an organ because it consists of tissues joined together to perform specific activities. Functions of the skin include regulation of body temperature, protection from physical and chemical damage, and sensing information from the environment.
9. Caused by forcible twisting of a joint, a sprain can result in injury to the bursae, ligaments, or tendons of the joint.

Page 37 • Understanding Main Ideas (Part B)

1. b
2. c
3. d
4. c
5. The sliding filament theory states that actin filaments within a sarcomere slide toward one another during contraction. Myosin filaments do not move.
6. Excess lactic acid in the bloodstream makes the blood more acidic. This stimulates rapid breathing, which supplies more oxygen to the muscle cells. The oxygen breaks down the lactic acid.
7. When exposed to the ultraviolet rays in sunlight, dermis cells produce vitamin D, a nutrient that aids calcium absorption. However, exposure to ultraviolet light can damage skin cells and accelerate the aging process.

Page 38 • Thinking Critically

1. Controllable factors are diet, exercise, smoking, and alcohol intake. Noncontrollable factors are gender, genetics, age, and body frame/weight.
2. Answers will vary but should reflect the reasoning that the increased workload imposed by exercising muscles stimulates bone cell information. Increased bone cell formation results in denser bone tissue.
3. The composition of a child's bones is different from an adult's bones. A child's bones have more cartilage and fewer minerals than an adult's. This

makes a child's bones less brittle and less likely to break in two.

4. By pressing a blood vessel against a bone, the paramedic can control bleeding temporarily.

Page 39 • Applying Scientific Methods

1. The graph shows that skeletal muscle contracts in less than five milliseconds after electrical impulse. Smooth muscle takes the longest to contract, about 200 milliseconds after electrical impulse. Answers are based on the amount of time between electrical impulse and mechanical activity.
2. The impulse duration for each muscle type is: about 3 ms for skeletal muscle; about 250 ms for cardiac muscle; about 50 ms for smooth muscle. The long duration in cardiac muscle insures that all muscle cells contract. In this way, the chambers of the heart reach maximum contraction as a result of each electrical impulse.
3. Smooth muscle contracts and relaxes more slowly than skeletal muscle. Because the fibers of smooth muscle are more interconnected than those of skeletal muscle, contraction is more diverse and widespread in smooth muscle.
4. Because electrical junctions are found between each cell juncture, stimulation can be spread quickly to other muscle cells in the heart. This would help maximize the number of cells that contract.
5. The soleus has the longer duration of contraction; it is about three times (100 milliseconds) longer than the gastrocnemius contraction (34 milliseconds).
6. The gastrocnemius muscle is responsible for fast movements, like running and jumping. So its contraction is fast. The soleus muscle is responsible for maintaining body position. Its contraction does not need to be as fast.

Student Recording Sheet

Page 41

Answers can be found on page 914 in the Teacher Wraparound Edition.

Chapter 35

MiniLab 35.1

Page 45 • Evaluate a Bowl of Soup

Analysis

1. Yes, sodium.
2. A serving of soup contains about 39% of its Calories from saturated fat. (6 g/serving × 9 Cal/g = 54 Calories of saturated fat per serving, 54 ÷ 140 = 39%)
3. Basically yes, although the sodium content is high.

MiniLab 35.2

Page 46 • Compare Thyroid and Parathyroid Tissue

Expected Results

Students will be able to differentiate between thyroid and parathyroid tissue.

Analysis

1. Students may notice that thyroid tissue contains many rather large spaces surrounded by a thin band of cellular tissue, while parathyroid tissue is composed of compact cells with no large spaces or follicles.
2. a. thyroid

   b. stored hormones (thyroxine or calcitonin)

   c. This tissue makes the hormones.
3. Both glands are located in the same general area of the neck. The parathyroids lie on the thyroid gland itself.

Investigate BioLab

Page 47 • The Action of the Enzyme Amylase on Breakfast Cereals

Data and Observations

Most cereals have both starch and simple sugar to start. Students should find the starch has rapidly disappeared in less than a minute or a few minutes at the most. Time will somewhat depend on how fine they grind their cereal and the amount of starch in the product to start.

Analyze and Conclude

1. Answers will vary but most cereals will contain starch. Amylase breaks down starch into simple sugars.
2. The cereal with the least starch will take the least amount of time.
3. No, 1 gram of carbohydrate, which includes both starch and simple sugars, yields 4 Calories of heat energy when broken down by the body.

Real World BioApplications

Page 49 • The Abdominal Thrust

Planning the Activity

Use this activity after students have studied the anatomy and function of the digestive system in Chapter 35 of the text, particularly the role of the pharynx and epiglottis in controlling the passage of food to the esophagus and stomach. This activity can also be used with Chapter 37 to extend the discussion of respiratory injuries or disorders.

Purpose

The structures and functions of the digestive system are reinforced as students examine the anatomy involved in the abdominal thrust. Students also learn the steps to this important first-aid skill.

Career Applications

The process of swift evaluation and decision-making described in this activity is essential to the occupation of emergency medical technician (EMT). EMTs give immediate care and transport the sick or injured to medical facilities. They determine the nature and extent of the patient's injuries or illness while also trying to determine whether the patient has epilepsy, diabetes, or other preexisting medical conditions. Following strict guidelines, certified EMT's employ procedures to give appropriate emergency care.

All EMTs, including those with basic skills (EMT-Basic) may do the following: open airways, restore breathing, control bleeding, treat for shock, administer oxygen, immobilize fractures, bandage wounds, assist in childbirth, manage emotionally disturbed patients, treat and assist heart attack victims, give initial care to poison and burn victims, and use automated external defibrillators to assist in the care of patients experiencing cardiac arrest. EMT-Intermediates and EMT-Paramedics have more advanced training that allows them to provide more extensive services.

Teaching Strategies

- After students have read the introduction, lead a general discussion about the causes and effects of choking. Point out that if the object blocking the air passage is not removed in 4 to 6 minutes, the victim will die. Ask students to discuss what they may know about the abdominal thrust. Then provide students with a brief introduction to the origins of this first-aid technique.

- Review the steps of the abdominal thrust in Part A with students. Point out that if a victim has collapsed or is too heavy to support, the abdominal thrust can be performed once the person is placed with his or her back on the ground. You may wish to ask a student volunteer to demonstrate the individual steps.
- Caution students that the abdominal thrust should only be performed as emergency first-aid for a choking victim. If not performed properly, it may cause injury. In particular, one should be careful not to apply pressure to the victim's ribs. Such pressure may break the ribs, especially if the victim is a child.

Answers to Student Worksheet

Part A

1. Students should realize that death or brain damage may occur if someone is deprived of oxygen for an extended period of time.
2. Blood becomes darker when there is a lack of oxygen, thus a person's skin may look bluish in color when he or she is choking.
3. If the abdominal thrust isn't done properly, it may not work. It may also result in damage to a victim's ribs or internal organs if the arms and fist are not correctly positioned.

Part B

1. Students should recognize that this phrase means that food or drink has entered the upper part of the trachea instead of the esophagus, or that food has lodged at the junction of the trachea and esophagus.
2. After studying the diagram, students should recognize that by pushing up on the diaphragm, you increase pressure inside the lungs, thus forcing out air. It should be understood that the forceful rush of air is what dislodges the object.

Reinforcement and Study Guide

Page 51 • Section 35.1

1. ingesting, digesting, absorbing, eliminating
2. increase
3. chemical, mechanical
4. amylase, salivary, starch
5. incisors, molars
6. respiratory tract
7. involuntary muscle contractions
8. pepsin and other digestive juices
9. true
10. slowly, a little bit at a time
11. Pancreatic enzymes break down, or continue the breakdown of, carbohydrates, proteins, and fats.
12. Bile is produced in the liver and is stored in the gallbladder before being released into the duodenum.
13. a. These molecules enter the circulatory system via blood vessels inside the villi.
    b. Indigestible materials pass into the large intestine.
14. Large Intestine
15. Small Intestine
16. Large Intestine
17. Small Intestine
18. Small Intestine, Large Intestine
19. Large Intestine
20. Small Intestine

Page 53 • Section 35.2

1. Fats
2. Carbohydrates
3. Proteins
4. Carbohydrates, Fats, Proteins
5. Proteins
6. Carbohydrates
7. Fats
8. Minerals
9. vitamins
10. fat-soluble, water-soluble
11. Calories, 1000
12. metabolize, eat

Page 54 • Section 35.3

1. nervous, endocrine	8. f
2. pituitary	9. a
3. hormone	10. e
4. demand	11. d
5. negative feedback	12. b
6. water	13. c
7. insulin	

Refuerzo y Guía de estudio

Página 55 • Sección 35.1

1. ingestión; digestión; absorción; eliminación
2. aumentas
3. digestión; mecánica
4. amilasa; salivales; almidón

5. incisivos; molares
6. tracto respiratorio
7. contracciones rítmicas de músculos involuntarios
8. pepsina y otros jugos digestivos
9. verdadero
10. lentamente; poco a poco
11. Las enzimas pancreáticas inician o continúan el desdoblamiento de carbohidratos, proteínas y grasas.
12. La bilis se produce en el hígado y se almacena en la vesícula biliar, antes de ser liberada en el duodeno.
13. a. Las moléculas entran al sistema circulatorio a través de los vasos sanguíneos de las vellosidades intestinales.

    b. Los materiales no digeridos pasan al intestino grueso.
14. intestino grueso
15. intestino delgado
16. intestino grueso
17. intestino delgado
18. intestino delgado; intestino grueso
19. intestino grueso
20. intestino delgado

Página 57 • Sección 35.2

1. grasas
2. carbohidratos
3. proteínas
4. carbohidratos; grasas; proteínas
5. proteínas
6. carbohidratos
7. grasas
8. minerales
9. vitaminas
10. liposolubles; hidrosolubles
11. Calorías; 1000
12. metabolizando; ingieren

Página 58 • Sección 35.3

1. nervioso; endocrino
2. pituitaria
3. hormona
4. demanda
5. retroalimentación negativa
6. agua
7. insulina
8. f
9. a
10. e
11. d
12. b
13. c

Concept Mapping

Page 59 • Carbohydrates, Fats, and Proteins in Nutrition

1. carbohydrates
2. simple sugars
3. body functions
4. indigestible cellulose
5. fatty acids
6. the liver
7. glycerol
8. fat
9. glycogen
10. proteins
11. amino acids
12. body cells
13. muscles
14. cell structure
15. hormones
16. chemicals for blood-clotting
17. enzymes
18. antibodies

Problem Solving

Page 60 • Interpreting a Blood Analysis Printout

1. The pancreas produces the hormones insulin and glucagon. Insulin signals the liver cells and muscle cells to take in glucose, lowering the blood glucose level. Glucagon signals these cells to release glucose, raising the blood glucose level. Together, these two hormones work to keep blood glucose levels fairly constant.
2. The blood glucose levels rose steadily and then stayed steady over four days following the operation. Without the pancreas, no insulin was present in the blood to signal the uptake of glucose into body cells.
3. The amount of fatty acids rose sharply right away. When glucose does not enter the cells, proteins and fats within the cells are broken down as sources of energy. Fatty acids are a by-product of fats being broken down.
4. After day 3, the amount of acid builds up, and the patient is at risk.

5. By giving the patient insulin, you would be able to lower blood glucose levels, and the effects of the operation could be overcome.

Section Focus Transparency 84

Page 61 • Food Processors

Purpose

- To recognize that the parts of the digestive system have specific functions

Teaching Suggestions

- Before projecting the transparency, ask students why they eat. (Most students will recognize that food is necessary to provide energy and building materials for cells that make up the body.) Ask what must happen to the food you eat before it can enter a cell. (It must be broken down.)
- Project the transparency, and have students describe the function of each device.
- Review with students the role of the cell membrane in transporting materials into and out of the cell.
- *Answers to questions on the transparency include:*

1. Knife—teeth and tongue; blender—stomach, small intestine; trash compactor—large intestine and rectum
2. The function is to break food down physically and chemically until it is in the form of molecules small enough to pass through cell membranes.

Section Focus Transparency 85

Page 62 • All the Things You Eat

Purpose

- To generate a list of nutrient substances as students understand them

Teaching Suggestions

- Before projecting the transparency, ask students to identify the six main nutrients. (carbohydrates, fats, proteins, vitamins, minerals, water)
- Ask students what would happen if they ate mostly one type of food, such as cake, candy, cookies, and other sweets. (possible lack of some essential nutrients) Discuss why eating a variety of foods is essential to maintaining good health.
- *Answers to questions on the transparency include:*

1. All foods contain vitamins and minerals, and most contain water. Muffin—carbohydrate, fat, vitamins; butter—fat; grapefruit and orange juice—carbohydrate, minerals, vitamins; bacon—fat, protein; egg—protein, fat, carbohydrate.
2. All except the grapefruit and orange juice contain fat.

Section Focus Transparency 86

Page 63 • Negative Feedback

Purpose

- To recognize and explain everyday examples of negative feedback

Teaching Suggestions

- Before projecting the transparency, ask students to describe how a negative feedback system operates. (The production of one hormone stimulates the production of a second hormone. When the second hormone reaches a certain level, it inhibits the production of the first hormone. This cycle of stimulation and inhibition maintains a steady internal environment.)
- Project the transparency, and have students describe the two situations depicted.
- Compare a negative feedback system with a positive feedback system. In a negative feedback system, such as a thermostat, the variable (temperature) remains constant. In a positive feedback system, such as bacterial growth, the variable (size of the population) continually increases.
- *Answers to questions on the transparency include:*

1. Shivering warms the body. Eating increases blood glucose levels.
2. Shivering—the person feels cold, shivers, warms up, stops shivering; Eating—the person eats, blood glucose levels rise, insulin is released, the liver takes in glucose, blood glucose levels decrease.

Basic Concepts Transparency 65

Page 65 • Regulation of Blood Glucose Concentration

Purpose

- To illustrate how the hormones of the pancreas regulate blood glucose levels

Teaching Suggestions

- Project the transparency and discuss how it illustrates a feedback process. The pancreas responds to blood glucose concentrations by producing one or the other of two hormones that either increase or decrease blood glucose concentration. Have students identify which hormone serves each function.
- Remind students that glucose provides a primary source of energy for body cells.

- Discuss the consequences of hypoglycemia, an abnormally low blood glucose concentration. Depending on the degree and length of hypoglycemia, a person might become lethargic or even go into a life-threatening coma. Relate this to the dangers of insulin shock in insulin-dependent diabetics.

Extension: Research Report

- Have students do library research on the most recent developments in the treatment of diabetes. Students should compare and contrast the use of genetically-engineered human insulin (Humulin) versus the use of animal insulin. Students should also report on transplants of pancreatic tissue or cells and on insulin pumps.

Answers to Student Worksheet

1. the amount and kind of food consumed and the production of the hormones glucagon and insulin
2. The process occurs in the liver.
3. Glucose-regulating hormones are produced in response to blood glucose concentrations.
4. negative feedback control
5. Glucagon is produced by the pancreas. It stimulates the liver to produce glucose from stored glycogen.
6. Insulin is produced by the pancreas. Insulin accelerates the transport of glucose from the blood into cells and the conversion of glucose into glycogen in the liver.
7. Blood glucose concentration rises after a meal. Thus, the doctor would have difficulty determining the significance of blood glucose concentrations if a person had recently eaten a meal.

Reteaching Skills Transparency 50

Page 67 • Function of the Small Intestine

Purpose

- To explore the functioning of the small intestine
- Skill: Interpreting scientific illustrations

Teaching Suggestions

- Have students outline the process of digestion, from early processing in the mouth, on through the stomach, to the intestines, and finally to either distribution to body tissues or elimination through excretion.
- Present the transparency. Discuss the structure of villi of the small intestine.

Extension: Cooperative Learning

- Divide the class into groups. Each group should investigate a digestive disorder such as ulcers, dysentery, or cholera. Each group should report on their findings, including a description of the disease and discussion of causes and treatments. They also should prepare posters or other displays to illustrate their findings.

Answers to Student Worksheet

1. In the mouth, food is cut, shredded, crushed, and ground down. Also, amylase breaks down starches into smaller molecules.
2. The esophagus moves food to the stomach. It has no chemical function.
3. In the stomach, food is mixed and churned. Also, pepsin breaks down proteins; hydrochloric acid provides the necessary environment for pepsin to act.
4. In the duodenum of the small intestine, food continues to break down through muscle contractions. Also, chemicals from other organs are mixed in with the food.
5. The pancreas has no mechanical function. However, it produces enzymes that break down carbohydrates, proteins, and fats, and it produces alkaline juices, which help neutralize stomach juices and food.
6. The liver produces bile, which breaks fats into small droplets and neutralizes acids.
7. The gallbladder is a storage area for bile.
8. The large intestine absorbs water and is the home of bacteria that synthesize some B vitamins and vitamin K.
9. A villus is a thin, small, fingerlike projection of the wall of the small intestine. Running through each villus is a network of blood vessels and a lymph duct.
10. Amino acids, fat molecules, and monosaccharides move from the small intestine into the villus; from there, they diffuse into the bloodstream.

Reteaching Skills Transparency 51

Page 69 • Information on a Food Label

Purpose

- To study the nutritional values of similar products
- Skill: Using numbers

Teaching Suggestions

- Bring in a variety of products (bread, cereal, salad dressing, microwave popcorn, and other familiar products) so students can examine the nutritional information on the food labels. Also bring in a set of standard-size serving dishes, a set of measuring spoons, and 1- and 2-cup measures. The goal is to enable students to see how much food is included in a serving of various products.

- Present the transparency. Explain that the labels are from actual, well-known canned soups. Both cans feature the same variety of soup. As a result, students are comparing "apples to apples," not "apples to oranges."
- Discuss the types of information included on the labels and in the list of Daily Values. Note the variables—especially serving size—that strongly affect the amounts of nutrients ingested. For example, most people consider a bag of microwave popcorn a single serving. However, the label indicates that a single serving is only half a bag. If a person eats the whole bag, he or she must double the totals listed on the nutritional label.

Extension: Challenge

- Have students investigate the FDA definitions of common labeling terms such as "fat free" and "low-fat." Then have them devise ways to inform shoppers about the meanings of the terms and the pitfalls that can befall an unwary shopper.

Answers to Student Worksheet

1. Answers will vary. The liquid that people use to dilute the soup will vary. They may use water, milk, or other liquid. Also, the amount of liquid used may vary from one person to another. When doing nutritional analysis, there is no way to predict the type of liquid or the amount the user will add. So the manufacturer eliminates these variables by analyzing only the condensed soup.
2.

	A	B
Total Fat	2 g	1.5 g
Sat. Fat	1 g	0.5 g
Cholesterol	15 mg	0 mg
Sodium	980 mg	460 mg
Total Carb.	9 g	18 g
Fiber	1 g	1 g
Sugars	2 g	11 g
Protein	3 g	1 g
Calories	70	90
Fat Calories	20	15

3. Soup A may be better for a person with diabetes.
4. Soup B may be better for a person with high blood pressure.
5. Soup B may be better for a person with heart disease.
6. Soup A may be better for someone who is trying to reduce his or her Caloric intake. Soup B may be better for someone who is trying to increase his or her Caloric intake.
7. Accept reasonable answers.

Chapter Assessment

Page 71 • Reviewing Vocabulary

1. d
2. g
3. m
4. a
5. e
6. b
7. l
8. c
9. k
10. f
11. n
12. i
13. h
14. j

Page 72 • Understanding Main Ideas (Part A)

1. c
2. d
3. a
4. b
5. b
6. b
7. b
8. a
9. b
10. d
11. d

Page 73 • Understanding Main Ideas (Part B)

1. The majority of endocrine glands operate under a negative feedback system. A gland makes and secretes a specific hormone. The hormone travels to its target tissue and an appropriate response occurs. Then information about the hormone's level or its effect on the body is fed back to regulate the gland's production of that hormone.
2. Glucagon increases blood glucose levels by binding to muscle and liver cells and signaling them to release glucose. Insulin signals liver and muscle cells to take in glucose, lowering blood glucose levels.
3. Steroid hormones diffuse through the target cell's plasma membrane and bind to receptor sites inside the cell. The hormone-receptor complex then travels to the nucleus and activates the synthesis of specific mRNA molecules. These mRNA molecules then activate the synthesis of certain proteins.

4. Amino acid hormones bind to receptors embedded in the target tissue's plasma membrane. From outside the target cell, amino acid hormones activate enzyme pathways within the cell.
5. The hypothalamus sends signals to the pituitary gland. The pituitary gland then releases hormones or stimulates other glands to release hormones.
6. The pituitary gland controls most of the other endocrine glands, including the thyroid gland, the adrenal glands, and glands that control reproduction.

Page 74 • Thinking Critically

1. Without insulin to signal the liver and muscle cells to take in glucose, blood glucose levels would become very high. Thus, a doctor may test the blood glucose level of a patient's blood.
2. The gallstones would effectively prevent the bile from reaching the duodenum. Bile is needed to break down the fats in preparation for digestion in the small intestine. Without bile, the patient would have great difficulty digesting fats.
3. The gallbladder serves as a storage area for bile. Even if it is removed, the liver can continue to produce and deliver bile to the small intestine. It just cannot store the bile.
4. No; because vitamin C is water-soluble, excess amounts of it are excreted and are not stored in the body. Therefore, vitamin C must be included regularly in the diet.
5. Water plays an important role in regulating body temperature. Without enough water, the body might suffer large temperature shifts. Oxygen and nutrients would not be able to enter cells as easily without water as a solvent. Water is also necessary for the process of digestion.

Page 75 • Applying Scientific Methods

1. a. 65
   b. 34
   c. 37
   d. 22
   e. 46
   f. 31
   g. 77
   h. 33
   i. 6
   j. 9
   k. 88
   l. 44
   m. 36
   n. 13
   o. 74
2. Sour cream, at 88 percent of the total Calories, has the highest percentage.
3. Yellowfin tuna has the lowest, at 6 percent.
4. 630 fat Calories
5. 837 fat Calories
6. Hamburger 21 g; cheese 33 g; whole milk 3 g = 57 g of fat consumed; female students would have 13 g left, and male students would have 36 g left.
7. chicken breast with and without skin, drumstick with and without skin

Student Recording Sheet
Page 77

Answers can be found on page 940 in the Teacher Wraparound Edition.

Chapter 36

MiniLab 36.1

Page 81 • Distractions and Reaction Time

Analysis

1. As students learn to anticipate the drop, their reaction time should improve.
2. The distraction probably increased their reaction time.
3. Answers may include being tired, sick, hungry, or otherwise preoccupied.

MiniLab 36.2

Page 82 • Interpret a Drug Label

Analysis

1. Student tables should show the following information: children under 12 years, people with high blood pressure, heart disease, diabetes, thyroid disease, asthma, or emphysema should avoid this drug; drowsiness is a possible side effect; should not be taken with antihypertensive or antidepressant drugs; will relieve nasal congestion associated with the common cold, hay fever, or sinustis; the correct dosage is one tablet every 12 hours.
2. The recommended dosage is the one that has been tested and proven to be safe. Over-the-counter medicines are potentially harmful if not used as directed.

Design Your Own BioLab

Page 83 • What drugs affect the heart rate of Daphnia?

Data and Observations: Sample Data

Drug	Heart rate/min
No drug	240
Coffee	270
Cola	270
Tea	260
Ethyl alcohol	215
Tobacco	300
Cough medicine	Heart rate varies with brand

Analyze and Conclude

1. Stimulants are coffee, tea, cola, and tobacco. Cough medicine may also be listed. Depressants are ethyl alcohol and cough medicine if it contains dextromethorphan hydrobromide.
2. Some students' hypotheses will be confirmed by their data; others' will be rejected.
3. Stimulants speed up the animal's heart rate. Depressants slow the heart rate.
4. Answers will vary. Differences may be due to how much water was on the slide when they added the drug-containing substance. Different *Daphnia* may be more or less sensitive to the drug.

Real World BioApplications

Page 85 • Looking Near and Far

Planning the Activity

Use this activity to extend student understanding of the nervous system and the eye in Chapter 36.

Purpose

Students examine the properties of concave and convex lenses and learn how lenses are used to correct nearsightedness and farsightedness.

Career Applications

Dispensing opticians fit corrective lenses (both eyeglasses and contact lenses) following prescriptions written by ophthalmologists or optometrists. Dispensing opticians recommend eyeglass frames, lenses, and lens coatings after considering the prescription and the customer's occupation, habits, and facial features. Dispensing opticians measure clients' eyes, including the distance between the centers of the pupils and the distance between the eye surface and the lens.

Some dispensing opticians specialize in fitting contact lenses, artificial eyes, or cosmetic shells to cover blemished eyes. To fit contact lenses, dispensing opticians measure eye shape and size, select the type of contact lens material, and prepare work orders specifying the prescription and lens size. Fitting contact lenses requires considerable skill, care, and patience. Dispensing opticians observe customers' eyes, corneas, lids, and contact lenses with special instruments and microscopes.

Materials Tips

Materials concave and convex lenses, comb, flashlight (see below) or penlight

The activity in Part B works well for lenses that are similar in diameter to the flashlight lens. If you are using smaller lenses and a flashlight, construct a cardboard shield with a small hole in it to place over the flashlight lens. This should produce a concentrated beam of light that can be directed through the lens. If multiple lenses and flashlights or penlights are not available, Part B may be performed as a teacher demonstration.

Safety Tips

Instruct students to use care when handling glass lenses. Lenses should be discarded if badly cracked or chipped.

Teaching Strategies

- Prior to the activity, you may wish to review with students the anatomy of the eye as well as how the eye forms an image.
- After students read the opening paragraph, begin a discussion about nearsightedness and farsightedness. You might ask students with either of these common eye disorders to interject anecdotal information about their eye problems. Have students compare eyeglasses designed to correct nearsightedness and farsightedness. Have students examine close and distant objects with each type of lens.
- You may wish to review and discuss the illustrations in Part A with students in order to assess their understanding of myopia and hyperopia.
- Have students work in pairs for Part B.
- You may wish to mention that another way to correct nearsightedness is through surgery known as radial keratotomy. Eye surgeons often use lasers to reshape the cornea.

Answers to Student Worksheet

1. Concave and convex lenses are called corrective lenses because they can correct for the shape of the eyeball, thus correcting vision.
2. After reading about eye disorders and performing experiments with different types of lenses, students should realize that nearsightedness can be corrected with a concave lens, whereas farsightedness can be corrected with a convex lens.
3. Student drawings should demonstrate knowledge of the topic. Concave lenses are used for nearsightedness because they make the light rays spread out before they reach the lens of the eye, thus allowing the focal point to fall on the retina and not in front of it. Convex lenses are used for farsightedness because they bring light rays together, allowing them to come to a focal point on the retina and not behind it.

Real World BioApplications

Page 87 • Relief from a Patch

Planning the Activity

Use this activity after students have learned about addiction and the dangers of smoking in Chapter 36 of the text.

Purpose

Students learn about the purpose and function of nicotine skin patches and evaluate a recent study on the effectiveness of this method to help quit smoking.

Career Applications

The experimental procedures and data evaluation presented in this activity mirror the procedures and evaluation processes practiced in applied research and product development. Biological and medical scientists who work in applied research or product development use knowledge provided by basic research to develop new drugs and medical treatments. These scientists generally rely on scientific technicians to set up, operate, and maintain laboratory instruments, monitor experiments, make observations, calculate and record results, and develop conclusions.

In addition to performing routine tasks, many technicians also develop and adapt laboratory procedures to achieve the best results, interpret data, and devise solutions to problems, under the direction of scientists. Science technicians make extensive use of computers, computer-interfaced equipment, robotics, and high-technology industrial applications such as biological engineering.

Teaching Strategies

- After students read the opening paragraph, ask them why they think people smoke. Discuss all responses, then discuss the addictive properties of the chemical nicotine. Elicit that nicotine is a stimulant. Many students will be aware of friends or family members who have tried to quit smoking. Have volunteers tell about some of these methods, then relate the addictive properties of nicotine and nicotine withdrawal symptoms to the difficulties of quitting smoking.
- Transdermal delivery of drugs through skin patches is related to the physical properties of the patch as well as to the anatomy and properties of the skin. You may wish to review the structure of the skin with students before they complete this activity. If possible, obtain some patches to show students. Remind students that, in addition to nicotine, other drugs administered transdermally include scopolamine for motion sickness and nitroglycerine for heart disease.

- You may wish to have a physician, nurse, or other health professional discuss with students nicotine patches and other methods to help people quit smoking.

Answers to Student Worksheet

Part A

1. Answers may vary. Nicotine patches can make it easier for a person to quit smoking by relieving the associated withdrawal symptoms. The method is convenient and easy to use.
2. Nicotine is an addictive substance. Patches are applied in successively smaller doses in order to withdraw ex-smokers gradually from nicotine dependence.

Part B

1. Approximately 30 percent of the patients receiving 21-mg patches, 20 percent of the 14-mg patch group, and 15 percent of the placebo group remained off cigarettes after 6 months.
2. The placebo group was the control; it helped researchers determine if the nicotine patch made a significant difference in people's behavior and symptoms.
3. Data indicate that nicotine patches are effective for reducing cigarette-withdrawal symptoms.
4. Most students will recognize that nicotine patches seem to be effective aids to help people quit smoking. Students should understand that if patches are effective in nearly 1 out of 3 smokers, then they are a worthwhile product. Students may point out that the success rate of the placebo group was only half that of the 21-mg patch group.

Reinforcement and Study Guide

Page 89 • Section 36.1

1. sensory neurons
2. carry impulses toward neuron cell bodies
3. carry impulses away from the brain and spinal cord
4. interneurons
5. axons
6. 4
7. 6
8. 2
9. 1
10. 5
11. 7
12. 3
13. cerebrum
14. cerebellum
15. brain stem
16. brain stem
17. cerebrum
18. cerebellum
19. brain stem
20. cerebrum
21. cerebellum
22. Parasympathetic
23. Sympathetic
24. Sympathetic
25. Parasympathetic
26. Sympathetic

Page 91 • Section 36.2

1. true
2. true
3. false
4. true
5. false
6. false
7. true
8. b
9. c
10. c
11. d
12. d

Page 92 • Section 36.3

1. A drug is any chemical that interacts with body functions. A medicine is a drug that can prevent, cure, or relieve a medical problem.
2. a pain reliever that depresses the CNS
3. A stimulant increases the activity of the CNS. A depressant decreases its activity.
4. being psychologically and/or physiologically dependent on a drug
5. With habitual use, the body becomes less responsive to a given amount of a drug.
6. Stimulant
7. Depressant
8. Stimulant
9. Stimulant
10. Depressant
11. Stimulant
12. Depressant
13. Stimulant

Refuerzo y Guía de estudio

Página 93 • Sección 36.1

1. neurona sensorial
2. transmite impulsos desde el cuerpo de la neurona

3. transmite impulsos hacia el cuerpo de la neurona
4. interneurona
5. axones
6. 4
7. 6
8. 2
9. 1
10. 5
11. 7
12. 3
13. cerebro
14. cerebelo
15. bulbo raquídeo
16. bulbo raquídeo
17. cerebro
18. cerebelo
19. bulbo raquídeo
20. cerebro
21. cerebelo
22. parasimpático
23. simpático
24. simpático
25. parasimpático
26. simpático

Página 95 • Sección 36.2

1. verdadero
2. verdadero
3. falso
4. verdadero
5. falso
6. falso
7. verdadero
8. b
9. c
10. c
11. d
12. d

Página 96 • Sección 36.3

1. Las drogas son sustancias químicas que afectan las funciones corporales. Las medicinas son sustancias químicas que al afectar las funciones corporales previenen, curan o alivian un problema médico.
2. un analgésico que deprime el SNC
3. Los estimulantes aumentan la actividad del SNC, mientras que los depresivos la disminuyen.
4. Es la dependencia física o psicológica a una droga.
5. El uso constante de una droga puede ocasionar que el cuerpo responda con menor intensidad o ya no responda a la misma cantidad de dicha droga.
6. estimulante
7. depresivo
8. estimulante
9. estimulante
10. depresivo
11. estimulante
12. depresivo
13. estimulante

Concept Mapping

Page 97 • Section 36.2

1. light pressure
2. eyelids
3. tip of tongue
4. palms of hands
5. fingertips
6. heavy pressure
7. organs
8. palms of hands
9. soles of feet
10. muscle tissue
11. nerve endings
12. lower layers
13. epidermis
14. temperature
15. heat
16. dermis
17. cold
18. skin surface

Critical Thinking

Page 98 • Section 36.1

1. In the patellar reflex, a sensory neuron transmits a message to the spinal cord, where it synapses directly with a motor neuron that sends an impulse back to the muscle that creates the leg jerk. In the withdrawal reflex, a sensory neuron transmits a message to the spinal cord, where it synapses first with an interneuron. The interneuron then transmits the message to a motor neuron that sends it to the muscle, causing the finger to be withdrawn from the flame.
2. The polysynaptic reflex occurs with stimuli that can cause pain and potential damage to body tissues. It is important that the conscious brain receive information about the source of the reflex almost as fast as the reflex occurs. In this way, it can identify the danger. This is not necessary in a monosynaptic reflex, such as the patellar reflex.

Section Focus Transparency 87

Page 99 • Take an Order

Purpose

- To recognize an analogy to a sensory response

Teaching Suggestions

- Project the transparency, and have students describe what is happening. (The girl is ringing a bell. The boy is responding to the bell by reaching for an order form.)

- Point out that the boy is responding to the ringing bell in two different ways—by glancing at the bell and by reaching for the order form.
- *Answers to questions on the transparency include:*
  1. the girl pushing the bell
  2. Accept any reasonable examples. One example is that when a person accidentally pricks a finger, the sensation triggers a response that causes an action—the person pulls the finger away.

Section Focus Transparency 88
Page 100 • Common Senses

Purpose

- To identify the body's senses and their stimuli

Teaching Suggestions

- Before you show the transparency, ask students which senses they are using as they are sitting in class. (Answers will vary, but students are probably seeing, hearing, perhaps feeling paper and pencil as they take notes.)
- Project the transparency, and have students describe the situation shown. (The boy is eating, sitting, looking at a clock, probably smelling something cooking, and feeling the warmth from the stove.)
- *Answers to questions on the transparency include:*
  1. The boy is tasting the celery, smelling the cooking, feeling the warmth from the stove, perhaps hearing the celery crunch, and seeing his surroundings.
  2. The stimuli are the celery, the warmth from the cooking, the aroma from the cooking, and light from the clock.

Section Focus Transparency 89
Page 101 • A Question of Poppies

Purpose

- To conduct a simple risk/benefit analysis on the growth of opium poppies

Teaching Suggestions

- Project the transparency, and have students note the products that come from opium sap.
- Review with students what they learned earlier in the chapter about how pain receptors in the body send signals of pain to the brain. Tell students that the drugs made from opium poppies are called opiates. These drugs are the only ones that are able to relieve severe pain, such as that experienced by many cancer patients.
- *Answers to questions on the transparency include:*
  1. Answers will vary. Students probably have heard of opium, morphine, codeine, and heroin.
  2. Students are likely to conclude that the beneficial products outweigh the dangerous products. Some might cite the problem of enforcing such a ban.

Basic Concepts Transparency 66
Page 103 • Structure of the Brain

Purpose

- To show the anatomy and functions of various parts of the human brain

Teaching Suggestions

- Project the transparency and ask students to identify the functions of the labeled structures. Provide correction or reinforcement for student responses.
- Explain that the cerebrum is divided into two hemispheres, each of which is subdivided into four lobes.
- Point out that each of the cerebrum's four pairs of lobes is involved in different activities. For example, the frontal lobes control such processes as making decisions, the parietal lobes receive information from the senses, the occipital lobes are involved mainly in the process of vision, and the temporal lobes are devoted to hearing and memory.

Extension: Activity

- Assign different groups of students to research and report on different parts of the brain such as the medulla oblongata, the pons, the midbrain, the hippocampus, the amygdala, the hypothalamus, the pituitary gland, the thalamus, the corpus callosum, and the cerebral cortex.

Answers to Student Worksheet

1. The cerebellum controls balance, posture, and coordination.
2. the central nervous system
3. The cerebrum is divided into two hemispheres. It controls intelligence, memory, language, skeletal muscle movements, senses, and all conscious activities.
4. Because of its many folds and grooves, the cerebrum has a large surface area. Because this surface area is large, more neurons can be located in the

cerebral cortex, the outer layer of the cerebrum that controls higher-level thinking processes.

5. The medulla oblongata controls involuntary activities such as breathing and heart rate.
6. The pons and midbrain serve as pathways connecting various parts of the brain with each other.
7. An injury to the cerebellum is likely to produce jerky movements.
8. A myelin sheath gives axons a white appearance. Masses of myelinated axons are called "white matter." Gray matter refers to the color of neurons that are not covered by myelin sheaths.

Basic Concepts Transparency 67

Page 105 • Organization of the Nervous System

Purpose

- To illustrate relationships among the different parts of the human nervous system

Teaching Suggestions

- Project the transparency and lead a discussion of its significance. First differentiate between the major anatomical divisions, that is, the central nervous system and the peripheral nervous system. Then differentiate between the somatic and autonomic systems. Finally, differentiate between the subdivisions of the autonomic system, the sympathetic and parasympathetic systems.
- Point out that certain organs, such as the lungs, are controlled by both the somatic and autonomic systems; people don't have to think about breathing but also can deliberately hold their breath. However, beyond a certain point, no one can hold his or her breath. This point is reached when the autonomic nervous system responds to high levels of carbon dioxide in the blood and stimulates breathing to rid the body of carbon dioxide.

Extension: Laboratory

- Use prepared slides of neurons and brain cross sections. Have students draw and label the parts they can identify.

Answers to Student Worksheet

1. the brain
2. the brain stem
3. the peripheral nervous system
4. a sensory neuron, an interneuron, and a motor neuron
5. The medulla oblongata, which controls involuntary activities such as heart rate, sends impulses to the autonomic nervous system, which then carries them to internal organs.
6. The sympathetic nervous system controls many internal functions during times of stress. The parasympathetic nervous system controls many of the body's internal functions when it is at rest.
7. The stimulus is picked up by receptors in the skin, initiating an impulse in the sensory neurons of the somatic nervous system. The impulse is carried to the CNS. From the brain, an impulse is sent to motor neurons, which transmit an impulse to your muscles. The response may be to raise your umbrella, run for shelter, or some other voluntary action.

Basic Concepts Transparency 68

Page 107 • Structure of the Eye

Purpose

- To review the structures of the eye and how they contribute to vision

Teaching Suggestions

- Use the transparency to have students trace the path of light through the eye.
- Point out that chemicals in rod cells are activated in dim light so that a person can see better in semi-darkness. Emphasize that this process takes time, which accounts for the fact that when we enter a darkened theater on a bright day, five minutes may pass before we can make out shapes.

Extension: Research

- Have students research how corrective lenses restore normal vision in people who are nearsighted or far-sighted. Encourage students to make drawings or models showing what happens to light entering a nearsighted and farsighted eye.

Answers to Student Worksheet

1. The image is upside down and reversed left to right. The brain interprets the image so that we see it correctly.
2. Rods and cones are located in the retina.
3. the lens
4. The optic nerve carries sensory impulses from the retina to the brain.
5. the pupil
6. Rods are adapted to vision in dim light. They help detect shape and movement.

7. Cones are adapted for sharp vision in bright light. They also help detect color.

Basic Concepts Transparency 69
Page 109 • Process of Hearing

Purpose

- To show how sound waves travel through the ear activating various structures that produce hearing

Teaching Suggestions

- Project the transparency and help students follow the path of sound waves from the outer ear to the brain.
- Be sure students understand that each of the diagrams B–D represents a magnification of a section of the previous drawing.
- After emphasizing that hearing is a response to mechanical stimulation, explain that this fact forms the basis for the development of hearing aids. For example, in a condition called otosclerosis, calcium deposits are laid down around the stapes, partly immobilizing it. A hearing aid increases the energy of sound waves, which makes the stapes vibrate with more force than it would otherwise.

Extension: Challenge

- Have students find out the effects of noise pollution on human hearing and behavior.

Answers to Student Worksheet

1. The outer ear captures sound waves and channels them into the middle ear.
2. the eardrum
3. The malleus, the incus, and the stapes are the bones of the middle ear. These bones carry the vibrations of the eardrum to the inner ear.
4. The mechanical stimulation of sound is converted into a nerve impulse in the cochlea, a fluid-filled, snail-shaped structure of the inner ear.
5. When the fluid in the cochlea vibrates, it causes the hair cells in the center of the cochlea to bend, initiating the movement of impulses along the auditory nerve.
6. the cerebrum and the cerebellum
7. The semicircular canals help you to maintain your balance.
8. Even though you have stopped spinning, the fluid in the semicircular canals of your ear would continue to move for a few moments. This movement of fluid causes the movement of hairs in the canals which, in turn, stimulate sensory neurons to carry an impulse to your brain. The "message" of this impulse is that you are still spinning.

Reteaching Skills Transparency 52
Page 111 • Structure of the Ear

Purpose

- To explore how the structure of the ear enables a person to hear
- Skill: Interpreting scientific illustrations

Teaching Suggestions

- Discuss the concept of sound as vibration, eliciting discussions of times when sound has been so intense that people have felt sound pulses on their skin. This can happen in a thunderstorm, a rock concert or other musical performance, or from a loud stereo.
- Present the transparency. Detail the process by which a sound vibration is sensed by the ear and passed on to the brain as a nerve impulse.

Extension: Demonstration

- Set up a series of demonstrations that enable students to see the ways that sound waves can affect fluids, diaphragms, and tissues. (Work with an instructor in physics for suggestions.) For example, to illustrate the effects of sound on a liquid, have students experiment with a bowl of water and one or more tuning forks—students strike the fork, then place the vibrating tines close to the surface of the water in a bowl. The vibrations will make ripples on the surface. Put graphite or other dark powder on a sheet of paper, then hold a vibrating tuning fork below the paper. The vibrations will make patterns in the powder. Another experiment uses two drums. When they are set next to each other and one is struck, the membrane of the other will vibrate.

Answers to Student Worksheet

1. Answers may vary. The outer ear is larger than the opening of the ear canal; as a result, the outer ear can capture incoming sound waves. The foldings of the ear channel the waves in toward the eardrum.
2. The malleus, incus, and stapes are parts of the middle ear.
3. When sound hits the eardrum, it vibrates. These vibrations are passed on to the malleus, incus, and stapes of the middle ear, which in turn pass the vibrations on to the cochlea.
4. The cochlea is the inner ear structure filled with fluid. The fluid picks up the vibrations of the

stapes. As the fluid moves, it moves against hair cells, making them bend.

5. Hair cells are hairlike structures that bend in response to waves of fluid in the cochlea. This bending stimulates the auditory nerve and impulses are sent along the nerve to the brain.
6. The semicircular canals are structures that are filled with fluid and lined with hair cells. They are part of the inner ear.
7. When the position of the head changes, the fluid in the semicircular canals moves the hair cells, which in turn stimulate nerves to carry impulses to the brain.
8. The other types are pain, light and heavy pressure, and heat and cold.

Reteaching Skills Transparency 53

Page 113 • Structure of the Skin

Purpose

- To discuss the sensory receptors in the skin
- Skill: Interpreting scientific illustrations

Teaching Suggestions

- Discuss the three types of stimulation: chemical, light, and mechanical.
- Present the transparency. Discuss the general structures in the skin, then discuss the touch receptors for heavy pressure, light touch, cold, and heat and their general location. Finally, discuss pain receptors, the free nerve endings close to the surface of the skin.

Extension: Demonstration

- Pressure receptors are also important *proprioceptors*, receptors in muscles, tendons, and ligaments that help tell the body the position of its various parts. (Distinguish between proprioception and the sense of balance, which is controlled by senses in the inner ear and reflects the position of the head in relation to the pull of gravity.) Proprioceptors also sense stretching and pain. To demonstrate the ways that proprioceptors function, have students close their eyes, then instruct them to position their arms, hands, head, and legs in various positions. Receptors sense increased pressure and stretching in muscles, ligaments, and tendons, so students should be able to follow the instructions with ease. Primates have a large number of proprioceptors—probably a reflection of the importance of the position of the body in climbing trees.

Answers to Student Worksheet

1. Nerve endings are found in the dermis, some free nerve endings extend into the lower layers of the epidermis.
2. The endings for light touch and pain (free nerve endings) are closest to the surface. Light touch would have to be close to the surface in order to detect very slight pressure. Pain receptors would have to be very close in order to alert the body to danger as quickly as possible.
3. The receptors for heavy pressure, cold, and heat are located deeper in the dermis.
4. Cold receptors are closer to the surface than heat receptors. That seems to signify that cold is more of a threat to the body than heat.
5. The hair follicle is surrounded by receptors—heavy pressure, light touch, and free nerve endings. This seems to imply that hairs will be very sensitive to touch.
6. Sweat glands are surrounded by heat receptors. This implies that heat receptors may have something to do with the production of sweat. Chapter 34 points out that as the body temperature rises, sweat is produced to cause a natural cooling process.
7. The major nerve may be buried more deeply in order to protect it from damage.

Chapter Assessment

Page 115 • Reviewing Vocabulary

1. h	8. f
2. g	9. b
3. d	10. k
4. m	11. j
5. n	12. c
6. l	13. e
7. i	14. a

Page 116 • Understanding Main Ideas (Part A)

1. b	5. b
2. c	6. d
3. c	7. b
4. c	

Page 117 • Understanding Main Ideas (Part B)

1. When a stimulus excites a neuron, sodium channels in the membrane open up, allowing sodium ions to rush inside. The inside of the neuron becomes more positively charged than the outside, a condition that

sets up a wave of changing charges down the length of the axon as the nerve impulse moves along it.

2. As an impulse reaches the end of an axon, the changing charges open calcium channels, allowing calcium to enter the end of the axon. The calcium causes neurotransmitters to be released. They then diffuse across the synaptic space to the dendrite of the next neuron.
3. The eye has special light receptors called rods, which are adapted for vision in dim light. The rods help the viewer to detect the shape and movement of objects in near darkness.
4. The semicircular canals are filled with thick fluid and lined with hair cells. The mechanical movements of the hairs stimulate the neurons to carry an impulse to the brain. Motor neurons in the brain then stimulate muscles in the head and neck to readjust the position of your head so you maintain your balance.
5. Sensory nerves of the somatic nervous system relay information mainly from your skin to the CNS, which relays a response through motor neurons of the somatic system to the skeletal muscles. Reflexes, which are automatic, also occur through the somatic system.

Page 118 • Thinking Critically

1. about 12 minutes
2. after about 40–50 minutes
3. Most animals live part of their lives in the dark and part in the light. Therefore, they must be able to see well in both. A retina that is able to vary its receptivity between light and dark environments in a matter of seconds would presumably help the animal find food and avoid predators.
4. Levels fall to almost zero.
5. Without gravity acting on the mineral grains, the astronaut's brain would not know how his or her head was positioned. Until the brain was able to adjust, he or she would experience the headaches and dizziness characteristic of space sickness.

Page 119 • Applying Scientific Methods

1. Answers will vary but may include that you would divide the hamsters into groups. Each group would be injected with a different specified dosage of the extract for a definite period of time, such as two or three weeks. You would provide continuous supplies of water and alcohol to the hamsters and measure their intake of each liquid daily.
2. One of the groups of hamsters will be given access to both water and alcohol but will receive none of the kudzu extract.
3. The amount of kudzu root extract given to the hamsters will be the variable.
4. The treated hamsters will avoid the alcohol and drink water instead. Those that receive more of the extract may have their alcohol craving restrained sooner.
5. You would want to observe previously treated hamsters to see if there is a relapse into alcoholism or if continuously treated hamsters develop a tolerance to the extract and require higher and higher doses to achieve results. You might also observe if any side effects occur.
6. Answers will vary but may include that if the extract interferes with the breakdown of alcohol in the body, then it might be that alcohol is addictive only after it is metabolized.
7. If in fact alcohol only becomes addictive after it is metabolized, doctors may be able to give patients doses of root extract (or some other enzyme-inhibitor) in order to prevent them from metabolizing alcohol, thereby reducing their alcohol cravings.

Student Recording Sheet

Page 121

Answers can be found on page 968 in the Teacher Wraparound Edition.

Chapter 37

MiniLab 37.1

Page 125 • Checking Your Pulse

Expected Results

Resting pulses will be around 80–90 beats per minute. After exercise, beats will be close to 120 per minute.

Analysis

1. A surge of blood through arteries corresponds with each ejection of blood from the heart.
2. Answers will vary. Average pulse after exercise is higher than resting pulse.
3. 70 mL × average resting pulse per minute = resting cardiac output in mL per minute

   70 mL × average exercising pulse per minute = exercising cardiac output in mL per minute

MiniLab 37.2

Page 127 • Testing Simulated Urine for Glucose

Expected Results

Test paper turns green in the presence of glucose. Water causes no color change.

Analysis

1. Any unknown that tests positive for glucose could indicate diabetes. High sugar intake may also result in glucose elimination in urine.
2. testing of normal and abnormal urine before testing of unknowns

Investigate BioLab

Page 129 • Measuring Respiration

Data and Observations

Answers among students could vary greatly. Average breathing rate is 11 to 12 breaths per minute. Tidal volume should be approximately 500 mL. The amount of air inhaled should be 5 to 6 L per minute.

Analyze and Conclude

1. Average breaths per minute and tidal volume per minute will differ among students.
2. Answers may vary from the average due to age, sex, size, and athletic condition.
3. After exercising, the breathing rate will be higher.
4. Answers will vary but may include: different individuals are expected to have somewhat different total volumes, differences from a real spirometer measurement could be due to differences in the elasticity of different balloons. By using a spirometer, the measurements would be much more accurate.

Real World BioApplications

Page 131 • The Biology of a Hiccup

Planning the Activity

Use this critical thinking activity to reinforce student understanding of the structure and function of the respiratory system in Chapter 37 of the text. It can also be used to exemplify the practical importance of biology.

Purpose

Students examine the structural and physiological cause of hiccups, then use their understanding of the respiratory system to hypothesize about the effectiveness of home hiccup remedies.

Career Applications

The critical thinking skills employed in this activity match those needed to be a health information technician (sometimes called a medical record technician). These technicians need a strong clinical background and critical thinking skills to analyze the contents of medical records. The records include information that patients provide concerning their symptoms and medical history, the results of examinations, reports of X rays and laboratory tests, diagnoses, and treatment plans.

Health information technicians organize and evaluate patient records for completeness and accuracy. Technicians assign a code to each diagnosis and procedure. They consult a classification manual and rely on their knowledge of disease processes. Technicians who specialize in coding are called health information coders, medical record coders, coder/abstractors, or coding specialists. Technicians also use computer programs to tabulate and analyze data to help improve patient care or control costs. Tumor registrars compile and maintain records of patients who have cancer to provide information to physicians and for research studies.

Teaching Strategies

- Begin the activity by having students read the introduction. Then ask students about home remedies for hiccups that they may have used or heard of. Point out to students that scientists may not know exactly what causes hiccups and why some home remedies work better than others; however, they are sure about the body parts involved. Ask students if they think a "cure" for hiccups may someday be developed. Have them give reasons for their views.

- Review the anatomy of the respiratory system in Figure 1 with students as they complete Part A. You may also wish to discuss and review the possible causes of hiccups. Students may not be familiar with some of the concepts dealing with the interaction of the central nervous system and muscular components.
- Point out that hiccups require medical treatment only if they are associated with other symptoms that suggest a serious problem. Because the phrenic nerve is long and extends to many internal organs, its function may be affected by disorders that require proper attention. For example, hiccups may be a symptom of peritonitis (an inflammation of the membrane lining the abdominal cavity), kidney disease, or heart disease. However, in these cases, symptoms other than hiccups would likely be present.

Answers to Student Worksheet

Part A

1. Students should recognize that most cases of hiccups involve stimulation of the stomach area, which may, in turn, influence the contraction of the diaphragm.
2. Eating or drinking too much may distend the stomach, thus stimulating the diaphragm or the phrenic nerve.

Part B

1. Accept all reasonable answers. Many students will say that holding your breath can help the diaphragm regain its rhythm because it forces the diaphragm to be temporarily inactive. Others may argue that by holding your breath, carbon dioxide builds up in the blood, thus influencing the breathing control mechanism in the brain.
2. Accept all reasonable answers. Students should recognize that if you breathe into a bag, carbon dioxide builds up in the air breathed in and eventually in the blood.
3. Accept all reasonable answers. Students may infer that this position puts pressure on the diaphragm, thus helping it to regain its rhythm.
4. Accept all reasonable answers. Students may infer that drinking water quickly distends the stomach and stimulates the diaphragm and/or phrenic nerve; drinking water may also cause the epiglottis to close and then open as it should.
5. Answers will vary. Some explanations may be similar to 1–4 above.

Reinforcement and Study Guide

Page 133 • Section 37.1

1. d	7. false
2. c	8. false
3. c	9. true
4. b	10. false
5. a	11. true
6. d	12. false

Page 134 • Section 37.2

1. red and white blood cells; platelets; carbon dioxide and other gases; hormones; enzymes; proteins; inorganic salts; antibodies; nutrients
2. About 70% combines with water in the plasma to form bicarbonate; the rest is carried by hemoglobin and/or dissolved in plasma.
3. Red Blood Cells
4. White Blood Cells
5. Red Blood Cells, Platelets
6. Platelets
7. Red Blood Cells
8. White Blood Cells
9. false
10. false
11. true
12. false
13. aorta
14. pulmonary arteries
15. pulmonary veins
16. left atrium
17. right atrium
18. left ventricle
19. right ventricle
20. to the left atrium; to the pulmonary arteries; to the aorta
21. one-way valves
22. pulse
23. true
24. the electrical changes in the heart
25. medulla oblongata
26. Systolic pressure

Page 136 • Section 37.3

1. to filter wastes from blood in order to maintain fluid homeostasis
2. It stores the waste solution, urine.
3. the basic filtering units in kidneys

4. 4
5. 2
6. 7
7. 6
8. 1
9. 5
10. 3
11. Ammonia, urea
12. osmotic pressure (or) sodium level, pH
13. glucose

Refuerzo y Guía de estudio

Página 137 • Sección 37.1

1. d
2. c
3. c
4. b
5. a
6. d
7. falso
8. falso
9. verdadero
10. falso
11. verdadero
12. falso

Página 138 • Sección 37.2

1. glóbulos rojos y blancos, plaquetas, dióxido de carbono y otros gases, hormonas, enzimas, proteínas, sales inorgánicas, anticuerpos y nutrientes
2. Aproximadamente el 70% se combina con el agua del plasma para formar bicarbonato. El resto es transportado por los glóbulos rojos y disuelto en el plasma.
3. glóbulos rojos
4. glóbulos blancos
5. glóbulos rojos; plaquetas
6. plaquetas
7. glóbulos rojos
8. glóbulos blancos
9. falso
10. falso
11. verdadero
12. falso
13. aorta
14. arterias pulmonares
15. venas pulmonares
16. aurícula izquierda
17. aurícula derecha
18. ventrículo izquierdo
19. ventrículo derecho
20. hacia la aurícula izquierda, a las arterias pulmonares y a la aorta, respectivamente
21. la presencia de válvulas unidireccionales
22. pulso
23. verdadero
24. los cambios eléctricos en el corazón
25. bulbo raquídeo
26. presión sistólica

Página 140 • Sección 37.3

1. filtrar los desechos de la sangre para mantener la homeostasis de los fluidos corporales
2. almacenar la orina, la cual es una solución de desecho
3. las unidades funcionales de filtración elementales de los riñones
4. 4
5. 2
6. 7
7. 6
8. 1
9. 5
10. 3
11. amoníaco; urea
12. presión osmótica (o) nivel de sodio; pH
13. glucosa

Concept Mapping

Page 141 • Circulation in Humans

1. right atrium
2. venae cavae
3. low O_2 high CO_2
4. right ventricle
5. lungs
6. pulmonary veins
7. high O_2 low CO_2
8. left atrium
9. left ventricle
10. aorta

Critical Thinking

Page 142 • Solving Respiratory, Circulatory, and Excretory System Problems

1. An overweight person's heart has to work harder to send blood to all parts of the body. After a heart attack, the person's heart can no longer respond as well to such a work load.
2. It would take that long for the athlete's red blood cells to increase in number so that his or her blood would be able to carry sufficient oxygen to the body cells. Only then would the athlete be able to perform efficiently at high altitudes.
3. Because blood pressure rises during exercise, you would get a much higher reading at that time than is considered normal for you.

4. The survivor's nephrons filter water from the blood. Most of the water is reabsorbed into the bloodstream to maintain the body's water balance. Little water is excreted as urine.
5. The plasma proteins must be leaking into the nephron capsules. Something must be wrong with the nephron for the plasma proteins to pass into the capsule.

Section Focus Transparency 90

Page 143 • Take a Breath

Purpose

- To relate the mechanics of breathing to a physical model

Teaching Suggestions

- Project the transparency, and direct attention to the bellows and the size of the fire in each illustration. Ask students what causes the difference in the size of the fire. (Air from the bellows fuels it.)
- Write the words *breathing* and *respiration* on the board, and have students provide a definition for each word. (*breathing*—process of moving air into and out of the lungs; *respiration*—process in which cells break down molecules of glucose to release carbon dioxide) Be sure students understand that breathing is just one part of respiration.
- *Answers to questions on the transparency include:*

1. Air rushes in as a result of reduced pressure inside the bellows.
2. Bellows—lungs; hands—diaphragm

Section Focus Transparency 91

Page 144 • The Blood Goes Around

Purpose

- To interpret a model of the circulatory system and to draw conclusions about the system's function

Teaching Suggestions

- Project the transparency, and have students follow the path of blood in the diagram. Ask students what the function of blood is. (to carry oxygen, nutrients, and cell wastes)
- Tell students that capillaries are microscopic blood vessels with walls that are only one cell thick. Explain that the thin walls are necessary so that materials can diffuse through the walls to and from the body tissues. Review the process of diffusion if necessary.
- *Answers to questions on the transparency include:*

1. One loop is devoted entirely to the exchange of oxygen for carbon dioxide; the other loop (from heart to lungs and back) releases carbon dioxide and picks up oxygen.
2. top—capillaries of the lungs; bottom—capillaries of the rest of the body

Section Focus Transparency 92

Page 145 • Saving and Discarding

Purpose

- To recognize that the kidneys are not just waste filters but are vital in maintaining the chemical balance of the body

Teaching Suggestions

- Before projecting the transparency, ask students what the function of the kidney is. (Most students will probably only identify its role in eliminating wastes.)
- Project the transparency, and have students describe the flow of blood through the kidney.
- *Answers to questions on the transparency include:*

1. Substances from the blood are being sorted out. Some are conserved by being passed back into the blood. Others are discarded by remaining in the urine.
2. Conserved—NaCl, H_2O, nutrients, HCO_3^-; discarded—K^+, H^+, ammonia, urea

Basic Concepts Transparency 70

Page 147 • Blood Types

Purpose

- To investigate the nature and interactions of ABO blood types

Teaching Suggestions

- Project the transparency and challenge students to identify the compatibility of various blood types. If needed, create a table on the chalkboard that lists blood types in the left-hand column. Label the second column "Antigen" and the third "Antibody." Have students fill in the table to help them identify compatible blood types.
- Explain that a person's blood type is inherited from his or her parents.
- Point out that antibodies are produced by the body in response to the invasion of any foreign protein, such as those of bacteria and viruses.

Extension: Laboratory

- Obtain blood typing kits that use simulated blood samples from a biological supply house. Have students perform the blood typing according to the directions given in the kit. Remind students about the antigen-antibody reaction that occurs if improper blood types are transfused. As an extended activity have students discuss why it is important for the correct blood type to be used during a transfusion and the risk created by Rh factor during some pregnancies.

Answers to Student Worksheet

1. An antigen is a foreign protein that stimulates an immune response in the body.
2. An antibody is a protein produced in the blood that reacts with its matching antigen.
3. Blood type is determined by the antigens on the membranes of red blood cells. Blood type is inherited from one's mother or father.
4. You have A antigens on your red blood cells and anti-B antibodies in your plasma.
5. If you were transfused with type B blood, the anti-A antibodies in the B blood plasma would react with the A antigens on your type A red blood cells, causing the blood to form clumps. The clumps can block blood vessels and cut off circulation.
6. Type AB blood has no antibodies but does have A and B antigens, whereas type O blood has no antigens but does have both A and B antibodies.
7. If a person with type O blood receives a transfusion from a person with type A, B, or AB blood, the recipient's antibodies will react with the donor's blood.
8. Since type O blood contains no antigens, it can be used in emergency transfusions for individuals with any blood type. Individuals with type AB blood can receive blood of any type because they carry no antibodies in their blood plasma.

Basic Concepts Transparency 71

Page 149 • Your Blood Vessels

Purpose

- To show the pathways of circulation to and from the heart, as well as the functioning of valves in the veins

Teaching Suggestions

- Project the transparency and discuss the top illustration. Explain that students are, of course, looking at a model of the circulatory system rather than a complete illustration. Be sure they understand the direction of blood flow and the function of each type of blood vessel.
- Now discuss the illustration at the bottom of the transparency. Explain that blood in the veins must sometimes flow uphill. A system of one-way valves working in conjunction with skeletal muscles prevents blood from flowing backward through the veins.

Extension: Laboratory

- Have students examine a prepared slide of an artery, a vein, and a capillary. Students should be encouraged to draw and label the various identifiable structures.

Answers to Student Worksheet

1. Arteries are large, elastic blood vessels that are thick-walled and muscular. They function to carry oxygen-rich blood away from the heart to the body tissues and brain.
2. The veins carry blood from the tissues back to the heart. Most of the oxygen carried by the red blood cells has been used by various tissues of the body, and therefore the blood is no longer a bright red.
3. Arterioles are blood vessels that are smaller than the smallest arteries. Arterioles enter tissues, where they branch into the smallest blood vessels, the capillaries. The capillaries are microscopic and have walls that are only a single cell in thickness. As capillaries leave the tissues, they join to form venules, which are similar in size to the arterioles. It is the venules that merge to become veins.
4. Blood in an artery is under great pressure, which forces the artery walls to expand a bit. When the artery wall shrinks back, it pushes on the blood. The result of having an alternately stretching and shrinking artery wall is that blood flows through the vessels with a steady pulsation rather than continually stopping and flowing.
5. Blood in the veins is under less pressure than it is in the arteries. There is insufficient pressure to prevent the blood from flowing backward if it must flow uphill against gravity, as in the veins of the arms and legs. Veins in these parts of the body are therefore equipped with valves.
6. When the skeletal muscles contract, the valves open, forcing blood toward the heart. When the muscles relax, the valves close, preventing blood from flowing backward and away from the heart.

Basic Concepts Transparency 72

Page 151 • Your Heart

Purpose

- To show the structures of the heart and their functions, as well as the interrelationship of the heart and lungs

Teaching Suggestions

- Project the transparency and discuss the structures shown in the top illustration. Then discuss the structures shown in the bottom illustration, focusing on blood flow and its oxygenation. Have students trace the pathway of a drop of blood after it enters the heart from the head or body.
- Point out that the coronary arteries deliver oxygenated blood to the heart muscles. When these arteries become sufficiently narrowed or blocked by a blood clot or deposit of fats, a heart attack occurs.
- Have students discuss how the transparency reveals the intimate relationship between the circulatory and respiratory systems.

Extension: Activity

- Have students examine a three-dimensional model of a human heart. Encourage them to compare the human heart with one or more other mammalian hearts.

Answers to Student Worksheet

1. The pericardium is a protective membrane that encloses the heart.
2. After they have filled with blood, the two atria contract, pushing the blood down into the two ventricles. Then, both the ventricles contract. The right ventricle pushes oxygen-poor blood out of the heart toward the lungs. The left ventricle pushes oxygen-rich blood out of the heart through the aorta.
3. The ventricles perform more work than the atria. The thicker, more muscular walls of the ventricles support this conclusion.
4. The pulmonary arteries transport blood from the heart to the lungs, whereas the pulmonary veins transport blood from the lungs back to the heart.
5. The vena cavae empty oxygen-poor blood from the body into the heart, whereas the aorta transports oxygen-rich blood from the heart to the body.
6. A heart valve is a one-way “swinging door” that keeps blood from backing up when each chamber of the heart contracts. This forces the blood to move in only one direction through the heart.
7. The drop moves from either the superior or inferior vena cava into the right atrium and then into the right ventricle. From there it moves through a pulmonary artery into the lung, where it drops off its carbon dioxide and picks up oxygen. The drop of blood then returns to the heart through a pulmonary vein and enters the left atrium, then the left ventricle, and finally the aorta, through which the drop of blood passes into the body.

Basic Concepts Transparency 73

Page 153 • The Urinary System

Purpose

- To review the structure and functions of the urinary system

Teaching Suggestions

- Project the transparency and discuss the illustrations shown, moving in turn from the macroanatomy of the upper left panel to the more detailed anatomy of the kidney, to the microanatomy of the illustrations below.
- Point out that some sources describe the urinary system as the major part of the excretory system, which also includes sweat glands, lungs, and the liver. Discuss how these organs perform excretory functions. Sweat glands excrete water, salts, and urea. The lungs excrete carbon dioxide and water. The liver removes bile pigments and some hemoglobin.
- Review homeostasis and cellular respiration. Explain that the kidneys maintain homeostasis by cleansing the bloodstream of the waste products produced by cellular respiration.

Extension: Research Report

- Have students do research on kidney dialysis. Students should report on how dialysis equipment functions and under what conditions it is used. Students should include the ways in which a dialysis machine is analogous to a kidney and its associated structures.

Answers to Student Worksheet

1. The kidneys filter waste from the blood and maintain homeostasis of body fluids.
2. The nephron is the filtering unit of a kidney. It is made up of a long, looping tube with a filtering capsule, called the Bowman’s capsule, at one end and a collecting duct at the other. The nephron filters the materials out of the blood under pressure. Most materials are reabsorbed back into the bloodstream as the liquid moves through the tubule. The liquid remaining in the tubule forms urine and is removed from the body.

3. The glomerulus is a capillary bed enclosed in the Bowman's capsule.
4. urea, water, salts, nutrients
5. blood cells, water, salts, nutrients
6. urine, excess water, salts
7. The ureters carry waste fluid from the kidney to the urinary bladder, where the fluid is stored until elimination.
8. The urethra is the structure through which urine is eliminated from the body.

Reteaching Skills Transparency 54

Page 155 • Circulatory Path Through the Heart

Purpose

- To study the path blood follows to the heart, to the lungs, back to the heart, and then on to the body
- Skill: Sequencing

Teaching Suggestions

- Review the heart's purpose: to circulate blood and to release carbon dioxide and reoxygenate the blood.
- Present the transparency. Discuss the fact that the right side of the heart receives carbon dioxide–rich blood from the body and sends that blood to the lungs; the left side receives oxygen-rich blood from the lungs and sends that blood to the rest of the body.
- Review the process of diffusion. Then discuss the action of the capillaries in the lungs, where carbon dioxide diffuses into the lungs and ultimately passes out of the body and where oxygen diffuses from the lungs into the blood and ultimately passes into cells throughout the body.

Extension: Cooperative Learning

- Divide the class into groups. Each group prepares a presentation about the circulatory system in other Animal Kingdom groups: mollusks, segmented worms, arthropods, echinoderms, fish, amphibians, reptiles, and birds.

Answers to Student Worksheet

1. Arteries are large, thick-walled, muscular, elastic vessels that carry blood away from the heart. Veins are large blood vessels that carry blood from the tissues back to the heart; veins have one-way valves that prevent backflow.
2. The heart is the muscle that pushes blood through the arteries. The blood in veins is under far less pressure, and in some cases muscles in the body help move blood through veins.
3. Capillaries are microscopic blood vessels with walls that are only one cell thick. Because of the thin walls, gases and other substances can diffuse easily through the membrane, passing from blood to tissues and vice versa.
4. The superior (upper) and inferior (lower) venae cavae carry blood from the body to the heart.
5. a. The right atrium receives venous blood from the body and pushes this blood into the right ventricle.
   b. The right ventricle receives blood from the right atrium and pushes this blood into the lungs.
   c. The left atrium receives oxygenated blood from the lungs and pushes it into the left ventricle.
   d. The left ventricle receives blood from the left atrium and pushes the blood out into the body.
6. Cells produce carbon dioxide during cellular respiration, which releases energy required for all cellular activities. Cells must have oxygen in order for cellular respiration to take place.
7. The gas exchange takes place in the alveoli and capillaries of the lungs.
8. The aorta carries oxygen-rich blood into the body.

Chapter Assessment

Page 157 • Reviewing Vocabulary

1. n	9. e
2. a	10. o
3. k	11. f
4. i	12. p
5. l	13. d
6. c	14. m
7. h	15. g
8. b	16. j

Page 158 • Understanding Main Ideas (Part A)

1. red bone marrow
2. valves
3. pulmonary veins
4. atria
5. true
6. proteins
7. glucose
8. water
9. true
10. true

11. artery
12. anti-B
13. Cellular respiration

Page 159 • Understanding Main Ideas (Part B)

1. The nasal cavity, trachea, and bronchi are lined with cilia that constantly beat upward toward your throat so that foreign particles can be expelled or swallowed. Also, cells in the trachea and the bronchi secrete mucus that can trap the particles.
2. When the ventricles contract, blood pressure rises sharply. This high pressure is called systolic pressure. As the ventricles relax, blood pressure drops; the lowest pressure occurs just before the ventricles contract again and is called diastolic pressure.
3. Toward the end of pregnancy or at delivery, the fetal blood may leak through the placenta and mix with the mother's blood. If the mother is Rh^-, she will produce antibodies against the Rh antigen. If she becomes pregnant again, the antibodies will cross the placenta and attack the red blood cells of an Rh^+ fetus. If the fetus is Rh^-, there is no problem.
4. The pacemaker generates an electrical impulse that spreads over both atria, signaling the two atria to contract at almost the same time. It also triggers cells at the base of the right atrium to send an electrical impulse over the ventricles, causing them to contract.
5. The urinary system removes nitrogenous wastes, controls the level of sodium in blood, and regulates blood pH by filtering hydrogen ions out of the blood and allowing bicarbonate to be reabsorbed.

Page 160 • Thinking Critically

1. 120 beats/min
2. 160 mL/beat
3. The heart rate has the greater effect because as the graph shows, cardiac output is at its maximum only when the heart rate reaches its maximum. Cardiac output is well below its maximum when stroke volume reaches its maximum.
4. Gas exchange between air and blood cannot take place. Unless this is remedied, the patient will die.
5. If the patient's blood flow is cut down, the amount of oxygen and nutrients that reach the brain is reduced. The patient may become confused and unable to perform normally.
6. Less water would be reabsorbed by the nephrons, so more water would be excreted from the body in urine.

Page 161 • Applying Scientific Methods

1. The sinus of the frog heart contracts slightly before the atrium. The atrium contracts slightly before the ventricle. The atrium and the ventricle contract at the same rate as the sinus.
2. It doesn't change the rate.
3. The atrium and the ventricle beat more slowly after the block.
4. You could tie another string around the heart, between the atrium and the ventricle.
5. The sinus and atrium continue to beat, but each at its own rate. The ventricle slows down considerably.
6. Answers will vary but may include that each area of the heart beats at its own rate unless influenced by the sinus or by the lower part of the atrium. Also, students may conclude that although the sinus controls the rhythm of the heart, other heart tissue can initiate contraction if the sinus is blocked.

Student Recording Sheet

Page 163

Answers can be found on page 992 in the Teacher Wraparound Edition.

Teacher Guide & Answers

Chapter 38

MiniLab 38.1

Page 167 • Examining Sperm, Egg, and Early Embryonic Development

Expected Results

Students will examine sperm, an ovary slide for eggs, and a sea star blastula for various structures.

Analysis

1. Students should be able to find the sperm head, which contains the nucleus and DNA for fertilization; acrosome cap containing digestive enzymes; midpiece, which contains mitochondria; and flagellum for movement.
2. The follicle cells protect the egg and produce the hormones estrogen and progesterone.
3. After fertilization of the egg by the sperm, the zygote divides by mitosis to produce the multicellular blastula (called a blastocyst in humans).

MiniLab 38.2

Page 168 • Making a Graph of Fetal Size

Expected Results

Graphs will show that the embryo grows fastest during the early periods of development.

Analysis

1. The embryo doubles in size during two 1-week periods: 3 to 4 weeks and 7 to 8 weeks.
2. All body systems are beginning to form.
3. 5th month

Investigate BioLab

Page 169 • What hormone is produced by an embryo?

Procedure

Data Table

Condition	hCG in urine?	+ Anti-hCG	= Joined hCG and anti-hCG?	+ Chemical C with anti-hCG?	Color
Not pregnant	———		———	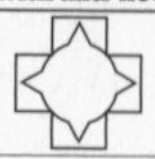	Green
Pregnant					Colorless

Analyze and Conclude

1. The chorion begins to release hCG as early as eight days after fertilization.
2. There is no chorion to relase hCG.
3. If pregnant, anti-hCG joins with hCG, preventing attachment to chemical C's hCG. No color appears. If not pregnant, anti-hCG attaches to chemical C's hCG and color appears.
4. To get an accurate result, hCG and anti-hCG must have a chance to bind before Chemical C is added.

Real World BioApplications

Page 171 • Tales from the Past

Planning the Activity

Use this activity after students have completed their study of Chapter 38 of the text to illustrate the importance of recognizing general patterns in human growth and development. The activity reinforces student understanding of variations in human structural characteristics and changes that occur with aging.

Purpose

Students examine how skeletal characteristics can be used to gain information about individuals from remains. Students then apply this method to solve a problem of individual identification.

Career Applications

The principles of observation, measurement, and comparison to a known sample used in this activity reflect the principles and theories of science and mathematics used by forensic technicians as they address criminal evidence. Forensic technicians work with criminal and forensic scientists as they perform a variety of advanced/specialized forensic scientific examinations and analyses of physical evidence gathered in law enforcement work. However, their jobs are more practically oriented than those of the criminal scientist. Forensic technicians set up, operate, and maintain laboratory instruments; monitor experiments; make observations; calculate and record results; and develop conclusions.

Teaching Strategies

- After students read the opening paragraph, ask them to think about how medical examiners, forensic anthropologists, and other scientists identify individuals from skeletal and dental remains. Point out that particular characteristics and features of teeth and bones are clues for these scientists. Remind them that, while human growth and development shows variation among individuals, there are general patterns or norms that are diagnostic of a person's sex, age, and stature. These norms are the result of extensive data collection, classification, and analysis by scientists. Emphasize the importance of precise measurements in this type of data collection.

- As students read about the skeletal characteristics in Part A, point out that many other skeletal and dental characteristics are used in practice. For example, the pattern of wear on the surfaces of molar teeth is a reliable indication of age. The diameter of the top of the humerus (upper arm bone) can help in determining sex. The fitting together of upper and lower teeth (bite) may provide clues about ethnic origin. You may wish to obtain additional reference sources and discuss some of these other criteria with students.
- Check students' understanding of Figure 3 by asking when the data would not be helpful in determining sex. (A width between 72 and 78 mm would be inconclusive.)

Answers to Student Worksheet

1. a. **Probable sex**—male
   Evidence used—shape of pubic bone, width of knee joint
   b. **Estimated age**—35–39 years old
   Evidence used—structure of pubic symphysis
   c. **Estimated height**—About 178–179 cm or 5' 10"
   Evidence used—length of femur
2. Dr. Ojeda is correct. The evidence indicates that the bones are from a tall male, not a short male.

Reinforcement and Study Guide

Page 173 • Section 38.1

1. to produce sperm and deliver them to a female
2. Being outside the body core, the scrotum maintains sperm at the cooler-than-body temperature conditions that they need to develop normally.
3. 300 million
4. 4
5. 2
6. 6
7. 3
8. 1
9. 5
10. puberty, sex characteristics
11. hypothalamus, pituitary, follicle-stimulating, luteinizing
12. sperm, testosterone
13. peristaltic muscle contraction and beating cilia
14. pituitary gland
15. true
16. estrogen
17. one meiotic division or a partial meiotic division
18. Luteal
19. Follicular
20. Flow
21. Luteal
22. Flow
23. Follicular
24. Follicular
25. Luteal
26. Flow

Page 175 • Section 38.2

1. oviduct
2. zygote
3. blastocyst
4. implants
5. embryo
6. amnion
7. umbilical cord
8. chorion
9. placenta
10. chorionic villi
11. Second
12. Third
13. First
14. First
15. Second
16. Third
17. First

Page 176 • Section 38.3

1. dilation, expulsion, and the placental stage
2. Oxytocin stimulates contraction of the uterine muscles and dilation of the cervix.
3. Continued contractions constrict the uterine blood vessels and prevent hemorrhaging.
4. age, gender
5. Human growth hormone, hCG
6. bones, skeletal muscles
7. protein synthesis, fat metabolism
8. Childhood
9. Adulthood
10. Adolescence
11. Childhood
12. Adolescence

Refuerzo y Guía de estudio

Página 177 • Sección 38.1

1. producir espermatozoides y depositarlos en el cuerpo de la mujer
2. Debido a que está por fuera del cuerpo, el escroto mantiene los espermatozoides a una temperatura más fresca que el resto del cuerpo, lo cual es necesario para el desarrollo normal de los espermatozoides.
3. 300 millones

4. 4
5. 2
6. 6
7. 3
8. 1
9. 5
10. pubertad; rasgos sexuales
11. hipotálamo; pituitaria; folículo estimulante; luteinizante
12. espermatozoides; testosterona
13. debido a contracciones peristálticas de los músculos y el agitar de los cilios
14. la glándula pituitaria
15. verdadero
16. el estrógeno
17. una división meiótica total o parcial
18. lútea
19. folicular
20. flujo
21. lútea
22. flujo
23. folicular
24. folicular
25. lútea
26. flujo

Página 179 • Sección 38.2

1. oviducto
2. cigoto
3. blastocisto
4. implanta
5. embrión
6. amnios
7. cordón umbilical
8. corión
9. placenta
10. vellosidades coriónicas
11. segundo
12. tercer
13. primero
14. primero
15. segundo
16. tercer
17. primero

Página 180 • Sección 38.3

1. la dilatación, la expulsión y la etapa placentaria
2. La oxitocina estimula la contracción de los músculos del útero y la dilatación de la cerviz.
3. Estas contracciones uterinas constriñen los vasos sanguíneos del útero y previenen una hemorragia.
4. edad; género
5. hormona humana del crecimiento; hGH
6. huesos; músculos esqueléticos
7. síntesis de proteínas; metabolismo de las grasas
8. infancia
9. edad adulta
10. adolescencia
11. infancia
12. adolescencia

Concept Mapping

Page 181 • Human Growth

1. Human growth
2. zygote
3. embryo
4. fetus
5. two years
6. puberty
7. teen years
8. slower metabolism
9. physical and intellectual activity

Critical Thinking

Page 182 • The Menstrual Cycle

1. FSH, because it is needed to stimulate growth of the follicle
2. Estrogen levels begin to rise sharply about the sixth or seventh day of the cycle and reach a peak shortly before ovulation, on the fourteenth day.
3. The FHS level begins to decrease because the follicle is already maturing and follicle production is no longer needed. The level of luteinizing hormone (LH) increases, so that ovulation may take place.
4. The level of LH reaches its peak almost immediately after estrogen reaches its peak, around the fourteenth day. This hormone is needed to cause ovulation.
5. There would be no mature follicle to go through the ovulation process.
6. Estrogen thickens the uterus and increases the blood supply to it. If ovulation was stimulated by luteinizing hormone before estrogen peaked, the uterus might not yet be a good medium for an early embryo.

Section Focus Transparency 93
Page 183 • Beginning Again

Purpose
- To realize that reproductive processes have nervous and hormonal control

Teaching Suggestions
- Project the transparency, and review with students the function of the cerebrum (controls such functions as conscious activity and memory) and the hypothalamus (controls homeostatic activities).
- Review with students what they recall from Chapter 35 about the role of hormones in the regulation of homeostasis. Tell students that hormones produced by the pituitary gland also serve important reproductive functions.
- *Answers to questions on the transparency include:*
  1. The cerebrum allows us to make rational and informed decisions about reproduction.
  2. Students are likely to have heard that the pituitary is the master gland and that it has something to do with controlling growth. (The pituitary gland and the hypothalamus work together to regulate the secretion of FSH and LH.)

Section Focus Transparency 94
Page 184 • From a Cell to a Human

Purpose
- To infer the different causes of twin births by examining the results

Teaching Suggestions
- Before projecting the transparency, have students review the process of mitosis in which a cell splits in two. Emphasize that the resulting cells have identical genetic material.
- Project the transparency, and point out the placenta in each set of twins. Remind students that humans are placental mammals; the placenta nourishes the embryo as it grows and carries wastes away from it.
- *Answers for questions on the transparency include:*
  1. The twins on the left are identical. There is one placenta for both.
  2. The identical pair results from a splitting of a single fertilized egg. The fraternal twins result from the fertilization of two separate eggs.

Section Focus Transparency 95
Page 185 • Birth, Growth, and Age

Purpose
- To realize that both growth and age cause changes in height

Teaching Suggestions
- Project the transparency, and have students study the data shown.
- Discuss with students the variation in height of individuals of the same age. Be sure students understand that there is a wide range of normal heights at any given age. Ask students what factors control height. (heredity, nutrition, environment)
- *Answers to questions on the transparency include:*
  1. Height increases through teens, reaching a maximum in the twenties. After middle age, height decreases slightly.
  2. Answers will vary, but students are likely to suggest changes in skeleton height are not dependent on activity.

Basic Concepts Transparency 74
Page 187 • Female Reproductive System

Purpose
- To illustrate the structures of the female reproductive system

Teaching Suggestions
- Project the transparency and discuss the functions of the labeled structures.
- Point out that one difference between the male and female reproductive systems is that the urethra is part of the male reproductive system but not part of the female system.
- Discuss the fact that the ovaries and testes are analogous structures that perform complementary functions. Have students identify those functions (production of sex cells and sex hormones).

Extension: Research Report
- Have students research fertility drugs, the use of which often results in multiple births. Students should explain when such drugs are used and how they work.

Answers to Student Worksheet
1. The bladder, urethra, rectum, ligaments, and bone are not part of the female reproductive system.
2. The ovary produces eggs.

3. The uterus is a spongy, pear-shaped organ that serves as the nurturing and developing site for the embryo and fetus during pregnancy. The uterus consists of a thick, muscular layer and a thin inner lining called the endometrium. The lower end of the uterus is the cervix, which opens into the vagina.
4. The egg ruptures from the surface of the ovary. The ovum is swept into the oviduct and enters the uterus.
5. The baby is delivered through the vagina at birth.
6. ligaments
7. cervix
8. Sperm production begins at puberty and continues throughout life. Eggs begin to develop before birth, then enter a resting stage. At birth, a female has all the potential eggs she will ever have. Beginning with puberty, and about once a month thereafter, one egg completes development.

Basic Concepts Transparency 75

Page 189 • The Menstrual Cycle

Purpose

- To review the events in the menstrual cycle and how they correlate with the production of various hormones

Teaching Suggestions

- Project the transparency. Discuss how the levels of pituitary hormones rise and fall on different days of the cycle. Then compare ovarian changes as well as changes in the uterine lining on those same days.
- Point out that the data provided in the transparency are for an average menstrual cycle, but that the length of the stages varies with the individual and may also vary from month to month.
- Discuss how various medications can be taken to regulate an irregular menstrual cycle. Have students hypothesize what such medications might contain.

Extension: Video Script

- Have students research and create a script and storyboard for a brief video on premenstrual syndrome, its symptoms and causes.

Answers to Student Worksheet

1. The menstrual cycle consists of flow stage, the follicular stage, and the luteal stage. The flow stage lasts about five days, the follicular stage lasts about nine days, and the luteal stage lasts about fourteen days.
2. luteinizing hormone
3. The pituitary gland releases FSH, which stimulates the development of a follicle in the ovary and causes estrogen to be released from the ovary.
4. After ovulation, the remaining tissue of the follicle develops into the corpus luteum, which secretes the progesterone needed to prepare the uterine lining for receiving a fertilized egg.
5. Estrogen levels are highest during the follicular stage, and progesterone levels are highest during the luteal stage.
6. The uterine lining is thickest during the luteal stage, when progesterone levels are at their highest.
7. If the egg is not fertilized, rising levels of progesterone and estrogen from the corpus luteum inhibit the release of FSH and LH, causing the corpus luteum to degenerate. This causes progesterone and estrogen levels to drop. At that point, the uterine lining begins to shed.

Reteaching Skills Transparency 55

Page 191 • Negative Feedback Systems

Purpose

- To examine the hormonal feedback circuits in males and females
- Skill: Comparing and contrasting

Teaching Suggestions

- Project the transparency and discuss similarities and differences between the two feedback systems.
- Point out that a feedback system is self-regulating.
- Make sure students understand the nature of the on and off "switches" involved in the feedback systems.
- Point out to students that the letters RH shown in the transparency stand for a type of releasing hormone secreted by the hypothalamus.

Extension: Research Activity

- Have students research and construct charts of feedback mechanisms not associated with reproduction. These include the regulation of blood sugar by insulin, the regulation of ion concentration by the kidneys, and the regulation of blood pressure and heart rate.

Answers to Student Worksheet

1. The hypothalamus and pituitary glands are located in the brain.
2. FSH, LH, and testosterone are involved in the male feedback system.

3. FSH, LH, estrogen, and progesterone are involved in the female feedback system.
4. The hypothalamus signals the pituitary to release FSH and LH, which stimulate sperm production. Increased production of sperm feed back into the system to inhibit FSH and LH production.
5. LH released from the pituitary stimulates the development of the corpus luteum. The corpus luteum in turn releases progesterone, which causes the uterine lining to thicken and increase its blood supply. If the progesterone level becomes too high, the hypothalamus is inhibited from signaling the pituitary to release FSH and LH. As a result, the corpus luteum degenerates and the progesterone levels drop. This drop in turn causes the uterus to shed its thick lining.
6. estrogen
7. The fertilization of an egg breaks the cycle.

Reteaching Skills Transparency 56

Page 193 • Fertilization and Fetal Development

Purpose

- To review the sequence of events resulting in fertilization and fetal development
- Skill: Sequencing

Teaching Suggestions

- Compare and contrast the egg produced by humans with eggs of other vertebrates.
- Point out that upon entry of a sperm into an egg, a change occurs in the membrane of the egg that keeps any other sperm from entering.
- Discuss prenatal testing. Point out that a more recently developed procedure than either ultrasound or amniocentesis is chorionic villus sampling. Point out that this procedure provides the same information as amniocentesis, but at an earlier time during pregnancy.

Extension: Cooperative Activity

- Organize students into groups. Have them research fetal alcohol syndrome and then create posters explaining the dangers of drinking alcohol during pregnancy.

Answers to Student Worksheet

1. A sperm and egg unite.
2. Fertilization occurs in the oviduct.
3. Implantation occurs in the lining of the uterus.
4. The chorionic villi are fingerlike projections that begin to grow into the uterine wall about 2 weeks after fertilization. Together with the maternal portion of the placenta, the chorionic villi form the placenta, the point of exchange between mother and embryo. Oxygen and nutrients from the mother diffuse into the chorionic villi for transport into the embryo.
5. The allantois is an outgrowth of the embryo's digestive tract. Its blood vessels form the umbilical cord.
6. The amniotic fluid cushions the fetus against mechanical shocks.
7. The umbilical cord is a ropelike mass of blood vessels that carry oxygen and nutrients to the embryo and waste products from the embryo to the placenta.
8. By the third month of pregnancy, the placenta has taken over the function of secreting estrogen and progesterone, which are needed to maintain pregnancy.

Chapter Assessment

Page 197 • Reviewing Vocabulary

1. h
2. e
3. b
4. a
5. c
6. f
7. g
8. d
9. Both are glands that secret alkaline fluids in which sperm are transported. The bulbourethral gland produces a sticky fluid that neutralizes the acidic environment of the urethra. The prostate gland secretes a thinner fluid that helps the sperm move and survive.
10. The epididymis is a coiled tube within the scrotum in which the sperm complete their maturation. The vas deferens is the duct that transports sperm from the epididymis toward the ejaculatory ducts and the urethra.

Page 198 • Understanding Main Ideas (Part A)

1. vagina
2. uterus
3. ovary
4. ovulation
5. oviduct

6. fertilization
7. zygote
8. blastocyst
9. implantation
10. b
11. c
12. d
13. c

Page 199 • Understanding Main Ideas (Part B)

1. hypothalamus
2. testosterone
3. FSH
4. LH
5. FSH
6. Sperm can develop only at a temperature that is about 3°C lower than normal body temperature.
7. The lining is shed.
8. It produces both progesterone and estrogen. The progesterone causes the uterine lining to thicken, to increase its blood supply, and to accumulate fat and tissue fluid in preparation for the arrival of a fertilized egg.

Page 200 • Thinking Critically

1. As the fetus begins to grow, the oviduct would probably not be able to accommodate its size. The fetus would probably die from lack of oxygen, because blood circulation would not be adequate.
2. Since the oviducts open into the pelvic cavity, a fertilized egg may fall into the cavity, or an egg may be fertilized there. After implantation, the embryonic membranes and the placenta would have to develop there to transport oxygen and nutrients to the fetus.
3. The fetus is not in the uterus, which opens into the birth canal, so it would have to be removed surgically.
4. Taking estrogen and progesterone in addition to that supplied by the body upsets the luteal phase by inhibiting the amount of LH secreted during ovulation. The decrease in LH prevents the normal preparation of the uterus for implantation.

Page 201 • Applying Scientific Methods

1. When Mrs. Smith ovulates in May and June, Mr. Smith is at home. During these months, Mrs. Smith may have the best chances of becoming pregnant. In March and April, there is less of a chance because Mr. Smith is away on the day of ovulation; however, because sperm can survive for several days, fertilization may still take place.
2. The change would have helped in March and April. In May and June, it is less likely the change would help.
3. If the egg is fertilized on the day of ovulation, there is a greater probability that the sperm will be a Y sperm, since they swim more rapidly than X sperm. An egg fertilized by a Y sperm will be a boy.
4. There would be an equal chance that they would have either a boy or girl because sperm can survive for a few days. Both X and Y sperm would have had enough time to reach the oviduct by the time the egg was released during ovulation.

Student Recording Sheet

Page 203

Answers can be found on page 1020 in the Teacher Wraparound Edition.

Chapter 39

MiniLab 39.1

Page 207 • Testing How Diseases are Spread

Expected Results

Apples 2 and 3 will develop spots and decay. Apple 1 will show little or no change. Apple 4 will show little or no change, because the alcohol may have inhibited the decay.

Analysis

1. Apple 1 is a control for comparison.
2. Apple 2 decayed the most, Apple 3 had brown spots, and Apple 4 may have shown little or no change.
3. Cleaning a wound with alcohol may destroy some pathogens and help prevent infection.

MiniLab 39.2

Page 208 • Distinguishing Blood Cells

Expected Results

The common percentages of white blood cells are: neutrophils, 60–70%; lymphocytes, 20–25%; monocytes, 3–8%; eosinophils, 2–4%; and basophils, 0.5–1%.

Analysis

1. neutrophils, lymphocytes
2. White blood cells have a nucleus, red blood cells don't.

Internet BioLab

Page 209 • Information on Emerging and Re-emerging Diseases

Data and Observations

Student data and observations will vary, depending on the diseases selected and the information resources used.

Analyze and Conclude

1. A pathogen is a disease-producing agent. Pathogens include some bacteria, viruses, parasites, and some fungi.
2. Emerging diseases are ones that have increased in the past 20 years. Re-emerging diseases are ones that have increased in incidence after a time of decline.
3. Answers may vary, but might include a change in resistance to an organism or a change in the organism itself.
4. Because people travel much more and much faster today, diseases can be spread more easily from country to country, and continent to continent.
5. Advantages include the fact that information is relatively easy to find and a search can be done from one convenient place such as a home computer. Disadvantages include the fact the information may be unreliable and hard to verify.

Reinforcement and Study Guide

Page 211 • Section 39.1

1. Infectious diseases area caused by pathogens that invade the body.
2. a series of experimental steps, developed by Robert Koch in 1876, used to identify infectious pathogens
3. a source of pathogens
4. airborne
5. vector
6. direct contact
7. true
8. false
9. false
10. true

Page 212 • Section 39.2

1. a physical barrier that prevents the entry of pathogens into the body
2. mucus
3. out of body tissues and into infected areas
4. true
5. monocytes that mature to become macrophages
6. viruses
7. d
8. c
9. b
10. a
11. Acquired immunity, resistance
12. antibody, cellular
13. antigens, antibodies
14. B cell, T cell, antibodies
15. T
16. killer T cell, pathogens
17. Antibody
18. Cellular, Antibody
19. Cellular
20. Cellular, Antibody
21. Antibody
22. Cellular
23. Active immunity develops as a result of direct exposure to antigens; passive immunity results

from acquiring antibodies through inoculations, or via the placenta or breast milk.

24. (1) naturally, when antibodies are transferred from mother to fetus or nursing infant; (2) artificially, via injection
25. a substance made up of weakened or dead pathogens, or parts of pathogens that, injected into the body, will cause active immunity
26. true
27. false
28. true
29. false
30. false
31. false
32. true
33. true

Refuerzo y Guía de estudio

Página 215 • Sección 39.1

1. Los patógenos que invaden el cuerpo causan las enfermedades infecciosas.
2. Una serie de experimentos, desarrollados por Robert Koch en 1876, que sirven para identificar los patógenos infecciosos.
3. una fuente de patógenos
4. a través del aire
5. vector
6. contacto directo
7. verdadero
8. falso
9. falso
10. verdadero

Página 216 • Sección 39.2

1. una barrera física que previene la entrada de patógenos al cuerpo
2. la mucosidad
3. la zona infectada, más allá de los tejidos
4. verdadero
5. monocitos que, al madurar, se convierten en macrófagos
6. virus
7. d
8. c
9. b
10. a
11. inmunidad adquirida; resistencia
12. por anticuerpos; celular
13. antígenos; anticuerpos
14. células B; células T; anticuerpos
15. T
16. células T asesinas; patógenos
17. anticuerpos
18. celular; anticuerpos
19. celular
20. celular; anticuerpos
21. anticuerpos
22. celular
23. La inmunidad activa se desarrolla a partir de la exposición directa a los antígenos. La inmunidad pasiva se produce al adquirir los anticuerpos a través de vacunas, la placenta o de la lactancia.
24. (1) de manera natural, cuando los anticuerpos son transferidos de la madre al feto o al lactante; (2) de manera artificial mediante una inyección.
25. una sustancia elaborada con patógenos muertos, patógenos debilitados o con partes del patógeno y que al ser inyectada en el cuerpo produce inmunidad activa
26. verdadero
27. falso
28. verdadero
29. falso
30. falso
31. falso
32. verdadero
33. verdadero

Concept Mapping

Page 219 • The Lymphatic System

1. tissue fluid
2. lymph capillaries
3. lymph veins
4. two ducts
5. lymph
6. bloodstream
7. lymph
8. nodes
9. white blood cells
10. lymphocytes
11. protect body
12. foreign substances

Problem Solving

Page 220 • Diagnosing Allergies

1. a. As a control, skin is scratched but no allergic material is rubbed in. The doctor can then determine whether the patient is reacting to the scratching rather than the test material.

b. Just rubbing the material into the scratch might not cause a reaction. Doctors may try a test where the suspected allergen is injected under the skin so that it mixes with blood.

2. a. Milk was drunk every day, but an allergic reaction did not occur every day.

   b. A reaction occurred on days 1, 7, and 14. On day 1, the person ate milk, eggs, fish, and chocolate. On day 7, the person ate milk, fish, chocolate, and nuts. On day 14, the person ate milk, eggs, and chocolate. Milk has been eliminated. The only other food common on all days is chocolate.

Section Focus Transparency 96

Page 221 • Don't Spread It Around!

Purpose

- To identify things people should do to prevent disease

Teaching Suggestions

- Before projecting the transparency, ask students to identify some disease-producing agents. (viruses, bacteria, fungi, protists) Ask students to name some diseases that they are familiar with. If possible, have students identify the organisms responsible for each disease.
- Ask students to identify ways in which disease is spread. (through air, water, soil, contact with others who are infected)
- *Answers to questions on the transparency include:*

1. The worker is washing her hands thoroughly after using the bathroom. The person sneezing covers her mouth and nose to avoid spreading disease-causing organisms.
2. Answers will vary, but students might suggest that the person is staying away from others during a period of contagion or that the person is getting rest to help the healing process.

Section Focus Transparency 97

Page 222 • Becoming Immune

Purpose

- To discover the value of obtaining immunity without having a disease

Teaching Suggestions

- Before projecting the transparency, introduce the concept of immunity. Ask students if they have ever been in a group of people who were exposed to a disease, such as chicken pox or measles. Ask if everyone in the group became infected. (Most students will indicate that not everyone did.) Ask students to explain why some people developed the disease while others did not. (Most students will have some understanding of immunity.)
- Project the transparency, and direct attention to the child in bed. Explain that the child has a disease, such as chicken pox.
- *Answers to questions on the transparency include:*

1. No, the child will have naturally acquired active immunity from the disease.
2. The child is receiving a vaccination, which will provide artificially acquired active immunity. Both result in active immunity.

Basic Concepts Transparency 76

Page 223 • Identifying a Pathogen

Purpose

- To study the procedure involved in identifying the causative agent of a disease

Teaching Suggestions

- Before projecting the transparency, lead a general discussion of what steps scientists would have to take to find out if a specific microbe causes a specific disease. Then tell students they will be examining a transparency that summarizes Koch's postulates, the steps scientists use in identifying an infectious pathogen. Have them study the transparency and complete the worksheet.
- Discuss student's responses to the worksheet to identify areas that need clarification or reteaching.
- Point out that when it is not possible to culture a pathogen, a cause-and-effect relationship can be inferred by isolating the same pathogens repeatedly from hosts that have a particular disease. For example, although it cannot be cultured, the organism that causes syphilis is always found associated with certain symptoms.

Extension: Class Report

- Have students research and report on the details of Koch's work. This includes discoveries related to the diseases anthrax, tuberculosis, bubonic plague, and sleeping sickness as well as the development of important techniques in bacteriology involving the staining and culturing of bacteria. Different groups of students can be assigned to research different subtopics.

Answers to Student Worksheet

1. Samples must be taken from an infected organism and examined under a microscope to find the pathogen potentially responsible for the disease.
2. Pure cultures of one or more suspected pathogens are grown to isolate the pathogen suspected of causing the disease under study.
3. A sample of a pure culture of the potential pathogen is being injected into a healthy host organism to determine if the organism develops the same disease found in Step 1.
4. In Step 4, samples are taken to discover whether the organism has indeed been infected by the pathogen found in Step 1 and isolated in Step 2. If the pathogens in steps 1 and 4 are identical, this would confirm that the pathogen is responsible for the disease.
5. Viral pathogens cannot be cultured outside of living cells.
6. In actual experimental research, the pathogen must be found in the host of every case of the disease. Therefore, many host organisms must be studied to preclude the possibility that some other pathogen is the actual cause or a corollary agent in the disease.
7. Koch's postulates can be used only if the suspected pathogen can be injected into a susceptible nonhuman subject. Using a human subject is considered ethically unacceptable.

Basic Concepts Transparency 77

Page 225 • Response to Injury

Purpose

- To show the processes initiated by tissue damage

Teaching Suggestions

- Project the transparency and discuss the sequence of events following injury. Discuss the nonspecific defense mechanisms involved and how they restore homeostasis.
- Explain that although the injury shown in the transparency was caused by physical force, there are other causes of injuries: chemical substances, extremes of temperature, and radiation.
- Discuss why an injury may or may not result in an infection.

Extension: Research Report

- In general, a doctor can predict how long it will take for an uninfected wound to heal. Have students research and report on processes involved in healing and how long each takes, as well as on ways to both shorten healing time and reduce scarring.

Answers to Student Worksheet

1. Inflammation can be caused by any injury produced by physical force, chemical substances, extreme temperatures, radiation, and infection.
2. Inflammation usually produces redness, swelling, pain, and heat.
3. Histamine is released by damaged tissue cells and white blood cells called basophils.
4. Dilation allows more plasma to diffuse from the bloodstream and enter the injured tissue to destroy toxic agents and restore homeostasis.
5. Redness results from dilated blood vessels, and swelling results from an increase in tissue fluid.
6. The phagocytes are white blood cells that ingest pathogens. Phagocytes include macrophages, neutrophils, and monocytes. Macrophages are present in body tissues. The other types of phagocytes circulate in the blood.
7. Pus is a collection of dead macrophages and body fluids that collect at the site of an infection.

Basic Concepts Transparency 78

Page 227 • Antibody and Cellular Immunity

Purpose

- To compare and contrast antibody immunity and cellular immunity, the two specific defenses against pathogens

Teaching Suggestions

- Walk students through the steps shown in each transparency. Point out that each transparency represents a sequence of reactions initiated when a pathogen enters the body. Discuss the consequences of a breakdown in either sequence.
- Have students compare and contrast the events taking place in each transparency, identifying similarities and differences.
- Be sure students understand the difference between B cells and T cells and the roles they play in immunity.

Extension: Guest Speaker

- Invite a representative from your local public health agency to discuss issues of immunity and disease control.

Answers to Student Worksheet

1. Nonself antigens are proteins recognized by the body as foreign substances.

2. Antibody immunity protects the body by first attacking the invading pathogen. Then antibodies specific to the invading antigen are produced. Some antibodies remain in the blood to respond to future invasions of the same pathogen.
3. T cells and B cells are two types of lymphocytes. Various T cells, which are produced in bone marrow and mature in the thymus gland, play roles in both antibody and cellular immunity. B cells, which are also produced from bone marrow but mature in the bone marrow, in turn produce antibodies that are released into the bloodstream. T cells do not form antibodies.
4. cellular immunity
5. Memory B cells and T cells are lymphocytes that are specialized for responding to a second attack by the invading pathogen.
6. Helper T cells are required in the chain of events that leads to antibody production. They also stimulate the production of cytotoxic T cells needed for a cellular immune response.
7. Cytotoxic T cells bind to infected cells and break through their cell walls, causing the infected cells to undergo lysis.

Basic Concepts Transparency 79

Page 231 • The AIDS Epidemic

Purpose

- To illustrate the structure of HIV and how this virus infects and destroys target cells

Teaching Suggestions

- Project the transparency and discuss how the human immunodeficiency virus is similar to and different from other viruses.
- Point out that the deadly effects of the AIDS virus are caused indirectly by the weakening of a person's immune system.
- Discuss how HIV is transmitted and how people can minimize their chances of being infected.

Extension: Research Report

- Have students do research on the spread of AIDS since it was first identified and the investigations medical scientists are conducting to find ways to prevent and treat the disease.

Answers to Student Worksheet

1. The virus is called the Human Immunodeficiency Virus.
2. The person may or may not have AIDS but, in either case, can transmit the virus to another person.
3. The outer knobs consist of proteins, which are antigens. A vaccine against AIDS could possibly be developed to trigger the body to produce antibodies specific to the antigen on the HIV knobs.
4. HIV is a retrovirus consisting of RNA and the enzyme reverse transcriptase wrapped in proteins and a lipid coat.
5. The virus's attachment protein is attaching itself to a receptor in the plasma membrane of a helper T-cell. The virus then penetrates the cell, leading to the fusion of the viral and T-cell membranes. The virus uses the host cell's RNA to synthesize viral DNA in the host cell.

Reteaching Skills Transparency 57

Page 233 • Human Body Systems

Purpose

- To introduce some of the characteristics and relationships of various human body systems
- Skill: Interpreting scientific illustrations

Teaching Suggestions

- Use the transparency to accompany this BioDigest on body systems and to assess prior knowledge.
- Point out that body systems interact with one another, although the functions of some are more closely interdependent than those of others. Discuss some of the closer relationships, such as those between the muscular system and the skeletal system, between the respiratory system and circulatory system, and between the nervous system and endocrine system.
- Project the base transparency and challenge students to identify selected structures in each of the body systems. Then superimpose the overlays to reinforce or correct answers.

Extension: Challenge

- Have students choose a physical activity, such as swimming, running in a long-distance race, or catching a ball, and describe how each body system contributes to the activity.

Answers to Student Worksheet

1. the skeletal system
2. the respiratory system
3. The muscular, nervous, and skeletal systems interact to provide mobility.
4. The ovaries in females are analogous to the testes in males because both produce gametes—sperm in males and eggs in females.

5. The urinary system keeps a homeostatic balance of water, salts, and other compounds in the body. In addition, the urinary system assures that levels of wastes do not accumulate.
6. In the circulatory system, the heart acts as a muscular pump. Arteries, veins, and capillaries transport circulatory fluids throughout the body. The blood contains components for body defense, gas exchange, and nutrients for cells.
7. the digestive system
8. the endocrine system

Reteaching Skills Transparency 58

Page 235 • Cells of the Immune Response

Purpose

- To study the types of immune response cells and their purposes
- Skill: Classifying

Teaching Suggestions

- Discuss the staining procedures used with blood cells and the fact that cells are classified primarily by stain rather than by function.
- Present the transparency. Work through it with students, filling in information as they provide the correct responses.
- Answers for chart: **Basophil:** Innate; Produces histamine, causing inflammation; blood vessels dilate, becoming more permeable to tissue fluid; **Eosinophil:** Innate; Phagocytic cells; **Neutrophil:** Innate; Phagocytic cells; **Macrophage:** Innate; Develops from monocyte; ingests and destroys pathogens by surrounding and engulfing them; **Helper T:** Adaptive; Activates killer T cells to replicate; activates B cells; produces memory T cells; **Killer T:** Adaptive; Attaches to infected cell and produces chemicals that lyse, or burst, the cell or produces chemicals that attract other macrophages; **Memory T:** Adaptive; "Early warning system" against the same antigen; **Memory B:** Adaptive; Attacks and marks antigens for destruction by macrophage; **Plasma:** Adaptive; Produces antibodies; **Antibodies:** Adaptive; Protein structures with sections that recognize one specific pathogen; sections bind with antigen structures; may block toxin production; attach to and deactivate virus.

Extension: Reading

- Have students read books by Paul deKruif, such as *The Microbe Hunters*. These books explore how researchers over the centuries have searched for causes and vaccines for diseases such as smallpox and rabies.

Answers to Student Worksheet

1. The innate immune system provides general defense against many pathogens; it is nonspecific. The acquired immune system provides specific defenses against specific pathogens; it is the job of the lymphatic system.
2. The skin provides a physical barrier to pathogens. Bacteria normally found on the skin help inhibit pathogens.
3. Mucus traps microbes that enter the respiratory and digestive tracts. Sweat, tears, and saliva contain the enzyme lysozyme, which can break down the cell walls of some bacteria.
4. a. A phagocyte is a white blood cell that ingests and destroys pathogens.
   b. A macrophage is a phagocyte that provides the first line of defense against pathogens.
   c. Pus is a collection of dead white blood cells and various body fluids.
   d. Histamine, produced by basophils when tissue damage occurs, causes blood vessels to dilate.
   e. Interferons are proteins that protect cells from viruses.
5. A vaccine is a substance consisting of weakened, dead, or partial pathogens or antigens that, when injected into the body, cause immunity. A vaccine causes the body to react as if it were naturally infected.

Chapter Assessment

Page 237 • Reviewing Vocabulary

1. g
2. i
3. d
4. e
5. a
6. b
7. c
8. h
9. f
10. A T cell is a lymphocyte that is produced in bone marrow and processed in the thymus gland. Different T cells perform different roles in immunity. A B cell is also a lymphocyte produced in bone marrow. It produces antibodies when activated by a T cell.
11. A phagocyte is a type of white blood cell that ingests and destroys pathogens by surrounding and engulfing them. A macrophage is one type of phagocyte—a very large phagocyte.

Page 238 • Understanding Main Ideas (Part A)

1. c
2. b
3. c
4. a
5. a
6. b
7. b
8. a
9. c

Page 239 • Understanding Main Ideas (Part B)

1. (1) They try to find a pathogen in the host in every case of the disease. (2) They isolate the pathogen from the host and grow it in a pure culture. (3) When they place a pathogen from the pure culture into a healthy host, it causes the disease. (4) The pathogen must then be isolated from the new host to prove it is the original pathogen.
2. Interferons are host-cell specific proteins produced by an infected body cell. The interferon diffuses into uninfected neighboring cells, which then produce antiviral proteins that can prevent the virus from multiplying.
3. A nonspecific defense mechanism is effective against a wide variety of pathogens. A specific defense mechanism achieves its goal by building up resistance against a specific pathogen or antigen.
4. A B cell is activated by a T cell to produce antibodies, which are released into the bloodstream. The antibodies bind to antigens to which they can fit. This binding results in an antigen-antibody complex.
5. Cytotoxic, or killer, T-cells produce clones that then travel to the infected site and release enzymes directly into the pathogens, causing them to lyse and die.
6. HIV, which causes AIDS, kills helper T cells that are important in developing the immune response.

Page 240 • Thinking Critically

1. Inflammation occurs as a reaction to the injury and to the pathogens introduced by the splinter. Macrophages migrate to the infected area and engulf large numbers of pathogens. After a few days, the infected area contains pus, which is made up of dead phagocytes and body fluids.
2. Antibodies recognize and initiate an immune response to proteins that are foreign to the body. If antibodies bind to the patient's own cardiac muscle cells, it may be because the proteins in muscle tissue must have something in common with the proteins in the rheumatic fever pathogen. This could lead to a mistake by which the body begins producing antibodies that attack its own tissues.
3. Without the cyclosporine, there would be an immune response to the organ transplant. The body would reject the new organ.
4. The danger of taking drugs that suppressed the entire immune system was that the patient became highly susceptible to infectious diseases.
5. They might think their child should be exposed to the disease so that he or she will produce antibodies and build up an active immunity to it.

Page 241 • Appyling Scientific Methods

1. When streptococci are placed in a drop of blood, human phagocytes stay away from those with M protein but not from those without it.
2. Every time the M protein changes, there is less chance that the human immune system will be able to identify and destroy the bacterium.
3. M6.1 has five A repeat blocks, whereas M6.2 has only three A repeat blocks. M6.1 has five B repeat blocks; M6.3 has only four B repeat blocks.
4. As soon as the body builds up an immune response to one form of the M protein, several other mutant forms appear, to which there is not an immune response.
5. Since both surfaces are negatively charged and like charges repel, you would expect that the phagocytes would not be able to make contact with the surface of the bacteria and would not be able to ingest them.

Student Recording Sheet

Page 243

Answers can be found on page 1046 in the Teacher Wraparound Edition.

Unit 10 BioDigest

Reinforcement and Study Guide

Page 245

1. protects tissues and organs
2. helps regulate the body temperature
3. produces vitamin D
4. contains many sensory receptors
5. softer, underlying tissues
6. muscle attachment
7. vital organs
8. blood cells
9. calcium and phosphorus
10. Oxygen passes from the alveoli in the lungs to the bloodstream.
11. Oxygen breaks down glucose to produce ATP for cells and to release CO_2.
12. Carbon dioxide passes from the cell to the bloodstream.
13. Carbon dioxide passes from the bloodstream to the alveoli in the lungs.
14. glands, bloodstream, target tissues, alter the metabolism of the target tissue cells
15. testes, prostate gland, penis, producing, transferring sperm cells
16. ovaries, uterus, egg cells, sperm cells, fetus
17. Possible answer: Skeletal system manufactures blood cells that travel through the circulatory system to bring oxygen and nutrients to the cells of the muscular system.
18. Possible answer: Circulation system carries waste products from food breakdown to the urinary system to be eliminated.
19. Answer should reflect: Hormones secreted by glands in the endocrine system alter the metabolism of target tissues in the reproductive system.
20. Answer should reflect: Oxygen supplied by respiratory system is carried by circulatory systems to cells; waste products from metabolism are carried by circulatory system to urinary and respiratory systems for excretion.
21. Answer should reflect: Fluids from capillaries of circulatory system bathe the cells and then are absorbed by the lymphatic system.

Refuerzo y Guía de estudio

Página 247

1. protege tejidos y órganos
2. ayuda a regular la temperatura corporal
3. produce vitamina D
4. contiene muchos receptores sensoriales
5. tejidos internos suaves
6. la inserción de músculos
7. órganos vitales
8. células de la sangre
9. calcio y fósforo
10. El oxígeno pasa desde los alvéolos de los pulmones hacia la sangre.
11. El oxígeno ayuda a desintegrar la glucosa para obtener ATP para las células. En este proceso se libera CO_2.
12. El dióxido de carbono pasa de las células hacia la sangre.
13. El dióxido de carbono pasa de la sangre hacia los alvéolos de los pulmones.
14. glándulas; torrente sanguíneo; tejidos blanco; alteran el metabolismo de las células del tejido blanco
15. testículos; próstata; pene; producción; transferencia de espermatozoides
16. ovarios; útero; óvulos; espermatozoides; feto
17. Respuesta posible: en el sistema óseo se forman las células de la sangre; éstas viajan a través del sistema circulatorio para llevar oxígeno y nutrientes a las células del sistema muscular.
18. Respuesta posible: el sistema circulatorio transporta los desechos de la digestión de alimentos hacia el sistema urinario, para su excreción.
19. La respuesta debe mostrar que las hormonas secretadas por las glándulas del sistema endocrino alteran el metabolismo de los tejidos blanco en el sistema reproductor.
20. La respuesta debe mostrar que el sistema circulatorio transporta el oxígeno, proporcionado por el sistema respiratorio, hacia las células y que el sistema circulatorio transporta los desechos del metabolismo hacia los sistemas urinario y respiratorio, para su excreción.
21. La respuesta debe mostrar que el sistema linfático absorbe los fluidos, que bañan las células, provenientes de los capilares del sistema circulatorio.

Student Recording Sheet

Page 249

Answers can be found on page 1056 in the Teacher Wraparound Edition.